CITIZENSHIP AND PUBLIC SERVICE:

VOLUNTARY AND STATUTORY RELATIONSHIPS
IN IRISH HEALTHCARE

*'During times of tumultuous change our principles
may be our only constant'*

Dr. David McCutcheon
Chief Executive Officer 1996-1999,
The Adelaide and Meath Hospital, Dublin,
incorporating The National Children's Hospital.

CITIZENSHIP AND PUBLIC SERVICE:

VOLUNTARY AND STATUTORY

RELATIONSHIPS IN IRISH HEALTHCARE

FERGUS O'FERRALL

First published in 2000 by The Adelaide Hospital Society
in association with Dundalgan Press (W. Tempest) Ltd.

Adelaide Hospital Society,
Adelaide and Meath Hospital,
Tallaght, Dublin 24.
E-mail address: info@adelaide.ie

ISBN 0-85221-140-6

Cover design: Graph X Design, Dundalk

The Wheel Logo incorporated on the cover has been designed
by Mr. Bill Fenton of Alexander Dunlop, Dublin.

Printed by Dundalgan Press (W. Tempest) Ltd., Dundalk

CONTENTS

v

CHAPTER 5

A Case Study: The Board of The Adelaide and Meath Hospital, Dublin, Incorporating The National Children's Hospital 1996–1999

CHAPTER 6

Perceptions and Prescriptions 225

CHAPTER 7

Conclusions 253

LIST OF TABLES

APPENDIX:

PREFACE

All the proceeds of this book will be given to support The Wheel which is a genuinely democratic movement of voluntary organisations and individuals who have come together in an exciting and innovative fashion . The Wheel expresses the values of active citizenship which is central to the argument of this book. A brief information note on The Wheel follows this Preface.

This book is dedicated to every citizen who undertakes responsibilities in society to care for other people's needs in a voluntary capacity and to giving such active citizens a more powerful voice in shaping our Republic.

As Dr. Mary Redmond stated prophetically in 1998:

> "The wheel of voluntarism is yet unturned. Think of how powerful it will be when it is turning, its spokes accommodating the rich diversity of the voluntary sector, its centre the distillation of the great energy which drives it"
> ('Social Enterpreneurship—A New Authority?' in *Are We Forgetting Something?* eds. H. Bohan & G. Kennedy (Dublin, 1999) P. 155).

The Adelaide Hospital Society, as a voluntary organisation serving healthcare since 1839, welcomes the development of The Wheel and is very pleased to facilitate the publication of this book as a contribution to the development of the voluntary and community sector in Ireland. We are honoured that Dr. Mary Redmond has graciously agreed to write the Foreword.

Serving healthcare since 1839

Professor DAVID McCONNELL

President
The Adelaide Hospital Society

THE WHEEL

What is The Wheel?

The Wheel is a movement for groups and individuals who wish to explore ways and means in which the community and voluntary sector might come together in a more cohesive and meaningful way. It recognises the importance of education and training, of communications and of information technology in advancing this objective.

"The Wheel" is a concept. Its spokes envisage the several communities of interest in the sector: its hub, the distillation of a great energy: its rims, the beneficiaries in the wider community. The Wheel has been spinning in the Republic and in Northern Ireland since February 1999.

What is it not?

The Wheel is not a hierarchy or funding agency. Nor is it a channel for funding.

It is not influenced by any interest or political party.

It is not a voice for the sector but can be the catalyst behind many voices within the sector.

What about other groups in the sector?

The Wheel recognises the very good work of many organisations working in the community and voluntary sector in Ireland and acknowledges their success in negotiations of various kinds, their influence and their results. There is no intention behind The Wheel to be divisive or to undermine this work.

The Wheel is independent of any one group. There is room for everyone. The autonomy of groups in the community and voluntary sector will be respected and will not be affected by membership of The Wheel.

The Wheel is forward thinking. It welcomes the use of modern telecommunication as a method of connecting the spokes of The Wheel.

What does The Wheel do?

Participative meetings are held every quarter, using round tables at which everyone meets as equals. These meetings constitute a "legislative" body whose decisions are carried further by working groups. All are welcome.

What about funding?

Funds for The Wheel are always welcome. The Wheel has set up a company limited by guarantee to receive and account for funds, called Rotha Teoranta, which has charitable status for tax purposes.

Where do I contact The Wheel?

At www.wheel.ie or by telephone on 01 874 9720 or by post to:

> The Wheel,
> Carmichael House,
> North Brunswick Street,
> Dublin 7.

> E-mail: info@wheel.ie

FOREWORD

Ireland's unprecedented economic success, instead of making voluntary organisations redundant, has greatly increased their importance. In almost every field policy makers are struggling with intractable problems that are not responding to orthodox solutions. The problems of ill-health, disability, drugs, housing, crime, employment and pollution are perhaps the most visible. The 1990s saw a significant decrease in Government spending on social welfare as a result of the dramatic drop in numbers out of work; yet the monies saved were not used to increase social investments elsewhere.

The Green Paper on *Supporting Voluntary Activity*, published in 1997, concluded that "The rapidly changing economic and social situation in Ireland requires serious consideration on how best to change society in order to make it socially and economically inclusive. There is a need to create a more participatory democracy where **active citizenship** is fostered. **An active voluntary and community sector** contributes to a democratic, pluralist, society . . ." (emphasis mine).

But phrases such a "more participatory democracy" and "active citizenship" are meaningless without public discussion and (at the least, some) consensus about the sort of citizenship or life to be pursued, its underlying values, norms, core assumptions and the development paradigm being advanced.

Most fundamentally, these phrases will be meaningless for as long as Ireland's public philosophy legitimating voluntary action is as inadequate as it is. The development of such a philosophy is a critical imperative if the voluntary sector is to build the infrastructure it so badly needs.

Dr. O'Ferrall has initiated a most important debate in this book and made a timely contribution to the imminent White Paper on the relationship between the voluntary sector and the State, by presenting a normative theory of active citizenship in a pluralist democracy as a convincing legitimisation of voluntary action in democratic societies. By standing back and reflecting upon his own experience as participant-observer in the development of the new public voluntary

Hospital at Tallaght, he has written a very valuable work for the whole voluntary sector (as well as for all involved in healthcare).

Key political and economic theorists have attributed very significant roles to voluntary action. In recent times there has been an emphasis on the value-expressive character of "active societies". Ireland, through the Green and White Paper process, is in the company of many countries which have taken initiatives to promote citizenship.

The voluntary sector in Ireland has a right as well as a responsibility to participate fully in developing and endorsing its legitimating philosophy. This is not something for an "inner circle" to do. All voluntary organisations, as part of an aspiring "Third Sector", need to seek and define values that go beyond themselves (such as the common good), a process that will lead to greater independence as well as synergy within the sector and ultimately to more fruitful interdependence (genuine citizen based partnerships) with the state and market sectors.

This is a most important book, setting out (for which one is grateful) a "usable theory", written by an historian with wide and long experience of voluntary organisations. He is by no means value-neutral about his subject: his commitment to the sector is both generally, and in the specific context of healthcare, self-evident.

Dr. MARY REDMOND

February 4th, 2000

Dr. Mary Redmond, a solicitor and company director, founded in 1986 The Irish Hospice Foundation of which she is Patron and in 1998 she instigated The Wheel, a new movement to harness Ireland's diverse voluntary sector.

ACKNOWLEDGEMENTS

I wish to acknowledge the help and support I have received in undertaking the research for this study which was undertaken at Trinity College, Dublin for the degree of M.Sc. in Health Services Management. I have benefited from the openness and helpful attitude of the Board and staff of the Adelaide and Meath Hospital, Dublin, Incorporating the National Children's Hospital; in particular the former CEO, Dr. David McCutcheon, the former Chairman, Mrs. Rosemary French, the former Acting CEO, Mr. Nicholas Jermyn, the former Vice Chairman and current Chairman, Mr. Gerry Brady and Ms Stephanie Keane, Personal Assistant to the CEO have fully co-operated at all times whenever I sought their help.

I wish also to thank the former Secretary-General of the Department of Health and Children, Mr. Jerry O'Dwyer and the officers of the Department of Health and Children, Ms Angela Fitzgerald, Mr. Vincent Barton and Mr. Tony Morris, for generous time which they provided to me for indepth interviews. In particular, Mr. Denis O'Sullivan from the Department, and my colleague on the M.Sc. Health Services Management Programme in Trinity College, greatly facilitated my research in the Department of Health and Children by providing sources for the research. Ms Laraine Joyce of the Office for Health Management both in discussion and in the provision of references was enormously helpful on issues of governance and management. Commissioner Christos Papoutsis, of the European Commission, helpfully sent me an up to date briefing on the promotion of the role of voluntary organisations in Europe and the work of the Social Economy Unit of Directorate-General XXIII.

I should like to thank the Canadian Council on Health Services Accreditation, and its Executive Director, Elma G. Heidemann, for permission to use and reproduce in Ireland as an appendix their 'Accreditation Standards for Governing Bodies'. I should like also to thank Eleanor Sawyer of the Canadian Healthcare Association for helpful information.

I owe a great debt to the Adelaide Hospital Society for generous support to me in undertaking this research. In particular, the President, Professor David McConnell and the Chairman, Professor Ian Graham have given me great encouragement and support in the course of the research. Also Ms Jacinta Gunning, in the office of the Society, patiently helped with the production of the transcripts of the interviews which assisted me greatly.

I would also like to thank Ms Eilish McAuliffe, Director of the M.Sc. Programme in Health Services Management, and Ms Marie O'Shea in the office of the Faculty of Health Sciences at Trinity College Dublin who provided help and advice from the beginning to the end of the research. My fellow students on the M.Sc. Programme provided stimulus and encouragement when needed over two busy years.

I should like to thank also the staff of the library of the Combat Poverty Agency which provided a very friendly and helpful centre for voluntary and community sector studies. Ms Nancy Larner of the Greenleaf Center for Servant-Leadership, Indianapolis, Indiana, most helpfully obtained material for me very quickly. The staff of the Library at Trinity College Dublin were most courteous and helpful at all times. Numerous other people responded promptly to my request for information and it is impossible to list each one separately. For books or information supplied I must, however, thank Professor Fred Powell of University College Cork, Dr. Arthur Williamson and Mr. Derek Bacon of the Centre for Voluntary Action Studies, The University of Ulster; Dr. Freda Donoghue, Director of the Policy Research Centre, National College of Ireland and her colleague, Ms Gwen Jaffro. Each of these has pioneered research in voluntary sector studies and I have benefited greatly from their published work. Dr. Williamson kindly invited me to participate in the formal constitution of the Association for Voluntary Action Research in Ireland and I have benefited greatly from the work and publications of this Association. Dr. Mary Redmond has provided much inspiration to the voluntary and community sector as she has encouraged the sector to meet together under the umbrella of 'The Wheel' using a direct democratic methodology and I have learned a great deal from her and from the innovative encounters at the 'round tables' of 'The Wheel'.

I owe my biggest single debt of gratitude to Ms Gemma Donnelly-Cox, of the School of Business Studies, Trinity College, Dublin who, as my Supervisor, provided the right combination of detailed advice and critical support while being exacting in terms of completing the research. Her colleague, Andrew O'Regan, Research Fellow at the School of Business Studies provided further insights and guidance to me at important points in the research. Professor John Murray, School of Business Studies, Trinity College, Dublin was most helpful in discussion providing guidance in relation to key issues of governance and management.

Finally I record my outstanding debt to my wife, Iris, who has so patiently lived with this research and has given so generously of her time in its production. It is true to say it would not have been possible but for her help and support. My children Eilís, Deirdre and Sinéad have contributed also by enduring with the great good humour their loss of access to the home computer and the piles of books and papers in at least three rooms of our home.

FERGUS O'FERRALL

March 2000

INTRODUCTION

'. . . *we are in the midst of a global "associational revolution" that may prove to be as significant to the latter twentieth century as the rise of the nation-state was to the latter nineteenth. The upshot is a global third sector: a massive array of self-governing private organisations, not dedicated to distributing profits to shareholders or directors, pursuing public purposes outside the formal apparatus of the state. The proliferation of these groups may be permanently altering the relationship between states and citizens, with an impact extending far beyond the material services they provide.*'

LESTER M. SALAMON 'The Rise of the Nonprofit Sector', *Foreign Affairs*, Vol. 73, No. 4, 1994, p. 109.

INTRODUCTION

Health services in Ireland are experiencing a period of rapid change especially in relation to the formal structures employed for planning, delivering and evaluating services.[1] Relationships between voluntary agencies and statutory bodies are bound to be high on the policy agenda in this context of structural change and development. This is apparent in *Shaping A Healthier Future A Strategy For Effective Healthcare in the 1990s* published by the Department of Health in 1994. This key document, known as 'the Health Strategy', signposted a major restructuring of the relationships between voluntary health agencies and statutory health boards. It stated that, for the first time, a specific statutory framework would be created between statutory health authorities and voluntary health organisations which would recognise the roles and responsibilities of both sectors.

This book will explore the implications for governance and management of the changes and developments which are occurring in voluntary and statutory relationships in response to 'the Health Strategy' with particular reference to public voluntary hospitals. The concern is particularly with the roles and operation of governing boards and relates to management only insofar as to consider management linkages to such boards as part of governance structures which enable effective management to occur. The phrase 'governance and management' refers to the overall governance structures embracing the board, the chief executive officer and senior management which relate to the governance responsibilities of the board. Voluntary and statutory relationships are an aspect of key importance in the growing literature concerning the voluntary or 'third sector'. Salamon, for example, observes that

> Perhaps the most decisive determinant of third-sector growth will be the relationship that nonprofit organizations can forge with government. The task for third sector organizations is to find a modus vivendi with government that provides sufficient legal and financial support while preserving a meaningful degree of independence and autonomy.[2]

[1] see a significant overview by the Secretary-General of the Department of Health and Children in J. O'Dwyer 'Reflections on Future Structures in the Health Services' in *The Irish Health System in the 21st Century*, eds. A.L. Leahy and M. Wiley, (Dublin, 1998), pp 37–51

[2] L.M. Salamon 'The Rise of the Nonprofit Sector', *Foreign Affairs*, Vol. 73, No. 4, 1994, p. 122

It is apparent that policy development concerning voluntary and statutory relationships generally is at an early formative stage in Ireland. This is the case also in the European Union.[3] This presents a major policy concern in respect of voluntary and statutory relationships in Irish health services where policy has developed in a separate stream more rapidly to the stage of legislation and implementation. The Health (Amendment) (No. 3) Act, 1996 and the Health (Eastern Regional Health Authority) Act, 1999 decisively set a new framework for voluntary and statutory relationships in health care well in advance of agreement on any general national framework. Such legislation has occurred in a context where voluntary health agencies and in particular public voluntary hospitals have poorly articulated their raison d'être and have received inadequate analysis in state policy documents concerning the health services. As O'Sullivan has noted

> A surprising point here is that voluntary agencies themselves have not been very effective at articulating their raison d'être and their distinctive contribution—some of the larger voluntary agencies could arguably do more to communicate the distinctiveness of their ethos or their contribution to healthcare'.[4]

As Salamon notes this 'absence' of the 'third sector' is a feature of the sector generally:

> The nonprofit sector has clearly arrived as a major actor on the world scene, but it has yet to make its mark as a serious presence in public consciousness, policy circles, the media or scholarly research. For emerging third sector organizations to be taken seriously by others, however, they must take themselves seriously first.[5]

This study is intended to contribute to Irish health policy studies by providing an analysis of the changing context of Irish health services in respect of voluntary and statutory relationships. This analysis will review the historical context of these relationships in Ireland as exemplified through the experiences of public voluntary hospitals and as compared

[3] see *Supporting Voluntary Activity A Green Paper on the Community and Voluntary Sector and its Relationship with the State*, (Stationery Office, Dublin [1997]) and *Communication From the Commission on Promoting The Role of Voluntary Organisations and Foundations in Europe*, (Office for Official Publications of the European Communities, Luxembourg, 1997)

[4] T. O'Sullivan 'Changing Relationships and the Voluntary and Statutory Sectors' in *A Healthier Future? Managing Healthcare in Ireland*, eds. E. McAuliffe and L. Joyce, (Dublin, 1998), p. 186

[5] L.M. Salamon 'The Rise of the Nonprofit Sector', *Foreign Affairs*, Vol. 73, No. 4, 1994, p. 121

with developments in the United Kingdom. The changing context in Irish health care requires to be placed within a broader theoretical framework concerning theories of voluntary action in democratic societies and it is hoped that this will prove valuable at a time of critical change in the structures of the health services.

Those who are responsible for governing and for managing health services are seeking to cope with fundamental and rapid change and this is especially the case in respect of acute hospitals. As the Secretary-General of The Department of Health and Children stated in 1998:

> Acute hospitals will continue to be subject to more extensive and rapid change than any other part of the health system. More resources will have to be invested in their management. The management structures in major voluntary hospitals and in major acute hospitals under health boards are likely to develop along similar lines. Steps are already being taken to delineate more clearly the governance and management functions within the large hospitals. Both functions are still relatively underdeveloped. Whereas considerable attention has been given to the strengthening of management in recent years, the responsibilities of governance have not been subject to the same degree of consideration and development.[6]

The Health Strategy noted in 1994 that the voluntary sector 'plays an integral role in the provision of health and personal social services in Ireland which is perhaps unparalleled in any other country'.[7] For example close to one half of acute hospital beds and two-thirds of mentally handicapped residential places are provided by 'voluntary' organisations or non-statutory agencies.[8] In the Eastern Health Board region (Counties Dublin, Wicklow and Kildare) in 1997 the Department of Health provided direct funding of £465.2 million approximately to 29 voluntary hospitals and agencies which employed over 15,000 people. In addition the Department also provided over £77 million to the six largest voluntary mental handicap organisations whose headquarters are located in the Eastern Health Board region and these organisations employed a further 3,000 people. Both these expenditures compare with the £399 million provided to the Eastern Health Board for its own services provided by approximately 9,000

[6] J. O'Dwyer 'Reflections on Future Structures in the Health Services' in *The Irish Health System in the 21st Century*, op. cit., p. 45

[7] *Shaping A Healthier Future A Strategy for Effective Healthcare in the 1990s*, (Department of Health, Stationery Office, Dublin [1994]), p. 33

[8] see T. O'Sullivan 'Changing Relationships and the Voluntary and Statutory Sectors' in *A Healthier Future? Managing Healthcare in Ireland*, eds. E. McAuliffe and L. Joyce (Dublin, 1998), p. 186

staff. Of this £399 million the Eastern Health Board provided almost £70 million to a range of voluntary providers of services.[9]

These figures indicate the importance of the 'voluntary sector' in the Eastern Health Board area which will be the focus of this study in respect of public voluntary hospitals.[10] However, the policy literature concerning the health services in Ireland devotes very little attention to the specific justification for, or to the role of, the voluntary sector compared to that given to the needs and concerns of the state and of the statutory bodies such as the health boards. In the policy statements, in the absence of any references to a theoretical approach to, or empirical studies of, the role of the voluntary healthcare sector, there are to be found simple assertions of the assumed contributions of voluntary bodies including such attributes as their pioneering and innovative role, their flexibility in response to needs, their access to a volunteer resource, their advocacy of the needs of clients, and their educational role which facilitates participation. It is assumed that voluntary organisations promote 'community spirit', independence and make some additional resources available.[11] A notable example of this in the recent literature is the major Report of the Commission on Health Funding September 1989 where beyond such perfunctory descriptions there is an absence of detailed policy consideration in over 400 pages of the Report in respect of how the voluntary sector in healthcare might be developed or promoted. The Commission stated:

> The role of voluntary organisations is immensely important. They reflect and stimulate the community spirit and humanitarianism of very many people outside of the formal health services, and in so doing they make available considerable additional resources, both human and financial.

[9] see *Interim Report of The Task Force on the Eastern Regional Health Authority June 1997*, (issued by the Department of Health in 1997), pp 8–9 and Appendix IV 'Voluntary Hospitals and Voluntary Mental handicap Agencies in the Eastern Region directly funded by the Department of Health'

[10] There are thirty hospitals listed as 'public voluntary hospitals' in *Administration Yearbook and Diary 1999* (Institute of Public Administration, Dublin, 1998), pp 132–136; twenty-four of these hospitals were in the Eastern Health Board area and situated in the County or City of Dublin. It should be noted that the category 'public voluntary hospital' includes voluntary hospitals with boards independent of the State and hospitals with boards appointed by the Minister for Health under the Health (Corporate Bodies) Act, 1961 which means they are not under the control of the statutory health boards. One of the above thirty, Our Lady of Lourdes Hospital, Drogheda has been transferred to the area health board recently.

[11] see, for example, *Shaping A Healthier Future A Strategy For Effective Healthcare in the 1990s*, Department of Health, Stationery Office, Dublin, [1994]), p. 33

They can also identify and meet needs quickly because of their closeness to the client-group which they serve; indeed, many services which are now provided or funded by the State were originally developed independently by such organisations.

The Commission went on to note that 'there is no formal framework or procedural guidelines' for the relationship between statutory and voluntary bodies so as to ensure their complementarity. The Commission called for the role of 'voluntary hospitals and other agencies' to be defined afresh and the parameters of responsibilities in the delivery of services to be set out clearly. It added significantly that such 'clarity is lacking in the present system'.[13]

The Commission's important contribution to the policy context from 1989 will be discussed below in Chapter 2 particularly in respect of contractual relationships for funding on the basis of clear agreements on the services to be provided.

The figures provided in the Commission's Report for the acute hospitals in 1987 at least raised the voluntary-statutory relationship as a policy issue: health board hospitals provided 7,061 beds and public voluntary hospitals provided 6,713 beds in the Republic.[14]

Since the Health Strategy was published in 1994 there are indications of the beginnings of an articulation of the policy concerns which are distinctive to the voluntary sector in health care.[15] This articulation

[12] *Report of the Commission on Health Funding September 1989* (Stationery Office, Dublin, 1989), p. 341

[13] ibid, p. 153

[14] ibid, p. 230; The Commission defined voluntary public hospitals as 'certain hospitals not owned by the State but which receive funding directly from the Department of Health acting as agent for the health boards. Some are owned by religious orders; others are incorporated by charter or statute and work under boards which, in many cases, are appointed by the Minister for Health' (p. xv); the poverty of policy in respect of voluntary health agencies is also apparent in *Health The Wider Dimensions (A Consultative Statement on Health Policy)*, (Department of Health [1986]) which contained two paragraphs on 'The Non-Statutory Sector' and one on 'Voluntary Hospitals' in over 40 pages of a major health policy statement.

[15] See T. O'Sullivan 'The Voluntary-Statutory Relationship in the Health Services', *Administration*, Vol. 42, No. 1, spring 1994, pp 3–24; P. Faughnan 'A Healthy Voluntary Sector: Rhetoric or Reality?' in *Reflections on Health Commemorating Fifty Years of the Department of Health 1947–1997* ed. J. Robins (Department of Health, Dublin, 1997), pp 232–249; T. O'Sullivan 'Changing Relationships and the Voluntary and Statutory Sectors' in *A Healthier Future? Managing Healthcare in Ireland*, eds. E. McAuliffe and K. Joyce, (Dublin, 1998), pp 181–197; in this context particular note should be taken of *Enhancing the Partnership Report of The Working Group on the Implementation of The Health Strategy in Relation To Persons with a Mental Handicap*, (Department of Health, [1997]) which will be discussed in Chapter 2 below

will benefit from the rapidly developing scholarly attention and policy focus upon the role of voluntary organisations in modern societies.[16] This study utilises the extensive international literature on the 'nonprofit' or voluntary sector as well as the increasingly important work on the sector now available from Irish sources.

David Billis has rightly observed 'that stumbling into change is the main hazard facing the voluntary sector'.[17] Policies have evolved in Irish healthcare and are being implemented without taking into account whether being a 'voluntary' agency implies any particular significance in respect of governance and management. Hence, for example, the Secretary-General of the Department of Health and Children expects that the 'management structures in major voluntary hospitals and in major acute hospitals under health boards are likely to develop along similar lines'.[18]

Objectives of the book

Given the background described above the objectives of this book are

(i)   to review the history of voluntary and statutory relationships in Irish healthcare with particular reference to hospitals and to place such relationships in a comparative context with particular attention to developments in the United Kingdom

(ii) to analyse critically the current policy context in which voluntary health agencies (and in particular public voluntary hospitals) operate with respect to governance and management issues

(iii) to review theories of voluntary action in society seeking to articulate a philosophy of voluntary action as a basis for more appropriate and effective voluntary and statutory relationships in healthcare and upon which governance and management approaches and practices may be built consistent with such a philosophy and with the vocation of voluntary organisations in democratic societies

---

[16] for a valuable introduction to this growing literature and research see L.M. Salamon and H.K. Anheier *The Emerging NonProfit Sector An Overview*, Johns Hopkins Non Profit Sector Series 1, (Manchester University Press, Manchester, 1996)

[17] D. Billis *Organising Public and Voluntary Agencies*, (London, 1993), p. 2

[18] J. O'Dwyer 'Reflections on Future Structures in the Health Services', op. cit., p. 45

(iv) to explore the implications which flow from the philosophical underpinnings of voluntary action and from the policy analysis for governance and management of voluntary health agencies generally and in particular to outline and assess models of governance and management associated with voluntary hospitals.

The basic question in this study is whether there is a convincing philosophical justification for voluntary action in society in general, and in healthcare in particular, and if there is what are the implications for governance and management of voluntary health care organisations and in particular public voluntary hospitals. My personal reflection will provide a description of how the study evolved (see pp 269-276 below). Readers might like to read this first.

Resources and methodology

(i) *Author's experiences as a resource*

The author of this study is a historian.[19] He has worked since 1977 in national voluntary organisations. He was Chief Executive of Macra na Feirme, a large national voluntary youth organisation and then Director of The National Bible Society of Ireland which is a member of the international movement of Bible Societies known as the United Bible Societies. He spent two years, 1983–85, as a public servant on secondment to the then Department of Labour as Special Adviser on Youth Policy. Since 1993 he has worked as Director of The Adelaide Hospital Society, a charitable voluntary organisation which is one of three foundations which formed The Adelaide and Meath Hospital, Dublin, Incorporating The National Children's Hospital in August 1996 and which moved its three base public voluntary hospitals to a new single campus in Tallaght, Dublin 24, in June 1998. The author has served on the Board of The Adelaide Hospital prior to his appointment as Director of the Society and has served on the Board of the new Hospital since 1996. He has thus been a privileged 'participant-observer' in respect of developments which of necessity have brought the concerns of this research study to the fore. The author's experiences and perspectives are rooted in the

---

[19] He obtained a Ph.d. in 1978 from Trinity College, Dublin, for a thesis entitled *The Growth of Political Consciousness in Ireland 1823–1847 A Study of O'Connellite Politics and Political Education*; he has subsequently published *Catholic Emancipation Daniel O'Connell and the Birth of Irish Democracy 1820–30*, (Dublin, 1985) and *Daniel O'Connell*, (Gill's Irish Lives, Dublin, 1981)

voluntary sector but it is hoped that his training as a historian and the methodology employed will bring the necessary degree of objectivity to the study.

This background is an important resource for this study which is based upon a historical-contextual and relational approach.[20] This approach aims to generate a deeper and more appropriate theoretical understanding of the dynamic relationships between statutory and voluntary organisations in order to provide a more explicit overall context and framework in which governance and management issues may be more effectively studied and addressed. A contextual and relational perspective is required to increase understanding both of the role of the state and of the role of the voluntary sector. This understanding, in turn, is a precondition for appropriate policy decisions and action in relation to the governance and management of voluntary organisations.

(ii)   *Developing 'usable theory'*

R.M. Titmuss in his classic study *The Gift Relationship* 'in examining the extent to which specific instruments of public policy encourage or discourage, foster or destroy the individual expression of altruism and regard for the needs of others' found himself compelled to raise 'great questions' about freedom and to enquire

> if this freedom is to be paramount do we not then have to regard social policy institutions as agents of altruistic opportunities and, thus, as generators of moral conflict and not simply as utilitarian instruments of welfare.[21]

Likewise this research study will raise immensely important theoretical questions which will trespass unto the territory of the political philosopher, as well as that of the historian, health policy analyst, organisation theorist, management theorist and perhaps other disciplines as well. Voluntary sector studies inevitably

---

[20] for a similar perspective see the important studies in *Government and Voluntary Organizations A Relational Perspective*, eds. Stein Kuhnle and Per Selle (Avebury, Aldershot, Hants, 1992) especially Chapter 1 'Government and Voluntary Organisations: A Relational Perspective', pp 1–33

[21] see R.M. Titmuss *The Gift Relationship From Human Blood to Social Policy*, (London, 1970), pp 12–13, p. 243

become multi-disciplinary in order to seek answers to the great questions they invoke. The stance adopted in this study is that theory is of immense practical importance. J.M. Keynes famously stated

> Practical men, who believe themselves to be quite exempt from any intellectual influences, are usually the slaves of some defunct economist. Madmen in authority, who hear voices in the air, are distilling their frenzy from some academic scribbler of a few years back.[22]

Ideas matter in governance and management. Theories are even more important and applying an appropriate theory may be the most practical asset available when deciding issues in governance and management for we never govern or manage in the absence of 'intellectual influences'. It is best to make our theory overt or else we are simply in the state so well described by Henrik Ibsen in his play *Ghosts:*

> It's not just what we inherit from our mothers and fathers that haunt us. It's all kinds of old defunct theories, all sorts of old defunct beliefs, and things like that. It's not that they actually live on in us; they are simply lodged there, and we cannot get rid of them. I've only to pick up a newspaper and I seem to see ghosts gliding between the lines.[23]

The substantial attention to context and theory in Part I of this study is intended to contribute to what Billis has called 'usable theory' – 'ideas that make sense and can be utilized by those whose business it is to cope with the complexity and chaos'.[24] It is hoped that such 'usable theory' will be of assistance in designing best practice governance and management structures appropriate to the twenty first century, in preference to 'all kinds of old defunct theories, all sorts of old defunct beliefs'. As Charles Perrow has noted:

> One test of good theory is that it have practical implications . . . relevant theory, however, is not the same as useful techniques . . . What good theory does is show how to analyze an organisation or an organization problem so that judicious selections of specific techniques can be made.[25]

---

[22] J.M. Keynes *The General Theory of Employment Interest and Money*, (1936), ch 24, v

[23] H. Ibsen *Ghosts*, (1881) Act 2

[24] D. Billis *Organising Public and Voluntary Agencies*, (London, 1993), p. 2

[25] Charles Perrow *Organizational Analysis: A Sociological View* (London, 1970) p. vii

(iii) *Methodology*

This study is based upon qualitative methods and approaches; of particular relevance will be historical analysis, health policy analysis, political
theory, management and organisation theory, case study and participant observation. The study commences with a historical and comparative analysis of voluntary and statutory relationships in Ireland with a
focus upon voluntary hospitals and health care (Chapter 1) followed by
an analysis of Irish health policy in the 1990s in respect of voluntary
and statutory relationships (Chapter 2). Health policy is not simply
concerned with content: it is about process and power. As Gill Walt
observes

> It is concerned with who influences whom in the making of policy,
> and how that happens. Although many agree that politics cannot be
> separated from policy, few books on health policy or health planning
> talk explicitly about political systems, power and influence, and
> people's participation in policy making.[26]

Walt's perspective is adopted in the analysis of Irish health policy in
the 1990s.

In Chapter 3 the extensive literature in relation to the nonprofit
and voluntary sector is reviewed in particular with respect to theories of
voluntary action. Recent political theory is examined in order to
outline a philosophy of voluntary action which will 'usable' in the Irish
policy context. Of particular relevance here are political theories of
liberalism rooted in the work of John Stuart Mill, of communitarianism
as described in the work of Amitai Etzioni and of 'civil society' as
described in recent work by political theorists such as John Keane. The
work of Hannah Arendt and civic republican theory emerges as of
particular importance in relation to a political and social philosophy of
active citizenship in which the voluntary sector would find legitimacy. A
fresh statement of a legitimating philosophy is essential for the
voluntary sector to enjoy a public policy context in which it might
flourish within appropriate voluntary and statutory relationships.

The three chapters which comprise Part I, therefore, provide an
analysis of the rapidly changing context of the relationships between
voluntary and statutory bodies. This analysis is vital in order to treat
successfully the implications for governance and management of these
dynamic relationships. Part I also suggests a philosophical basis upon

---

[26] G. Walt *Health Policy An Introduction To Process and Power*, (London, 1994), p. 1

11

which evaluations might be made of appropriate models of governance and management for voluntary organisations. Part II is specifically concerned with implications for public voluntary hospitals. It commences with an assessment of governance and management in hospitals, exploring the available practices and models in the international literature in order to enquire whether there are models and practices appropriate in particular to voluntary healthcare provision. (Chapter 4). A detailed case study is undertaken of The Adelaide and Meath Hospital, Dublin, Incorporating The National Children's Hospital established in August 1996. This large public voluntary teaching Hospital, the result of a merger of three base hospitals, developed a distinctive model of governance and management. The relationships between the Hospital and the Department of Health and Children and the effects of such relationships upon governance and management in the Hospital are explored in detail. (Chapter 5). Selected interviews conducted with 'key informants' with central roles in the case studied, explore voluntary and statutory perspectives on the key issues raised in respect of governance and management in healthcare in Chapter 6.

This chapter will attempt normative prescriptions for governance and management of voluntary organisations and in particular for public voluntary hospitals, arising from the context, theory and experiences documented in the study. Chapter 7 provides a critique of the 'managerialist' approach to governance and management which is contrasted with a citizen-based voluntarist approach. This concluding chapter will be concerned with how far the basic question concerning the philosophical justification for voluntary action has been answered and what benefits might flow from the study. The chapter suggests that the study has provided

(a) an explicit philosophical framework for voluntary action in Irish society

(b) clarification as to the definition and assumptions made in respect of what constitutes a 'voluntary' agency in the Irish health services

(c) delineation of appropriate future roles and relationships between voluntary and statutory agencies in the context of optimum healthcare provision

(d) analysis of governance and management models now available to hospitals and a unique description of the experiences of one large public voluntary hospital; some recommendations are made in respect of board development, education and training together with interrelated management development proposals

(e)   an outline of some key concepts and approaches which are now central to developing governance, leadership and management of voluntary services in healthcare and specifically in public voluntary hospitals

(f)   a contribution to the emerging policy framework for the Irish voluntary sector particularly in the light of the policy discourse stemming from the Green Paper published in 1997 and the proposed White Paper in the Irish Republic.

The study concludes with a reflection by the author on the method, theory and data employed.

PART I

The Changing Context

CHAPTER 1

Voluntary and Statutory Relationships: The Irish Experience to 1989 in a historical and comparative context

'The excellence of the work of a democratic State depends largely upon the quality of its citizens. Individuals do not become intelligent and public-spirited citizens merely by keeping the law, paying rates and taxes, and recording their votes at elections. They require opportunities of insight into the lives of their fellows and into the practical work of group administration. This kind of insight is given by active participation in the work of voluntary associations and of public bodies alike: it is all an expression of voluntary citizenship.'

CONSTANCE BRAITHWAITE *The Voluntary Citizen: an enquiry into the place of philanthropy in the community* (London, 1938), p. 80

'Ultimately this is a story about the nature of the State in independent Ireland, in particular the relationship between the State and voluntary institutions, most specifically in this instance, the Catholic Church.'

MARY E. DALY 'An Atmosphere of Sturdy Independence: The State and the Dublin Hospitals in the 1930s' in *Medicine, Disease and the State in Ireland, 1650–1940*, eds. G. Jones and E. Malcolm (Cork University Press Cork, 1999) p. 234

17

1. INTRODUCTION

The purpose of this chapter is to trace voluntary and statutory relationships in Ireland against the background of the growth of the modern 'welfare' state up to 1989. Developments in the United Kingdom are documented initially for comparative purposes. As will be briefly described below there was a keen awareness in Ireland of the impact of the welfare state on health service development in the United Kingdom from the 1940s so it is valuable to compare developments in both countries. Ireland shared with the United Kingdom traditions of governance and public administration prior to independence in 1922 and Irish policy developments frequently followed United Kingdom models and patterns in the decades after 1922. It will emerge that the Catholic majoritarian effect in the Irish State provides the most significant factor in the contrasting experiences of both states. Voluntary action in Ireland, with particular reference to public voluntary hospitals is described and the influence of the Roman Catholic Church and Catholic social thought on the voluntary sector is explored.

2. THE VOLUNTARY IMPULSE AND THE GROWTH OF THE MODERN STATE: THE UK EXPERIENCE

Since the eighteenth century voluntary agencies have played a major part in a wide range of social developments in western societies. Voluntary organisations in the United Kingdom as elsewhere have been greatly influenced and shaped by whether the state was prepared to assume certain responsibilities for services in society.[1] Over the last two hundred years the balance between voluntary organisations and the state has shifted remarkably and is currently undergoing considerable flux and development. The twentieth century has been characterised by the increasing responsibilities assumed by the state and the emergence of the 'welfare state' particularly since the 1940s.

The impact of the growth of the modern state on voluntary organisations may be traced in the United Kingdom through a succession of studies and reports.[2] In 1934 Elizabeth Macadam's *The New Philanthropy*

[1] a useful bibliographic summary of the literature to 1985 is Margaret Harris and David Billis *Organising Voluntary Agencies A Guide Through the Literature* (London, 1985); valuable historical perspectives may also be traced in the contributions to *The Nonprofit Sector A Research Handbook* ed. W.W. Powell, (New Haven and London, 1987)

[2] a valuable introduction to these is F. Prochaska *The Voluntary Impulse Philanthropy in Modern Britain* (London, 1988) see also D. Owen *English Philanthropy 1660–1960* (London, 1964)

observed in Great Britain 'a system of combined statutory and voluntary social service developed during the last forty years which is quite unrivalled elsewhere. This unique partnership I called the new philanthropy'.[3] Constance Braithwaite's *The Voluntary Citizen An Enquiry into the Place of Philanthropy in the Community*, published in 1938, attempted to address the urgent problem of 'evolving the right relationships between the State and its citizens' as 'we are faced with the very difficult task of combining a large degree of public control of economic life with a preservation and extension of the spirit of democracy'. Braithwaite argued that philanthropy 'is essentially an expression of voluntary citizenship' and she believed that

> The excellence of the work of a democratic State depends largely upon the quality of its citizens. Individuals do not become intelligent and public-spirited citizens merely by keeping the law, paying rates and taxes, and recording their votes at elections. They require opportunities of insight into the lives of their fellows and into the practical work of group administration. This kind of insight is given by active participation in the work of voluntary associations and of public bodies alike: it is all an expression of voluntary citizenship. The qualities of citizenship desirable in the democratic community of the future are far more likely to be developed by this kind of means than by methods of mass propaganda and deification of the State'.[4]

The public debate in the 1940s on the 'welfare state' is marked by two classic studies of voluntary action. The first study, edited by A.F.C. Bourdillon, sought to identify the characteristics and place of voluntary social services in the modern state arguing that the essential characteristics of a voluntary organisation are not the products of its work

> . . . but of their mode of birth and method of government. A voluntary organisation properly speaking is an organisation which, whether its workers are paid or unpaid, is initiated and governed by its own members without external control. Such a body may well undertake work on behalf of a statutory authority, but if it is to qualify as a voluntary organisation it is essential that it should select or co-operate in selecting what that work shall be and how it shall be done.[5]

[3] E. Macadam *The New Philanthropy A Study of the Relations between the Statutory and Voluntary Social Services* (London, 1934) p. 18, p. 285

[4] Constance Braithwaite *The Voluntary Citizen; an enquiry into the place of philanthropy in the community* (London, 1938) pp 78–80

[5] A.F.C. Bourdillon, Introduction, *Voluntary Social Services their Place in the Modern State* ed. A.F.C. Bourdillon (London, 1945), p. 3

It was clear that the roles and functions of voluntary organisations would undergo major transformations as the 'welfare state' developed. In terms of post-World War II social reconstruction questions in social policy were bound to revolve around how voluntary action should relate to state provision. Bourdillon noted the gaps in the literature 'on this subtle subject' and the need for further study 'particularly by those who would approach the subject from the historical point of view'. She felt that the key to the whole subject 'is to be found in the idea of historical development. The extreme difficulty of arriving at an agreement on definitions is mainly due to the fact that the matter in need of definition is in a perpetual state of growth and that the ideas of several generations co-exist at the present time'.[6] Many of the early proponents of the welfare state assumed that voluntary agencies would simply wither away as the state assumed its full role in society. It is important however to note that the second classic text of the 1940s is by the key figure behind the philosophy of the new 'welfare state', Sir William Beveridge, who argued for a vital role for voluntary action in society and for a fruitful balance between voluntary organisations and statutory bodies.

Beveridge saw his 1948 report on *Voluntary Action* as an 'appropriate sequel and completion' to his work which he began with his famous report in 1942 on *Social Insurance and Allied Services*. He was particularly concerned to foster voluntary action, that is action 'not under the directions of any authority wielding the power of the State' but action 'for a public purpose—for social advance'. He believed that the defining characteristic of voluntary action was 'independence from public control'. Such independence does not mean lack of co-operation between voluntary and statutory bodies but voluntary action 'does imply that the agency undertaking it has a will and a life of its own'. Beveridge believed that 'the vigour and abundance of Voluntary Action outside one's home, individually and in association with other citizens, for bettering one's own life and that of one's fellows are the distinguishing marks of a free society'. *Voluntary Action* dealt with both the mutual aid motive and with the philanthropic motive in considerable detail. Beveridge was clearly very worried about how 'Voluntary Action is being affected by a continual stream of legislation'. In this changing environment he focused upon the challenge of reconciling the responsibilities of the State with the vital need to sustain a society characterised by voluntary action:

[6] ibid, p. 8

It is clear that the State must in future do more things than it has attempted in the past. But it is equally clear, or should be equally clear, that room, opportunity, and encouragement must be kept for Voluntary Action in seeking new ways of social advance. There is need for political invention to find new ways of fruitful co-operation between public authorities and voluntary agencies.[7]

It is important to note that Beveridge's *Voluntary Action*, though central to his particular brand of liberal collectivism, became a 'forgotten text' in social policy: the editors of the Beveridge anthology of his writings in 1987 argue that *Voluntary Action* 'is a crucial lost text' which provided a blueprint for the development of voluntary provision in a state of enlarged responsibilities.[8] In the 1940s in Britain there occurred in the creation of the National Health Service, for both ideological and pragmatic considerations, a transfer of 'the vast network of charity hospitals from voluntary auspices to central government control, representing a massive shift of resources to the public sector'.[9] Beveridge's belief in the value of voluntary action carried little weight in the first flush of the new Welfare State.

The subsequent debates of the 1950s and later may be traced in studies by Trevelyan and Rooff.[10] Rooff's analysis is pertinent to voluntary and statutory relationships as they developed historically in Britain. She explores in detail the long history and deep roots behind the combinations of voluntary and public action in social policy since the seventeenth century and which evolved into a unique partnership of voluntary and statutory action in twentieth century Britain. In particular she traces a number of types of partnership such as 'dual control' in respect of education or 'spheres of influence' where a negative form

[7] see Lord Beveridge *Voluntary Action A Report on the Method of Social Advance* (London, 1948) pp 8–10; Beveridge presented a supplemental volume *The Evidence for Voluntary Action Being Memoranda by Organisations and Individuals and other Material Relevant to Voluntary Action* eds Lord Beveridge and A.F. Wells (London, 1949); on Beveridge generally see J. Harris *William Beveridge A Biography* (Oxford, first published 1977 and revised edition 1997); it is notable that the revised edition devotes much more attention to *Voluntary Action* than did the first edition. See also *A Beveridge Reader* eds. K. Williams and J. Williams (London, 1987)

[8] *A Beveridge Reader*, op. cit., p. 1 and p. 145

[9] for the place of health services in the UK's voluntary sector see J. Kendall and M. Knapp *The Voluntary Sector in the UK* Johns Hopkins Non Profit Sector Series 8 (Manchester University Press, Manchester, 1996); p. 2 for quotation

[10] see John Trevelyan *Voluntary Service and the State* (London, 1952) which is important in respect of hospital services and Madeline Rooff *Voluntary Societies and Social Policy* (London, 1957)

of partnership obtained as in the Poor Law arrangements whereby certain activities were left to voluntary provision and others assumed by State agencies.

In the context of the later revival of confidence and interest in the role of the voluntary sector in social services note should be made of the influential but unofficial Aves Committee's *Report on the Voluntary Worker in the Social Services* (London, 1969). This Report laid a tentative basis for a rehabilitation of volunteer work within the British philosophy of social welfare and implicitly suggested the need for a coherent theory of voluntarism in the changing context.

The Wolfenden Committee Report *The Future of Voluntary Organisations*, published in 1978, stands as a landmark in the more recent United Kingdom literature. It provides an overview of the voluntary sector and its inter-relationships with other sectors and also raised issues about the internal working and effectiveness of individual agencies. The Wolfenden Committee made a distinction between the voluntary, the informal, the statutory and the commercial systems for meeting social need; their Report saw the voluntary sector as subsidiary to the informal and statutory sectors in respect of meeting social needs but sought more scope for voluntary endeavour within the statutory framework. The study by Gladstone, published in 1979, reviewed the record of the welfare state and argued for a change of approach towards 'welfare pluralism' and more voluntary action.[11] This was followed in 1981 by an important study by Hadley and Hatch which provided a critique of the expansion of centralised statutory services and suggested that a pluralist, participative and decentralised pattern of services was required which could maximise the contribution of the informal and voluntary sectors within a framework of priorities and standards set by the statutory sector.[12]

In the 1980s the voluntary sector began to receive greater attention in terms of policy studies and academic focus at national and international levels.[13] The apologetic tone which dominated discussion of the

[11] F. Gladstone *Voluntary Action in a Changing World* (London, 1979)

[12] R. Hadley and S. Hatch *Social Welfare and the Failure of the State* (London, 1981); see also the international study R.M. Kramer *Voluntary Agencies in the Welfare State* (University of California Press, 1981) and N. Johnson *The Welfare State in Transition: the Theory and Practice of Welfare Pluralism* (Brighton, 1987)

[13] for the relatively strong research tradition in the UK on the voluntary sector embracing historians, legal scholars, social policy analysts, management theorists and practitioners see J. Kendall and M. Knapp *The Voluntary Sector in the UK* John Hopkins Non Profit Sector Series 8 (Manchester University Press, Manchester, 1996) p. ix

role of the voluntary sector during the heyday of the 'welfare state' disappeared and a new phase of more positive and ambitious thinking about the role and influence of voluntary organisations emerged. Maria Brenton's study *The Voluntary Sector in British Social Services* (London, 1985) provides an important overview of the relationships between voluntary and statutory agencies in the mid-1980s when the limits of the 'welfare state' were clearly evident and the debates on 'welfare pluralism' and 'partnership' were well underway. The upsurge in interest in the potential of non-governmental alternatives to the delivery of social services by the State was by then very apparent raising ideological issues of fundamental importance as to the role and responsibilities of the State. Upon the resolution of these issues would depend the answer as to whether the voluntary sector would have an integral role or a marginal role in society and in the provision of services. There had emerged a very clear need for a coherent theory of voluntary action that would specify the role of voluntary organisations in advanced economies and societies of the late twentieth century.[14] This brief survey of the literature in the United Kingdom in respect of voluntary and statutory relationships has indicated a relatively rich discourse concerning such relationships in a democratic society with important themes such as voluntary citizenship, the need for scope for voluntary organisations in a free society, and the search for appropriate relationships with the state through 'partnership' which would be supported by a more explicit theory of voluntary action. The experiences of voluntary action in Ireland contrast markedly and will now be outlined with a focus on healthcare provision. Reference will be made to UK developments in healthcare as appropriate.

3. VOLUNTARY ACTION IN IRELAND WITH PARTICULAR REFERENCE TO VOLUNTARY HOSPITALS

There is evidence that traditional Irish culture was characterised by co-operation and mutual aid amongst neighbours in order to complete agricultural tasks such as harvesting, or turf cutting. The words 'comhar' ('co-operation') or 'meitheal' ('a working party') were used

---

[14] see R. Kramer *Voluntary Organisations in The Welfare State: On the Threshold of The '90s* Working Paper 8 (The Centre for Voluntary Organisation, The London School of Economics and Political Science, London, 1990) for an useful overview of the literature of the 1980s on the interrelationships of the voluntary sector and the Welfare State

in this context.[15] The eighteenth and nineteenth centuries were characterised in terms of social action by a wide range of philanthropic and voluntary charitable bodies which are receiving increasing scholarly attention.[16] Perhaps because of traditional social and cultural factors and because of the particular motivations of, and indeed conflicts between, the various religious denominations, Ireland has been notable for the range and extent of voluntary action in society. Freda Donoghue provides a brief overview of the development of philanthropy and voluntary action in Ireland in her valuable Working Paper for the Johns Hopkins Comparative Nonprofit Sector Project.[17] In this context note might be made of the Irish co-operative movement in agriculture from the 1890s, and the development of major rural organisations such as the Irish Countrywomen's Association, Muintir na Tire, and Macra na Feirme. In addition Irish language organisations, especially the Gaelic League and sporting organisations particularly the Gaelic Athletic Association, are major voluntary movements in the Irish context.[18] For a range of reasons perhaps especially those associated with a relatively impoverished independent state, voluntary organisations resisted the encroachments of the 'welfare state' longer and more successfully in Ireland than was the case in the United Kingdom.

Voluntary hospitals were established during the eighteenth and nineteenth centuries by philanthropic individuals, groups of doctors or religious bodies in response to a genuine concern for the condition of the sick poor and also in response to the growth of a more clinical hospital-based approach to the teaching of medicine. This voluntary hospital movement can be traced through the establishment of the Charitable Infirmary (1718) Dr. Steevens' Hospital (1720) Mercer's Hospital (1734) the Rotunda Lying-In Hospital (1745) and The Meath

[15] see C.M. Arensberg and S.T. Kimball *Family and Community in Ireland* (Cambridge, Mass., 1968); H. Brody *Inishkillane* (Harmonsworth, 1974)

[16] see, in particular, M. Luddy *Women and Philanthropy in Nineteenth Century Ireland* (Cambridge, 1995)

[17] Freda Donoghue 'Defining The Nonprofit Sector: Ireland' *Working Papers of the John Hopkins Comparative Nonprofit Sector Project* No. 28, edited by L.M. Salamon and H.K. Anheier (Baltimore: the Johns Hopkins Institute for Policy Studies, 1998), pp 2–4

[18] The histories of such organisations is often best approached through biographical studies; see for examples G. Mitchell *Deeds Not Words the Life and Work of Muriel Gahan* (Dublin, 1997); J.E. and G.W. Dunleavy *Douglas Hyde; A Maker of Modern Ireland* (University of California Press, Berkeley and Los Angeles, California, 1991); T. West *Horace Plunkett: Co-operation and Politics An Irish Biography* (Gerrard's Cross, Buckinghamshire, 1986); there are organisational histories also see for example, J. Miley *A Voice For the Country Fifty Years of Macra na Feirme* (Macra na Feirme, Dublin, 1994)

Hospital (1753), in the eighteenth century and St. Vincent's Hospital (1834), the Adelaide Hospital (1839), the Mercy Hospital, Cork (1857) and the Mater Misericordiae Hospital in Dublin (1861) in the nineteenth century.[19]

Health care is integral to and develops out of the wider religious, scientific, philosophical and political beliefs embedded in the culture which surrounds it. Thus exploration of voluntary and statutory relationships in providing health services requires an examination of the mentalités which governed such relationships. In the nineteenth century, statutory provision, based mainly on the Poor Law, was minimal and social needs were generally met, if they were met at all, by voluntary endeavour. This reflected the limited conception of the role of the State that prevailed until the twentieth century. As Rooff states 'For a great part of the 19th century the prevailing social philosophy denied the responsibility of the community for the welfare of its adult citizens . . . Until the 1870s Individualism dominated thought, and Laissez-Faire was widely accepted as the proper role of the State'.[20] In the nineteenth century the State had assumed some responsibility for medical relief of the poor in the context of the Poor Law and through workhouse hospitals and the dispensary medical service. The State also assumed some responsibilities in respect of public health seeking to prevent and contain outbreaks of infectious diseases.

The origins of the current arrangements for preventing and treating illness have been analysed by Ruth Barrington's valuable history of the Irish health services from 1900–1970.[21] A key feature of the development of the Irish health services in the twentieth century has been the gradual expansion of State responsibility. The Irish

---

[19] There is an extensive institutional literature on these hospitals which is discussed and listed in G. Jones, E. Malcolm 'Introduction: An Anatomy of Irish Medical History' in *Medicine, Disease and the State in Ireland 1650–1940*, ed. J. Jones and E. Malcolm (Cork University Press, 1999), pp 1 - 17; for examples see P. Gatenby *Dublin's Meath Hospital 1753–1996* (Dublin, 1996); J.B. Lyons *The Quality of Mercer's The Story of Mercer's Hospital 1734–1991* (Dublin, 1991); F.O.C. Meenan *St. Vincent's Hospital 1834–1994 An Historical and Social Portrait* (Dublin, 1995); D. Mitchell *A 'Peculiar' Place The Adelaide Hospital Its Times, Places and Personalities 1839 to 1989* (Dublin {1989}); see also Davis Coakley's three important works *The Irish School of Medicine Outstanding Practitioners of the 19th Century* (Dublin, 1988); *Robert Graves Evangelist of Clinical Medicine* (Dublin, 1996); *Irish Masters of Medicine* (Dublin, 1992)

[20] Rooff *Voluntary Societies and Social Policy* op. cit., pp 3–4

[21] R. Barrington *Health, Medicine and Politics in Ireland 1900–1970* (Dublin, 1987); the summary of the relationships between voluntary hospitals and the state which follows is based on this study

hospital system had a long and complex evolution of which the main features were hospitals funded by religious or voluntary action and hospitals, such as country infirmaries, supported by public funds. Voluntary hospitals, while independent of statutory control, were often in receipt of government grants but they existed in what was well described as 'an atmosphere of sturdy independence'.[22] As Barrington notes 'the only link between the State and these hospitals was through an annual grant voted by parliament towards their upkeep, a legacy from the days of the Irish parliament in the eighteenth century. This grant was not used to influence the activities of the hospitals in any way'.[23] The voluntary hospitals were particularly important for the medical schools associated with them and for the clinical training of doctors and of nurses. Doctors on the staff of the hospitals were not remunerated for their services but they gained entry to private practice and income from medical tuition through association with a hospital of repute. These voluntary hospitals were governed and managed by either Catholic or Protestant governors or boards as the Churches wished to provide for the spiritual as well as the medical needs of the patients. The voluntary hospitals sought to provide for the poorer sections of the population within their wards while the wealthier section of the population were treated as private patients often in their homes. There was an increasing trend, however, for those who could afford to pay the cost of medical treatment to be admitted to 'pay beds' or private accommodation closely associated with the hospitals. Barrington observes:

'The voluntary hospitals, both Catholic and Protestant, enjoyed great prestige, through their boards of management, subscribers and medical staffs. Their physicians and surgeons were the leaders of the medical profession in Ireland, dominating medical organisation, medical teaching and the affairs of the professional colleges such as the Royal Colleges of Physicians and Surgeons. These hospitals, with relatively high standards of medical, surgical and nursing care, set the standard by which the county and workhouse infirmaries were judged by contemporaries.'[24]

---

[22] see the valuable analysis of the state and the voluntary hospitals by M.E. Daly 'An Atmosphere of Sturdy Independence': The State and the Dublin Hospitals in the 1930s' in Jones and Malcolm *Medicine, Disease and the State in Ireland 1650–1940*, op. cit., pp 234–252; the phrase came from the Hospital Commission Report, 1933–4, published in 1936 see Daly, p. 245

[23] Barrington, op. cit., p. 14

[24] Barrington, op. cit., p. 16

As the view gained acceptance in Western societies that access to medical care should be based on need rather than charity or ability to pay, that such access was a right of all citizens in democratic societies, the State began to assume much greater responsibility for the welfare of its citizens. This inevitably led the State to encroach on the voluntary providers and it was obliged to relate to the Churches, especially the powerful Catholic Church, in a new way. The twentieth century has been marked by tense and often subterranean conflicts in this regard.

Barrington notes that by the late 1920s

> 'the voluntary hospitals in Dublin were in a desperate way. The value of their endowment funds was reduced by inflation during and after the First World War and income from new charitable sources fell away. At the same time, costs rose as advances in radiology, pathology and surgery required new facilities and staff. The hospitals were increasingly dependent on income from paying patients and organised collections. The income from paying patients in six voluntary hospitals in Dublin averaged £2,000 a year before the war; in the 1920s the income had risen to an average of £24,000.'[25]

A conflict was inevitable between the charitable commitment to the poor and the need to remain financially solvent. The voluntary hospitals could only provide accommodation for poor patients as far as their charitable income would permit. This led to *The Public Charitable Hospitals Act, 1930* which authorised a monopoly in the promotion of sweepstakes on horse races for Dublin hospital purposes. The first step towards greater involvement by public authorities in the affairs of these hospitals was the authorisation and supervision of the hospitals sweep-stakes.[26] As Barrington notes 'As unprecedented amounts of money became available for hospital development, the state, in its role of guardian of the common good, was challenged to develop a hospital policy for the whole country and for both voluntary and public hospitals'.[27] *The Public Hospitals Act, 1933*, clearly indicated that voluntary hospitals would be expected to work in harmony with an overall plan for hospital development in Ireland. In the 1930s the State, for the first time, asserted the right to direct the development of

---

[25] Barrington, op. cit., p. 108

[26] The Adelaide Hospital refused to participate in the Hospitals Sweepstakes and attempted an 'Anti-Sweep combine' with Mercer's Hospital and Dr. Steevens' Hospital but these two Hospitals did soon participate so The Adelaide Hospital 'alone stood out for over 30 years' see D. Mitchell *A 'Peculiar' Place* op. cit., p. 164

[27] Barrington, op. cit., pp 111–112

hospital services in the public interest.[28] A Hospital Commission was established and charged with the task of surveying hospital facilities in each area, reporting on applications from voluntary hospitals for grants from the sweepstakes funds and with power to inspect any hospital and examine receipts and expenditures. The *Public Hospitals Act, 1933*, was denounced as 'the death knell of all voluntary hospitals in this country' and was viewed, according to Barrington, by the voluntary hospitals 'as an act of piracy by the government'.[29] In fact the voluntary hospitals faced stark choices: accept some state control in return for the necessary resources, close or become wholly private. The developing context for hospital care had led to a changing role for the voluntary hospital not only in Ireland but in Britain and the United States. By the1930s medical advances had made the hospital the pivot of modern medicine and many more were seeking hospital treatment than previously. Barrington notes that the Irish voluntary hospitals 'remained independent of the state but it was an uneasy independence. A reduction of sweepstake funds or an ill-disposed Minister could bring about a radical change in fortune; and it is understandable that their attitude to the state should have become somewhat paranoid'.[30] As Daly notes 'the 1933 Act came into effect without any clear understanding as to the extent of State power to intervene in the running of voluntary hospitals. The Government's hand was weakened because the funds came, not from the exchequer, but from a sweepstake which had been initiated by the voluntary hospitals'.[31]

By 1935, the proportion of patients treated free in voluntary hospitals had fallen to 40%.[32] This underlined the need for the state to plan hospital provision for the whole population. The Hospital Commission began its work in September 1933. In the period of its first report, 1933–36, it found just over 14,000 acute hospital beds, of which 63% were in publicly owned hospitals and the remaining 37% in voluntary hospitals. The Commission, while recommending an expansion of the voluntary hospitals to meet the needs of Dublin, was critical of the situation existing in the voluntary hospitals in Dublin:

[28] ibid, p. 117

[29] Barrington, op. cit., p. 118

[30] ibid, pp 118–119

[31] M.E. Daly 'An Atmosphere of Sturdy Independence: The State and the Dublin Hospitals in the 1930s' in *Medicine, Disease and the State in Ireland 1650–1940*, eds. Malcolm and Jones, op. cit., p. 244

[32] Barrington, op. cit, p. 119

facilities were out of date, co-operation between specialists was lacking, and medical teaching was falling behind international standards. It recommended amalgamation into two general hospitals in south Dublin and two for north Dublin. As Barrington observes

> In a clear warning to the voluntary hospitals, it suggested that St. Kevin's, the former workhouse for south Dublin, be developed as the chief hospital and clinical teaching centre in Dublin, if the voluntary hospitals failed to respond to the challenge of providing sufficient accommodation for the poor.[33]

The voluntary hospitals, in effect, were now required to see themselves as part of a system and to respond to national policy for hospital provision. The Hospital Commission emphasised that the hospitals should be run as charitable institutions, that they treat a certain proportion of patients without charge and that the Minister, by supervision and inspection, should insist that these conditions were met.

The hospital system expanded in the 1930s and 1940s with thirteen new county hospitals, seventeen district hospitals and eight fever hospitals being completed by 1942.[34] The Dublin voluntary hospitals were slow to accept and respond to the new arrangements established by the *Public Hospitals Act, 1933*. The Commission blamed their refusal to co-operate on 'the tenacity with which those hospitals cling to their time-honoured claim for complete individual independence'.[35] Yet the hospitals' income from charitable sources fell off sharply as the funds raised by the sweepstakes rose and this led to increasing hospital deficits as demand grew upon hospital services. Voluntary hospitals received no payment from local authorities for the treatment of poor patients, but were obliged to maintain beds for non-paying patients if they wished to benefit from the sweepstake funds. Therefore, as Barrington notes 'it is not surprising that they should have accumulated deficits'.[36] Medical consultants and denominational interests, especially those of the Catholic Church, resisted any scheme which would interfere with the management and control of voluntary hospitals while the Government, through the Department of Local Government and Public Health, was concerned with securing adequate

[33] Barrington, op. cit., p. 121
[34] Barrington, op. cit., p. 124
[35] ibid, p. 124
[36] ibid, p. 125

accommodation for free patients and with protecting its rights of inspection.[37]

The rise in deficits was the occasion for greater Government involvement in hospital management. Payments from the Hospital Trust Fund were only approved on the basis of accounts submitted and hospitals were asked to send in quarterly statements of expenditure. The Commission remarked that 'hospitals should be looked upon as business establishments as far as their management is concerned'.[38] The tensions generated by the hospitals' deficits damaged relations between the State and the hospitals. It is important to quote Barrington in this regard:

> 'The hospitals, on the one hand, could point to the fact that they were responding to the increasing demand for hospitalisation without due recompense from the state. They resented demands that they should improve their management, instead of being paid for the job they were doing. All the major hospitals had been established long before the new state was set up. The Protestant hospitals were suspicious of the overwhelmingly Catholic ethos of the state and its government; the Catholic hospitals jealously guarded their special position against state interference. By maintaining a policy of minimal co-operation with the Hospitals Commission, the hospitals made clear their determination to retain their independence of the state. Their medical staff, who had most to lose from any change in the status quo, and who were dismayed by the rapid development of a modern public hospital network outside of Dublin, became increasingly anxious about state interference with the voluntary hospitals.[39]

Sir William Beveridge's Report *Social Insurance and Allied Services*, published in 1942, had a considerable influence on public opinion in Ireland where it was widely read and discussed. Beveridge's combination of radical proposals for comprehensive social insurance and a universal health service with conservative views on the role of the state and the need for voluntary initiative and responsibility had appeal for those in Ireland seeking health reforms. Irish political and social philosophy was dominated by the fact that the majority of the people were Roman Catholic and effectively under the social control of orthodoxies as propounded by a conservative Catholic hierarchy. Tom Inglis states:

[37] see M.E. Daly 'An Atmosphere of Sturdy Independence: The State and the Dublin Hospitals in the 1930s' in *Medicine, Disease and the State in Ireland 1651–1940* eds. Malcolm and Jones, op. cit., pp 246–250

[38] quoted in Barrington, op. cit., p. 125

[39] Barrington, op. cit., p. 126

The Catholic Church has had enormous influence in the health field in modern Ireland . . . Twenty-six of the 63 hospitals in the Republic are Catholic voluntary hospitals. The ownership and control of hospitals and the representation of Catholic religious on the boards of public hospitals has meant that the church has been able to exert considerable influence on the way medicine is practised, written and talked about; on the teaching, training and appointment of doctors and nurses; and over hospital ethics and the type of medical procedures available to patients.[40]

As Joseph Lee has observed in respect of the drafting of the 1937 Irish Constitution: 'republican rhetoric had to be reconciled with Catholic reality'.[41] The distinctive Catholic contribution to social thought in the 1930s and 1940s concerned a corporatist (or vocationalist) reorganisation of Irish society.[42] The stimulus to this had been Pope Pius XI's 1931 encyclical *Quadragesimo Anno*. In brief, this approach saw the task of the state as a facilitating one allowing activity by voluntary groups within society to flourish. It enshrined in paragraph 79 the important principle of subsidiarity 'It is an injustice . . . to assign to a greater and higher association what lesser and subordinate organisations can do'.

This principle of subsidiarity not only coloured the approach of many in the 1930s and 1940s when there were bitter clashes over health services and the role of the state in Ireland but it has remained an important European approach being adopted, for example, in the 1992 Maastricht *Treaty on European Union* in respect of member states and the Union (Article 3B). It continues to be cited in defence of publicly funded Catholic hospitals against a perceived risk of encroachment by the state.[43] As O'Sullivan has observed:

---

[40] see T. Inglis *Moral Monopoly The Rise and Fall of the Catholic Church in Modern Ireland* 2nd Edition (University College Dublin Press, Dublin, 1998) p. 226 and for origins of this control see pp 125 - 128

[41] J. Lee *Ireland 19132–1985 Politics and Society* (Cambridge, 1989), p. 206

[42] see J. Lee 'Aspects of Corporatist Thought in Ireland: the Commission on Vocational Organisation 1939–43' in *Studies in Irish History* eds. A. Cosgrave and D. McCartney (Dublin, 1979) and his analysis in his *Ireland 1912–1985* op. cit., pp 271–77; E. McLoughlin 'Ireland: Catholic Corporatism' in *Comparing Welfare States: Britain in International Context* eds. A. Cochrane and J. Clarke (Sage, London, 1993) pp 205–237; see also T. Brown *Ireland A Social and Cultural History 1922–1985* (London, 1985), pp 160–1

[43] Address by Archbishop D. Connell at the Annual General Meeting of Mater Hospital, 3 September 1996 cited in T. O'Sullivan 'Changing Relationships and the Voluntary and Statutory Sectors' in *A Healthier Future? Managing Healthcare in Ireland* ed. E. McAuliffe and L. Joyce, (Dublin, 1998) p. 188

31

Subsidiarity is an important principle which draws attention to the important role played in civil society both by voluntary organisations and by individuals who take initiatives in contributing to the voluntary sector; and to the need for such organisations and individuals to enjoy the freedom to take appropriate initiatives.[44]

Developments in the United Kingdom during the 1940s, however, impacted upon such concepts of voluntary-statutory relationships in Irish healthcare leading to radical challenges to church dominance and to the principle of subsidiarity.

The British White Paper *A National Health Service*, which followed the famous Beveridge Report, led to much consideration about what course health reforms should take in Ireland. Beveridge believed that comprehensive social insurance could only provide against loss of income, one of the 'five giants on the road of reconstruction—the others are Disease, Ignorance, Squalor and Idleness'. To combat disease he recommended a 'health service providing full preventive and curative treatment of every kind to every citizen without exceptions, without remuneration limit and without an economic barrier at any point to delay recourse to it'.[45] There were great fears in Catholic and medical circles of 'state medicine'. In 1946 in Northern Ireland hospitals were placed under the jurisdiction of a new Hospitals Authority, but the Mater in Belfast, the only Catholic voluntary hospital in the province, remained outside the system until 1972.[46] Bishop John Dignam, Bishop of Clonfert produced a plan in 1945 which was 'an explicit alternative to a state-organised medical service' which was dismissed by the Government.[47] The Irish Government prepared for a new and expanded health service and established a separate Department of Health in 1947. The controversial Health Acts of 1947 and 1953 were resisted by the medical profession and the Catholic Church, both acting in collaboration from time to time, in order to avert what was perceived as the beginning of a state-controlled health service. The Catholic Church continued to favour an approach to service provision by Catholic voluntary and community organisations

[44] O'Sullivan, op. cit., p. 190

[45] W. Beveridge *Social Insurance and Allied Services* November 1942, Cmd 6404 (London, 1942) p.6 and p. 162

[46] see A Clifford *The Mater Hospital (Belfast) and the National Health Service Past, Present and Future* (Athol Books, Belfast, 1990)

[47] see Bishop Dignam, *Social Security: Outlines of a Scheme of National Health Insurance* (Sligo, 1945) and comment in Barrington, op. cit., pp 150–1

which would reduce the need for state intervention. A notable proponent of this approach was Archbishop John Charles McQuaid.

The underlying tensions between Catholic ideology and state responsibilities came to the surface in the major 'Mother and Child' controversy which stemmed from the attempt to implement Part III of the 1947 Public Health Act. Events in Britain 'provided the catalyst' for a 'the *real* clash of interests' between the Department of Health and the Irish Medical Association.[48] The approach of both the Medical Association and the Catholic Church, as expressed in the Dignam plan, for example, 'invoked the spirit of vocationalism, that vogue of Christian social teaching which often allowed vested interests to present themselves as a defence against 'bureaucratic totalitarianism'.[49] From the Department of Health's point of view there was 'an obvious need to give coherence to the multifaceted structure which included voluntary hospitals, local authority dispensaries, charitable institutions, insurance societies, and myriad private practitioners. It was a system which had displayed inertia in the face of oppressively high rates of tuberculosis and infant mortality'.[50] The Catholic bishops denounced state health care for all mothers and children as 'a ready-made instrument for future totalitarian aggression . . . we have no guarantee that state officials will respect Catholic principles in regard to these matters.'[51] Barrington observes in regard to the published correspondence concerning this clash: 'The evidence that real power in the country lay not with elected representatives but with the Catholic Hierarchy generated a crisis of confidence in the democratic institutions of the state and the ideals of republicanism'.[52] The doctors and the bishops both defended a means test: the doctors because it was 'a key procedure to ensure the survival of the private practitioner as a species in the face of the Department of Health's vision of a free comprehensive health service for all' while the bishops' desire for a means test 'was based on a need to ensure the prevalence of Catholic ethics within medicine'.[53] The role of the voluntary hospitals following the crisis of 1950–51 might

[48] see Eamonn McKee 'Church-state relations and the development of Irish health policy: the mother-and-child scheme, 1944–53' *Irish Historical Studies* Vol. XXV, No. 98, November 1986, pp 159–194 for a very detailed examination of this critical episode.

[49] McKee, op. cit., p. 163

[50] ibid, p. 165

[51] see R.F. Foster *Modern Ireland 1600–1972* London, 1988, p. 572

[52] Barrington, op. cit., pp 218–219

[53] McKee, op. cit., p. 185

thus be seen to be a defence of vested interest against changes originating in the Department of Health; increasingly, however, they became dependent on Exchequer funding. The Exchequer began to meet the actual deficits of voluntary hospitals by way of grants to the Hospitals Trust Fund since the sweepstake income was no longer large enough to meet the deficits. Under the 1952 White Paper *Proposals for Improved and Extended Health Services*, health entitlements through a medical card scheme to cover 80% of the population posed, according to Barrington 'the biggest threat yet to the position of voluntary hospitals and to the private practice and income of hospital consultants'.[54] The Catholic bishops were critical of the tendency towards 'the elimination of the voluntary hospitals and the establishment of a monopoly of State hospitals' when opposing the Health Bill, 1952.[55] What steps had the voluntary hospitals taken to shape their own future in the changing context since independence of the State in the 1920s?

From the 1920s various initiatives had been taken in Dublin to explore amalgamation of some of the voluntary hospitals into an agreed voluntary central hospital in order to provide better services and a better context for medical education. Others, such as St. Vincent's Hospital, planned for decades to move from old buildings to new sites and new buildings. For decades the planning of possible mergers proved fruitless for a range of reasons not least the complex legal work involved in mergers of independent voluntary legal entities. Eventually seven voluntary hospitals associated with Trinity College Dublin 'federated' under The Hospital Federation and Amalgamation Act, 1961 as the Federated Dublin Voluntary Hospitals. Difficulties ensued in selecting sites for the new hospital and only partial amalgamation occurred in relation to pathology and consultant appointments. The eventual outcome, in fact, was two large hospitals: Sir Patrick Dun's Hospital, Mercer's Hospital and the Royal City of Dublin Hospital closed and their services were transferred into the new St. James's Hospital (1971) governed by a corporate body appointed by The Minister for Health. The Meath, Adelaide and National Children's Hospital merged under an amended Royal Charter of The Adelaide Hospital in 1996 and moved to a new Hospital at Tallaght in 1998.[56]

[54] Barrington, op. cit., p. 227

[55] ibid, p. 236

[56] see brief accounts of these developments in J.B. Lyons *The Quality of Mercer's* op. cit., pp 161–8; D. Mitchell *A 'Peculiar' Place* op. cit., pp 161–2, pp 238–245

Voluntary hospitals from the 1950s operated in a context of an expanded public hospital network and were ever more dependent upon Government funding. By the 1960s there were calls for the establishment of free medical health services and the Labour Party in 1965 called for a national health authority which would 'take over voluntary hospitals'.[57] The 1966 White Paper *The Health Services and their Further Development* pointed to more regionalised hospital services and the Report of the Consultative Council on the General Hospital Services *Outline of the Future Hospital System* (The Fitzgerald Report) published in 1968 recommended radical changes including a single administrative system for public and voluntary hospitals. This major report was not accepted or implemented but it has continued to inform more piecemeal developments in the hospital system. The *Health Act, 1970,* which created regional health boards, opened a new era in the Irish health services and placed the voluntary hospitals under more central regulation in respect of consultant appointments through Comhairle na nOspideal. The voluntary hospitals would have probably agreed with the comment on the Health Act, 1970 in the annual Report of The Adelaide Hospital for 1971

> The Act marked a further stage in the process—now well established—of the gradual diminution of the powers and responsibilities of the lay personnel who had for so many years given of their time and experience in the administration of the voluntary teaching hospitals. Increased State control and the trend towards the replacement of voluntary workers by civil servants was continuing and was likely to make the recruitment of competent persons to serve on the boards of voluntary hospitals an increasingly difficult task, as well as removing the incentive of those voluntary workers on whose support this Hospital had relied so much since its foundation.[58]

In 1973 Mr. Brendan Corish TD as Minister for Health issued a public statement on a 'General Hospital Development Plan' which may be seen in hindsight to be a prime policy document in respect of the development of the Irish hospital system into the 1990s. Broadly this policy foresaw three major acute public hospitals on the northern side of Dublin and three on the southern side and this has now been largely fulfilled with the new developments of St. Vincent's Hospital in Elm Park (1970), St. James's Hospital (1971), and the Adelaide & Meath Hospital at Tallaght (1998) on the southside joining Beaumont

[57] Barrington, op. cit., p. 260

[58] quoted in D. Mitchell *A 'Peculiar' Place* op. cit., pp 223–4

Hospital (1987), the Mater Hospital and James Connolly Memorial Hospital, Blanchardstown on the northside. The 1980s were characterised by severe financial restraint in the public sector and this led to a period of rapid reduction in public beds and the closure of a range of public voluntary hospitals and the transfer of their services to larger hospitals resulting in services being focussed in the above six major acute hospitals. The vulnerability of voluntary hospital boards, the lack of understanding of the responsibilities and commitment of voluntary board members, the predatory attitude of the State to voluntary assets and the pain felt at the end of so many long established hospitals are all well captured in the letter of W.A. Watts, Chairman of Mercer's Hospital to Mr. P.W. Flanagan, Secretary of the Department of Health, 6 February 1985, in reply to the Secretary's letter seeking the transfer of the capital assets of the sale of Mercer's Hospital to the Minister for Health.[59] The Irish health system was the subject of a major scrutiny by the Commission on Health Funding whose Report in 1989 set the terms for the policy developments of the 1990s which will be discussed in detail in the next chapter.

It was apparent that the mentalités which had originally shaped the voluntary hospital movement had become largely defunct in a radically changed environment.

4. VOLUNTARY ACTION: RELIGIOUS OR SECULAR?

The above description of Irish voluntary action in healthcare demonstrates how reliant it was upon a religious justification in contrast to the secular justification advanced in the discourse described in respect of the United Kingdom. Indeed as a result of the predominance of the Catholic Church Irish intellectual life in the decades after independence has been characterised as very impoverished in respect of social or political thought. Lee writes

> Those responsible for the formulation of social policy had little contact with the supply of ideas in Ireland, much less in the wider world. Catholic thinking, or assumed Catholic thinking, or selected Catholic thinking, may have influenced some. However, what is striking about social policy in the first generation of independence is not the demand for Catholic principles among policy-makers, but the general indifference in policy formulation to any social thought Catholic or otherwise.

[59] see letter republished as appendix in J.B. Lyons *The Quality of Mercer's The Story of Mercer's Hospital 1734–1991*, (Glendale, Dublin, 1991), pp 207–8

Lee notes the dominance of economists in policy studies since the 1960s but the economists who were influential were more impressive 'as technicians than as thinkers'. Other relevant disciplines remained underdeveloped until the 1980s and 1990s.[60]

Ruth Barrington in respect of her study of health policy has observed

One of the characteristics of Irish Catholic moralists in the 1940s and 1950s was their assumption that the moral law was there for all to see and that it could be applied in only one way. On this assumption, the Hierarchy's claim to be the guardian of moral law in society was easily translated into a claim to be the arbiter of which social policy was acceptable by the criterion of the moral or social teaching of the Church. The overwhelmingly Catholic ethos of Irish life and the absence of competing native ideas on social issues meant that the Hierarchy's assumptions and claims went almost unchallenged.[61]

Prior to the 1960s Irish social policy, insofar as policy developed at all, emerged in an era of cultural protection and religious defensiveness.[62] The era of almost total Catholic dominance of Irish life from the 1920s and the erosion of this dominance from the 1970s to the 1990s has been documented in major studies by Blanshard, Whyte, Inglis, Keogh, O'Reilly, Heskett, Hug and Cooney.[63] Tom Garvin has explored how this 'popular nationalist alliance between fundamentalist Catholicism and 'republicanism' gradually crumbled' and how the politics of 'cultural defence and the fear of the modern' has slowly given way from

[60] Lee *Ireland 1912–1985* op. cit., pp 578–586; the noted Irish sociologist Eileen Kane agrees with Lee's assessment see her important article E. Kane 'The Power of Paradigms: Social Science and Intellectual Contributions to Public Discourse in Ireland' in *On Intellectuals and Intellectual Life in Ireland: International Comparative and Historical Contexts*, ed. L. O'Dowd (Institute of Irish Studies, QUB and The Royal Irish Academy, 1996), pp 132–155

[61] Barrington, op. cit., p. 152

[62] see T. Brown *Ireland A Social and Cultural History 1922–1985* (London, 1985) passim

[63] see Paul Blanshard *The Irish and Catholic Power An American Interpretation* (The Beacon Press, Boston, 1953); J.H. Whyte *Church and State in Modern Ireland, 1923–1979*, 2nd Edition (Gill and Macmillan, Dublin, 1980); T. Inglis *Moral Monopoly The Rise and Fall of the Catholic Church in Modern Ireland* 2nd Edition (University College Dublin Press, Dublin, 1998); D. Keogh 'The Role of the Catholic Church in the Republic of Ireland, 1922–1995' in *Building Trust in Ireland–Studies Commissioned by the Forum for Peace and Reconciliation* (Blackstaff Press, Belfast, 1996) pp 85–213; E. O'Reilly *Masterminds of the Right* (Attic Press, Dublin, 1992); T. Heskett *The Second Partitioning of Ireland? The Abortion Referendum of 1983* (Brandsma Books, Dublin, 1990); C. Hug *The Politics of Sexual Morality in Ireland* (Macmillan Press, London, 1999); J. Cooney *John Charles McQuaid Ruler of Catholic Ireland* (The O'Brien Press, Dublin, 1999)

about 1960 to a 'secular patriotism, which does not rely on tribal and religious identities'.[64]

The extensive voluntary activity present in Irish society found no independent secular advocate nor was it based on any coherent theoretical expression. It might also be said that analyses of the role of the state in a democratic Republic were not developed thus compounding the problem of identifying the contribution of voluntary action. This left the voluntary sector vulnerable to the rapid expansion of state responsibilities and to the increasing centralisation of Irish government and administration. As Lee notes 'The intense centralisation of government helped foster further the dependency syndrome throughout society. Citizens were expected to behave responsibly despite having little responsibility to exercise'.[65]

Despite the absence of a validating social or political philosophy the development of voluntary organisations in Irish society in recent decades has been remarkable in a number of areas notably women's organisations and community and anti-poverty organisations. A 'third strand' has been incorporated into the 'social partnership' of unions, employers and farmers consisting of representatives of women's organisations, unemployed, disadvantaged, youth, the elderly, people with disability, environmental interests and others. This 'third strand' is now represented in the National Economic and Social Forum and was consulted about the three year 'social partnership' agreement *Partnership 2000 for Inclusion, Employment and Competitiveness* agreed in 1996. In this way the 'voluntary sector' has a recognised, if limited 'voice', in the shaping of national agreements with the Government.[66]

In other countries, however, notably the United Kingdom and the United States, there have been historically developed political theories and traditions as well as practices which explicitly advocated voluntary action and limits to State responsibilities. In Ireland, aside from the Catholic principle of subsidiarity, the voluntary sector had little official

---

[64] see T. Garvin 'Patriots and republicans: an Irish evolution' in *Ireland and the Politics of Change* eds W. Crotty and D.E. Schmitt (London, 1998) pp 144–155; for the 'slowness' of the change see T. Garvin 'The Politics of Denial and Cultural Defence: the Referendums of 1983 and 1986 in context' *The Irish Review*, No. 3, 1988, pp 1–7

[65] Lee *Ireland 1912–1985* op. cit., p. 560

[66] The National Women's Council of Ireland comprised over 135 women's organisations in 1997 representing an estimated 300,000 women see Yvonne Galligan 'The Changing Role of Women' in *Ireland and the Politics of Change*, op. cit., p. 112; see Niamh Hardiman 'Inequality and the Representation of Interests' in *Ireland and the Politics of change*, op. cit., pp 122–143

or public understanding when the state expanded rapidly its responsibilities into every area of Irish life from the 1960s. Indeed the growing
antipathy to the Catholic Church, which had so badly misplayed its
hand in the Mother and Child Scheme, coloured official and public
attitudes to voluntary social services. As Lee perceptively notes 'the
furore over the Mother and Child Scheme, which appeared to reflect
church dominance over the social policy of the state, served to conceal
the relative lack of church influence on wider social policy'.[67] As we
have seen the church and vested interest had marched hand in hand to
the apparent detriment of effective healthcare outcomes for the
population.

Catholic bishops might rail against the emerging 'welfare state' but
public discourse and public policy was not informed by any coherent
view of citizenship which would give theoretical underpinning or
coherence to the place of voluntary organisations in a democratic
society. In his study Lee has an important section on 'character' . He
notes that 'Irish society had difficulty grasping even the idea of public
morality'.[68] Lee delineates the 'begrudger character' and 'the
begrudger mode of discourse' in Irish society up to the 1980s which
was inimical to a civic and political culture of active citizenship and
which, as we have seen, was argued by Beveridge and others as
necessary for voluntary action to flourish. Lee observes 'The lack of a
viable civic culture testifies to the slender hold of the idea of the public
good. The communal ethic was devised to discourage disturbance of
the natural order of things . . .'[69]

Traditional Ireland had largely succeeded notes Lee 'in excluding
from the agenda of moral discourse doctrines potentially subversive of
the material interests of the dominant social elements'.[70] The close
connection between Catholicism and Irish culture has left 'the civic
culture so vulnerable to a rapid decline in the role of institutional
religion'.[71] In addition the pronounced weakening of nationalism has
confronted Irish society with a major challenge to define and inculcate
a civic culture for a modern republic. There has been in Irish society, as
Ó Tuathaigh has put it,

[67] Lee *Ireland 1912–1985*, p. 578
[68] Lee *Ireland 1912–1985*, p. 645
[69] ibid, p. 650
[70] ibid, p. 654
[71] ibid, p. 657

an unusual congruence of community values and symbols defined in religious terms and the legislative framework and symbols of a national state. Their congruence was acceptable to the majority of the citizens, even though it was sharply at odds with the republican tradition to which the official rhetoric of the state gave regular obeisance between the twenties and the late fifties.[72]

Ó Tuathaigh comments that 'as the nineteen-sixties gave way to the seventies it was clear to all but the most wilfully blind that the particular kind of community cohesion based on a kind of 'moral protectionism' and high religious conformity, which had characterised the Irish state since the nineteen-twenties, was no longer a viable model for the future development of society'.[73]

5. CONCLUSION

The developments prior to 1989 which have been traced above in respect of voluntary and statutory relationships in the Irish health system are characterised by the increasing role of the statutory sector. This occurred both through legislative measures, such as the Health Act, 1970, and other regulatory instruments, and it occurred through the increasing reliance of all health service providers on public funds. This meant that public voluntary hospitals became almost completely dependent on the State for their financial resources and so increasingly accountable to the Department of Health.

Given the developing power of the State it might have been expected that there would have been an explicit articulation in this changing context of the role of the voluntary sector in the Irish health system. The fact that this did not happen illustrates the dominance of the religious values as expressed by the Churches, especially the Catholic Church, as the justification for voluntary organisation and action in healthcare. This left the voluntary sector vulnerable to the decline in the role and power of the Catholic Church, which became a feature of Irish society from the 1970s, and the result was that the voluntary providers, such as public voluntary hospitals were embraced, however reluctantly, by the developing statutory framework and provision.

[72] M.A.G. O'Tuathaigh 'Religion, Nationality and a Sense of Community in Modern Ireland' in *Community, Culture and Conflict Aspects of the Irish Experience*, ed. M.A.G. O'Tuathaigh (Galway University Press, 1986) p. 73

[73] ibid, p. 76

There was no coherent public policy which sought to define the place of voluntary bodies in a democratic Republic nor did the voluntary organisations themselves succeed in articulating a philosophical justification which would have application in an increasingly secular context. It is important, however, to note that the Catholic Church through Catholic voluntary hospitals, enshrines a prescriptive ethos for such hospitals through written codes of Catholic medical ethics. The Protestant Churches, through Protestant voluntary hospitals, placed the freedom of conscience of each individual person at the centre of their approach to medical ethics; by eschewing written denominationally-based codes such Protestant voluntary hospitals had the potential, at least, to evolve into inclusive hospitals catering for increasingly diverse religious views in an emerging pluralist society. This essential difference between the religiously-based voluntary hospitals in Ireland proved a significant factor in the new governance arrangements of the public voluntary hospital—The Adelaide and Meath Hospital, Dublin, Incorporating The National Children's Hospital—which is the subject of a detailed case study in Chapter 5 below.

Voluntary organisations generally continued to be defensive and reactive and their lack of clarity and definition profoundly affected their governance and management in the face of the more challenging and stringent environment in which they had to operate. A detailed analysis of this policy context in the 1990s follows in Chapter 2. This will be followed by an attempt in Chapter 3 to meet the need for a coherent democratic theory concerning voluntary and statutory relationships in Ireland which has been shown to be absent historically and which is essential if effective governance and management arrangements are to be developed in both sectors.

CHAPTER 2

The Policy Context in Irish Healthcare 1989–1999
An Analysis

'Despite the importance of the activities of the voluntary sector and the role it has traditionally played in Irish society, there is no policy at national level within which its contribution may be located. There is no clear statement of principles which underlie the relationship between the voluntary and statutory sectors in general. Neither is there agreement as to the relative spheres of competence and legitimacy or the balancing of functions between the voluntary and statutory sectors within the health arena.'

PAULINE FAUGHNAN 'A Healthy Voluntary Sector: Rhetoric or Reality?' in *Reflections on Health Commemorating Fifty Years of the Department of Health 1947–1997*, ed. J. Robins (Department of Health, Dublin, 1997), p. 238

1. INTRODUCTION

The purpose of this chapter is to describe the key actors, both voluntary and statutory, in the Irish healthcare system and to provide an analysis of the policies which govern voluntary and statutory relationships at present. The analysis will explore whether an appropriate policy framework is in place to address the legitimate requirements of both statutory and voluntary healthcare agencies with respect in particular to public voluntary hospitals. Appropriateness of policy will be assessed on whether an explicit theoretical and empirical basis for the policy exists which provides both a rationale for the policy and a measure for evaluation of policy effectiveness in terms of outcomes as measured against the policy objectives. In addition the analysis will seek to identify any positive or negative implications in respect of governance and management arising from the existing policies.

The previous chapter has traced the historical developments in the Irish healthcare system to the period inaugurated by the Health Act, 1970 and the creation of the statutory health boards and of Comhairle na nOspideal. The context which followed in the 1970s and 1980s was of increasing statutory responsibility and increasing vulnerability for the public voluntary hospitals. There are a number of reasons for such vulnerability. The public voluntary hospitals became almost totally dependent upon public funding and were required to submit to the necessary regulations and annual budgetary requirements that public funding necessitated.[1] In addition the voluntary hospitals were now subject to increasing statutory regulation especially in respect of consultant appointments due to the work of Comhairle na nOspideal. The voluntary hospitals failed to produce a publicly articulated raison d'être for their role as voluntary healthcare agencies. There was little attempt, for example, by such agencies to argue that voluntary agencies might play an important role in promoting active community participation in developing and implementing strategies for health.[2] The vulnerability of the public voluntary hospitals was dramatically revealed during the rationalisation of the late 1980s when public funding was reduced

---

[1] see National Economic and Social Council Report *Some Major Issues in Health Policy* (Stationery Office, Dublin, 1976), p. 49, p. 53 which notes the change in 1974 from a system of capitation fees to a system of annual grant in aid which required submissions of annual budgets in advance of expenditure.

[2] such an argument might have been made, for example, based upon the World Health Organisation *Health For All by the Year 2000* Programme issued in 1985 which had as a basic tenet such active community participation.

leading to the closure of a range of long-established public voluntary hospitals including Dr. Steeven's Hospital, Dublin; Barrington's Hospital, Limerick; Sir Patrick Dun's Hospital, Dublin; Monkstown Hospital, Dublin and the Royal City of Dublin Hospital, Baggot Street, Dublin.

2. THE NEW POLICY ENVIRONMENT 1986–1999

The years since 1986 have been characterised by a rapidly developing new policy environment for the Irish health services: Table 1 lists the major policy milestones which are of particular importance for this study.

Table 1   Major Policy Milestones in Irish Health Services 1986–1999

1986	*Health: The Wider Dimensions*
1989	*Commission on Health Funding*
1990} 1991}	Dublin Hospital Initiative Group (Kennedy Reports) Minister's Statement on the restructuring of the Eastern Health Board Region
1992	Dublin Hospital Advisory Group Review of Tallaght Hospital Project (unpublished report)
1994	*Shaping A Healthier Future*
1996	Minister's Statement on the Restructuring of the Eastern Region Health (Amendment) (No. 3) Act, 1996 'the accountability legislation'
1997	Public Service Management Act, 1997 Freedom of Information Act, 1997 *Statement of Strategy:* Department of Health & Children *Interim Report of the Task Force on the Eastern Regional Health Authority* *Enhancing The Partnership* Report
1998	*Strategy Statement 1998–2001: Working for Health and Well-Being*
1999	Health (Eastern Regional Health Authority) Act, 1999

SOURCE: Adapted and expanded from Table 1.7 in T. O'Hara 'Current Structure of the Irish Health Care System—Setting the Context' in *The Irish Health System in the 21st Century*, eds. A.L. Leahy and M.M. Wiley, (Dublin, 1998), p. 28

In 1986 Department of Health Consultative Statement on Health Policy entitled *Health The Wider Dimensions* contained very limited acknowledgement of the potential role of what it described as the 'non-statutory sector' as follows:

> The considerable involvement of the non-statutory sector in the Irish health system is a very concrete expression of community participation . . . The role of the non-statutory sector has evolved over a long period and these agencies are now involved not just in the delivery of services on an agency basis but also participate in the process of policy development through their pioneering work with various care groups . . . this non-statutory input is an important element in the health system which should be preserved. However, problems of integration between the statutory and non-statutory sectors have arisen in the past and a further objective of the re-organisation now proposed is to introduce arrangements which will lead to greater cohesion between both sectors. The extent to which the non-statutory sector is dependent on exchequer funding lends further emphasis to the need for such cohesion.[3]

One main issue in health policy identified in this significant 1986 statement has remained a major policy concern: 'The proposed re-organisation of health administration is designed to strengthen health planning, to maintain a significant role for the non-statutory sector, and its integration with the statutory agencies, and to ensure a mechanism for community participation'.[4] There was a very significant and revealing paragraph on 'Voluntary Hospitals':

> Traditionally, the voluntary hospitals have played a prominent role in the provision of services. Statutorily, these hospitals provide services on behalf of health boards. In practice most voluntary hospitals see themselves as independent providers of service with health boards having little say in their operation. Up to now, both the Department of Health and the health boards have acquiesced in this. It is clear that such a situation can no longer be allowed to continue and the appropriate relationships between these hospitals and those responsible for the delivery of the services must now be firmly established. This is one of the questions addressed in the re-organisation proposals submitted to Government.[5]

Note might be made of the significant use of the word 'acquiesced' in this quotation in relation to the future of voluntary hospitals.

---

[3] *Health The Wider Dimensions (A Consultative Statement on Health Policy)* (Department of Health, n.d. [1986]), p. 21

[4] ibid, p. 22

[5] ibid, p. 33

Concern about hospital management was also very evident in 1986 both in respect of 'the essential management structures and expertise' which had 'by and large, been neglected' and in relation to the role of each hospital, its range of services, the population served and its relationship with other hospitals and community services.[6]

Health The Wider Dimensions signposted the major policy issues which have continued to feature in subsequent policy documents and discourse, in legislation and re-organisation proposals between 1986 and 1999. The Commission on Health Funding whose major and influential Report was issued in 1989 contained more substantive comments on the role of voluntary organisations:

> The role of voluntary organisations is immensely important. They reflect and stimulate the community spirit and humanitarianism of very many people outside of the formal health services, and in so doing they make available considerable additional resources, both human and financial. They can also identify and meet needs quickly because of their closeness to the client-group which they serve; indeed, many services which are now provided or funded by the State were originally developed independently by such organisations.

Significantly the Commission went on to state that 'there is no formal framework or procedural guidelines for the relationship between statutory and voluntary bodies so as to ensure their complementarity'. The Commission noted the range of problems relating to the discretionary nature of annual funding by statutory bodies of voluntary bodies and the difficulties of co-ordination, reporting relationships and accountability appropriate to the provision of public funding. It referred to an unpublished management consultant's report of 1982 which identified 'an insufficient understanding and appreciation of each other's contributions on the parts of those in the statutory and voluntary sectors'. The Commission sought an approach 'which will ensure that all publicly-funded agencies, whether statutory or voluntary, work together in the most efficient and effective way, without jeopardising the independence and flexibility which are the voluntary organisation's most important attributes'. The Commission recommended that those responsible for 'the management of services in each region should, with the involvement of the voluntary organisations, determine the services required' and that the funding of each voluntary organisation 'should be related to the provision of a specific

[6] ibid, p. 33

47

agreed level and type of service' and that 'there should be an agreed basis for the evaluation of each agency's contribution' though medium term contracts. This laid the basis for policy lines which continued to be stressed in the 1990s.[7]

At the centre of any policy analysis in the 1990s must be *Shaping A Healthier Future A Strategy for Effective Healthcare in the 1990s*, published by the Department of Health in 1994, which has a claim to be the most significant policy statement in the history of Irish healthcare. It is popularly referred to as 'the Health Strategy' and it created a new policy environment for the health services.

The Health Strategy addressed in general terms the role and contribution of the voluntary sector in healthcare identifying one of 'the strengths' of the Irish healthcare system the 'strong voluntary sector which provides an integral part of the public system without foregoing the benefits of independence and flexibility'. However as Faughnan noted in 1997

> 'The current Health Strategy addresses the structures within which large voluntary organisations will continue to deliver services. However, the issue of appropriate roles of the voluntary and statutory sectors in the provision of basic services has not yet been debated and is critical to the future service-providing role of the voluntary sector.'[8]

3. THE KEY ACTORS IN THE CONTEXT OF DEVELOPING POLICY

The power to decide what health services should be provided and how they will be governed and managed does not reside in any one person or institution. A combination of Government, Department of Health and Children, advisory and executive agencies, professional bodies and voluntary organisations all play roles though their degree of power and influence varies from issue to issue.[9] This section will describe the key actors in respect of voluntary and statutory relationships in a rapidly

[7] *Report of the Commission on Health Funding September 1989*, (Stationery office, Dublin, 1989) p. 27, pp 341–3; the management consultant's report referred to was Inbucon Management Consultants: *Community Care Review Report for Department of Health* (1982, unpublished)

[8] see P. Faughnan 'A Healthy Voluntary Sector: Rhetoric or Reality?' in *Reflections on Health Commemorating Fifty Years of The Department of Health 1947–1997*, ed. J. Robins (Department of Health, Dublin, 1997), p. 235

[9] for a valuable overview of the structure see T. O'Hara 'Current Structure of the Irish Health Care System—Setting The Context' in *The Irish Health System in the 21st Century*, eds. A.L. Leahy and M.M. Wiley (Dublin, 1998), pp 3–36

changing policy environment: the Department of Health and Children, the health boards and the public voluntary hospitals. This description will take account of the most recent developments which have radically altered the context of these relationships. The description will provide the basis for a critical analysis of some key policy concepts which have emerged as central to the relationships in particular, 'partnership', 'service planning' and 'voluntary' as defined in policy documents.

(a)   *The Department of Health and Children*

One of the key objectives of the Department Health and Children is to support the Minister in the formulation, development and evaluation of health policy. In 1997 the Department of Health and Children issued a *Strategy Statement* which includes the mission statement of the Department:

> In a partnership with the providers of health care, and in co-operation with other government departments, statutory and non-statutory bodies, to protect, promote and restore the health and wellbeing of people by ensuring that health and personal social services are planned, managed and delivered to achieve measurable health and social gain and provide the optimum return on resources invested.[10]

The key word used is 'partnership' with 'providers'. Social partnership has evolved as a major framework for Irish political, economic and social governance. However, in the health system it is important to explore the possible meanings and the import of 'partnership' between statutory and voluntary providers and the role of the Department in funding such 'partnerships'. Before exploring in more detail the concept of 'partnership' there are a number of recent major legislative and other measures to be noted which are fundamental to shaping the Department's current role in policy formation:

The Public Service Management Act, 1997
This Act makes the submission of a *Strategy Statement* by each Department necessary. It makes explicit the responsibilities of the Secretary-General of a Department (and other officers to whom responsibilities might be assigned) to manage and to be accountable for delivering outputs specified in the assignments. This accountability

---

[10] see *Working For Health and Well-Being Strategy Statement 1998–2001* (Department of Health and Children, 1998); this document follows the Department's first Strategy Statement published in May 1997

is both to the Minister and to the committees of the Houses of the Oireachtas. This Act emerged as part of a wider Strategic Management Initiative (SMI) in the Irish public service which is still in its early stages and which is designed to manage the public services better and to make them more responsive to the people served by them.[11]

The Freedom of Information Act, 1997
According to a former Assistant Secretary of the Department of Health and Children, Dr. Ruth Barrington, this Act is 'having a profound effect on the management and organisation of the Department. A culture that protected information on the basis that to disclose it might be inimical to the interests of the Minister must now cope with a culture in which a citizen has a right to information, a right that can only be refused on certain limited grounds'.[12] The full effect of the Act which came into effect in April 1998, will not be clear for a number of years but it is bound to be significant in relation to health services which affect issues of vital concern to citizens.

The Department of Health and Children is now obliged to function under new statutory arrangements which are changing both the culture and the management style of the public service.

The method most frequently used by the Department in developing significant policies is to establish expert groups, working parties, task forces or commissions.[13] The Department has recently confirmed that 'this model is one which the Department will continue to use when it is necessary to reach a consensus on major policy issues'.[14] Most of these policy groups set up a process to obtain submissions from any organisation or individual before recommendations are made. However, there

[11] for an evaluation of the effectiveness of 'Strategy Statements' see the two articles by J.F. Keogan and D. McKevitt, 'Making Sense of Strategy Statements: A User's Guide' *Administration* Vol.45, No. 3, (Autumn 1997) pp 3–25 and 'Another Set of Strategy Statements: What is the Evidence on Implementation?' *Administration*, Vol. 47, No. 1, (Spring, 1999) pp 3–25; for consideration of public service reform in this context see W.K. Roche 'Public Service Reform and Human Resource Management' *Administration*, Vol. 46, No. 2, (Summer 1998) pp 3–24

[12] R. Barrington 'The Future Political, Legislative and Social Framework of the Health Services' in *The Irish Health System in the 21st Century*, eds. A.L. Leahy and M.M. Wiley, (Dublin, 1998), p. 88

[13] recent examples are listed in O'Hara 'Current Structure of the Irish Health Care System–Setting The Context', p. 11 and include *Enhancing The Partnership: Report of the Working Group on the Implementation of the Health Strategy in Relation to Persons with a Mental Handicap, 1997* which will be discussed in detail below

[14] see *Enhancing The Partnership*, op. cit., p. 27

are some fundamental implications of this approach to policy development which should be noted with respect to 'partnership' between voluntary and statutory bodies. Firstly, the membership and terms of reference are controlled by the Minister and by the Department. Secondly the policy status of such groups may be unclear in terms of public scrutiny or parliamentary scrutiny: there is no obligatory or agreed 'green' paper to 'white' paper process involving Government and Oireachtas approval. Thirdly the Minister and the Department are free to ignore, select or approve any policy recommendations from such groups. These defects were apparent for example in the Task Force on the Eastern Regional Health Authority established in November 1996 to pave the way towards the publication of the Health (Eastern Regional Health Authority) Bill, 1998 which was a highly significant policy development in respect of voluntary and statutory relationships.

(b)   *The Health Boards*

By international standards the range of functions of Irish local authorities is narrow. Local authorities have no role in policing, public transport or personal social services and very little in health or education.[15] The health boards, established under the Health Act, 1970, have statutory responsibility for administering the services provided for in health legislation and by ministerial initiative. The establishment of the eight health boards was a major step in a longer term process of change in the way Irish health services are organised: 'the change from a locally controlled and locally financed system to an increasingly centralised and centrally financed health system'.[16] The population served by health boards ranges from just over 200,000 in the Midland Health Board to nearly 1.3 million (or 36 percent of the total Irish population) in the Eastern Health Board area.[17]

In respect of health board governance Section 4 (2) of the Health Act, 1970 specifies in broad terms the constitution of each health board and how the boards are to be managed. Membership of the boards is drawn from a combination of three main interest groups

[15] see *Better Local Government A Programme for Change* (Department of the Environment, Stationery Office, Dublin, 1996), p. 7

[16] R. Barrington *Health, Medicine and Politics in Ireland 1900–1970* (Dublin, 1987), p. 280

[17] see O'Hara 'Current Structure of the Irish Health Care System—Setting The Context', op. cit., pp 18–19

- Elected public representatives from County and Borough Councils. Such representatives are to be a majority of each board and are intended to provide a responsiveness to local interests.

- Professional representatives. These are mainly officers and staff of the health board, and include doctors, nurses, dentists and pharmacists, elected by their peers.

- Nominees of the Minister for Health (three on each Board). Initially these nominees represented excluded professional groups, but increasingly they tend to represent the 'consumers' of health services.

The Eastern Health Board, the largest Health Board, and one of particular significance for this study given the large presence of public voluntary hospitals in the Dublin region, had 38 members. These included 13 professionals (nine medical practitioners, one pharmacist) three ministerial appointees and 22 public representatives.

The 1994 Health Strategy identified several weaknesses in the structure of the Health Boards. These included

- A lack of clarity with regard to the respective roles and responsibilities of health boards and their Chief Executive Officers.

- Inadequate accountability within the structures.

- Over involvement by the Department of Health in the detailed management of the services.

The Health (Amendment) (No. 3) Act, 1996 has as its primary purpose to address these weaknesses. This Act provides a legal framework within which the Minister for Health and Children determines the budget of each health board and the health board must adopt a service plan consistent with this budget between 21 and 42 days of receipt of the letter of determination. Under this Act health boards must have regard to certain matters in performing functions. These include

- *Resource allocation:* securing the most beneficial, effective and efficient use of whatever resources are available to the board.

- *Co-operation with voluntary bodies:* 'the need for co-operation with voluntary bodies providing services similar or ancillary to services which the health board may provide, to people residing in the functional area of the health board'.[18]

---

[18] Health (Amendment) (No. 3) Act, 1996, Section 2 (1)(b)

- *Multi-sectoral co-operation.* Co-operating with and co-ordinating its activities with those of other health boards, local authorities and public authorities who perform functions related to the health of the population of the health board.

- *Implementing Government* policy giving due consideration to the policies and objectives of the Government insofar as they may affect or relate to the functions of the health board.

1998 was the first year in which these new accountability arrangements for the health boards were implemented in full.

The health boards and the voluntary sector in health provision are increasingly working to a common agenda and in common structures. Health boards, in co-operation with the voluntary hospitals and the agencies providing services for people with a mental handicap, established the Health Service Employers' Agency which conducts industrial relations negotiations on behalf of health service providers. Health boards are also seeking to co-ordinate materials management across the health system as a whole. Under the Health (Eastern Regional Health Authority) Act, 1999 a joint executive agency for the health boards will be established so that they can co-operate and co-ordinate their activities more effectively. All providers are engaged in a process to strengthen and adapt management practice on an ongoing basis led by the Office for Health Management established in 1997.[19] The purpose of the Office is to facilitate management development for the health services in Ireland. It is the Office for Health Management for example, that is organising the 'Governance Initiative' process initiated in 1998 to explore governance and management issues in the hospital system.

In this context of closer institutional arrangements and many common objectives that the policy of developing the health boards into health authorities which would be responsible for funding all service provision both voluntary and statutory in their functional areas is being progressed by the Department of Health and Children.

(c) *Public Voluntary Hospitals*

The historical background to voluntary hospitals in the Irish health care system was described in Chapter 1. In the hospital sector of the

---

[19] this Office was established following the publication of *A Management Development Strategy for the Health and Personal Social Services in Ireland* (Commissioned and published by the Department of Health, 1996).

Table 2 General Hospital Sector 1998

	IR£m
Regional hospitals	420
Public Voluntary hospitals	628
Health Board County hospitals	276
Health Board District hospitals	47
Health Board long stay hospitals	109
Payments to patients in Nursing Homes	43
Ambulance services	40
Total	1,563

Total health expenditure was approximately IR£3.1 billion
SOURCE: Department of Health and Children

health system 29 public 'voluntary' hospitals account for nearly 50 per cent of the hospital budget in a public general hospital network made up of 62 acute hospitals as Table 2 indicates. The voluntary hospitals were funded by the Department of Health and Children directly in 1999 but this has changed in the Eastern Health Board area under the new Eastern Regional Health Authority.[20]

There is a very significant definitional problem in respect of 'voluntary' in regard to Irish hospitals. The traditional voluntary hospitals which survived into the 1990s such as St. Vincent's Hospital, Dublin, owned and managed by the Sisters of Charity, or The Mater Misericordiae Hospital, Dublin, owned and managed by the Sisters of Mercy have been joined

> by a new group—those hospitals which are administered by boards established by the Minister for Health under the Health (Corporate Bodies) Act, 1961. These are Beaumont Hospital, St. James's Hospital and St. Luke's Hospital, all in Dublin . . . Perhaps these are not voluntary in the sense of the original group of hospitals but they are sufficiently close to them in their nature to justify 'voluntary' as a generic description for non-health board public hospitals.[21]

[20] see O'Hara 'Current Structure of the Irish Health Care System—Setting The Context', op. cit., p. 12, pp 25–6

[21] see B. Hensey *The Health Services of Ireland*, completely revised 4th Edition, (Dublin, 1988), pp 120–1

This 1988 comment by a long serving public servant in the Department of Health, who served until 1981, is revealing for two reasons. Firstly, it indicates a Departmental cast of mind which is amply evident in subsequent policy statements that sees the 'non-health board hospitals' as essentially of the same 'nature' irrespective of whether they have a board appointed under statute by the Minister for Health or a board appointed by a voluntary body such as the Sisters of Charity. Because of this approach to 'public voluntary hospitals' it is unclear in policy as to whether being 'voluntary' necessarily involves independence and autonomy in the governance and management of the organisation concerned. Secondly there was a very significant if small addition to the above quotation which reads: '(another will be added when a new hospital planned for Tallaght, Co. Dublin is built)'. It was contemplated that this new Hospital would be governed by a board appointed by the Minister under the 1961 Act. In fact after a prolonged period involving years of controversial negotiations the Royal Charter of the Adelaide Hospital was amended in 1996 to govern the new Hospital thus retaining the voluntary nature of the Board of Management.[22] The *Report of the Commission on Health Funding* in 1989 stated concerning voluntary hospitals that 'in a modern health service their role must be defined afresh and the parameters of responsibilities in the delivery of services set out clearly. Such clarity is lacking in the present system'.

The definitional problem has not been addressed in Irish health policy despite the availability of an internationally accepted 'structural—operational' definition of the Johns Hopkins Comparative Nonprofit Sector Project since the early 1990s: Five key criteria have been identified in this definition for defining nonprofit or voluntary organisations: organisations with some kind of formality or institutional reality; institutionally separate from government; non-profit distributing; self-governing; and meaningful voluntary input or activity.[23] The Commission in 1989 recollected that the 1968 Fitzgerald Report on the future hospital system in Ireland had recommended that voluntary

---

[22] see *Health Act, 1970 (Section 76) (Adelaide and Meath Hospital, Dublin, Incorporating the National Children's Hospital) Order 1996 and Health (Amendment) No. 2) Act, 1996* and *Charter of the Adelaide and Meath Hospital, Dublin, Incorporating The National Children's Hospital* published by the Board of the Hospital 1996; this will an important aspect of the case study undertaken in Chapter 5 below

[23] see F. Donoghue 'Defining The Nonprofit Sector: Ireland', Working Paper No. 28, *The Johns Hopkins Comparative Nonprofit Sector Project*, (Institute for Policy Studies, The Johns Hopkins University, Baltimore, 1998)

hospitals should remain under independent ownership and management but that they should enter into contractual arrangements with the regional hospital boards which it had recommended for a planned hospital service. These regional hospital boards never became operational: 'consequently, the Department of Health became closely involved in the organisation and management of voluntary hospitals, which it was funding directly . . .' The 1989 Commission on Health Funding again recommended that ownership and management of voluntary hospitals remain with the voluntary owners but they recommended that all hospitals be licensed by a new body proposed by the Commission, a Health Services Executive Authority, and that they should have a designated role and catchment area. There would be 'formal agreements' between the Executive Authority and each hospital and each hospital would receive 'global budgets for the provision of an agreed level of service'.[24]

The Department's policy, therefore, to transfer the direct funding of voluntary agencies including public voluntary hospitals to the health boards or to the new Eastern Regional Health Authority has had a long gestation. It is intended to provide representation for the voluntary sector on the health boards when they become health authorities and there will be representation of the voluntary sector and voluntary hospitals on the new Authority which has replaced the Eastern Health Board in March 2000. The rationale for this transfer is that the direct funding of voluntary agencies by the Department 'impedes the effective co-ordination, development and evaluation of services at a local level and reduces the Department's capacity to achieve its objectives'.[25]

The Department places these proposals in the context of 'partnership' stating that the 'voluntary sector is, and will continue to be, a most important partner in the provision of health and personal social services. The Department of Health and Children will continue to respect and protect the independence and operational autonomy of voluntary agencies.'[26] The Department believes that the proposals 'are being progressed by the Department in partnership with all concerned. An example of this partnership process is the Task Force established to

---

[24] see *Report of the Commission on Health Funding*, op. cit., p. 153 and Ch. 12, pp 228–258

[25] *Working for Health and Well-Being Strategy Statement 1998–2001*, (Department of Health and Children, 1998), pp 15–16

[26] ibid, p. 15

oversee and manage the implementation of the proposals to restruc-
ture the health services in the Eastern Health Board area, which
includes among its membership persons drawn from the voluntary
sector, the Department and the Eastern Health Board . . . A vital
element of its ongoing work is close consultation and co-operation with
all service providers in the Eastern region'.[27]

Under these proposals the public voluntary hospitals will each have
service agreements with the new Authority which will link funding to
agreed levels of service to be provided by the hospital concerned. The
Health (Amendment) (No. 3) Act, 1996 known as 'the accountability legislation', introduced in respect of health boards, as described above, is
also now applied 'in an administrative way' in respect of public
voluntary hospitals directly funded by the Department.[28] In effect the
Department regards such voluntary hospitals as being bound in the
same way as health boards by this Act.[29] In this way the process has been
put in place for the transfer of this service planning process to the new
Authority from the Department in March 2000 under the Health
(Eastern Regional Health Authority) Act, 1999.

This Act defines a 'voluntary hospital' as a hospital which is substan-
tially funded by the Authority or an Area Health Board under the
Authority 'and the governing body of which is not the Authority or an
Area Health Board or any committee of those' and a 'voluntary body' is
defined as 'a voluntary body which provides or proposes to provide a
service similar or ancillary to a service that a health board may
provide'. The Act provides that 'voluntary service providers' will be
voluntary bodies which provide a service by arrangement with the
Authority or an Area Health Board under the Authority and the
Authority shall 'have regard to the right of voluntary bodies' which
provide such services 'to manage their own affairs in accordance with
their independent ethos and traditions'. Such 'arrangements' shall
include written service agreements 'covering a period of not less than 3
years and not more than 5 years and specifying—

[27] ibid, p. 16

[28] see Letters of Determination issued by The Department of Health and Children to
public voluntary hospitals in 1997 and 1998 governing 1998 and 1999 allocations of
funds.

[29] the dramatic effects of this in 1998 in relation to governance and management of the
new Hospital at Tallaght will be detailed in Chapter 5 below

(i) the principles by which both parties agree to abide for the duration of the agreement, and

(ii) such standards relating to the efficiency effectiveness and quality of the services to be provided as may be agreed between the parties'

There will be a written annual service agreement specifying the services to be provided and the funds to be made available for these services.[30]

4. THE CORE POLICY CONCEPTS

The Health Strategy of 1994 embraced a range of core policy concepts in seeking to re-orient the Irish health system 'by reshaping the way services are planned and delivered'.[31] These include concepts which are generally acknowledged to be excellent aspirations such as 'equity', 'quality of service' and 'accountability'. The Health Strategy also embraced the concepts of 'health gain' and 'social gain' as a means of directing services towards providing a demonstrable benefit to those who use health services. These concepts involve sophisticated systems of measuring and evaluating outcomes which are, as yet, not very well developed in the Irish health care system.

Comparative casemix budgeting was introduced in 1993 in the acute hospital sector as a result of proposals for reform of the budgetary process first made in the Commission on Health Funding in 1989. A casemix budgeting model is in place in 30 hospitals with more than 5000 acute in-patient discharges in order to assess the average cost per case more accurately. Budgetary adjustments are calculated on the basis of an average of the hospital's casemix adjusted costs and the average cost for the hospital group (teaching or non-teaching). Gains or losses are cumulative in the sense that they are carried from year to year.[32] There is, therefore, a move away from incremental budgeting on a purely historical basis. In addition policies seek to relate the level of funding to agreed levels and types of service through service planning.

[30] *Health (Eastern Regional Health Authority) Act, 1999,* Section 2 and Section 8(3)(f), Section 10(3)(4); the public voluntary hospitals will make such agreements directly with the new Authority and the Act is not to be construed as prejudicing the performance of the new public voluntary hospital at Tallaght of its functions under its Charter (Section 8(4))

[31] *Shaping A Healthier Future,* op. cit., p. 8

[32] see Angela Fitzgerald Fergal Lynch 'Casemix Measurement: Assessing the Impact in Irish Acute Hospitals' *Administration,* Vol. 46, No. 1, Spring 1998, pp 29 - 54

However as one public servant with responsibility in this area in the Department of Health and Children has noted:

> . . . The emphasis is now switching to evaluating the effectiveness of the services provided. This is the critical distinction between outputs such as number of services provided, number of clients seen or number of sessions worked, and outcomes which are concerned in the actual result of the intervention . . . Evaluating outcomes of health services is a very difficult task . . . Techniques for this form of evaluation are still in their infancy . . .[33]

In order to implement the Strategy and the policy inherent in the concepts espoused it is proposed to develop the 'partnership' between statutory health agencies and voluntary agencies within a new statutory framework involving principally the health boards (renamed health authorities) and the 'voluntary' providers as outlined above. The health authorities would take responsibility for funding all providers within their areas by having 'service agreements' with 'voluntary' providers. Funding will be linked to agreed levels of service to be provided. The Health Strategy 'envisaged that these agreements will, in general, be for terms of a number of years' in order to provide continuity but that funding would be agreed on an annual basis.[34] In terms of the relationships between voluntary and statutory health agencies and the governance and management of these agencies these core concepts of 'partnership' and 'service agreements' need to be examined very carefully particularly in a context where there exists such a lack of clarity as to what is understood by 'voluntary' in the health care system.

(a) *Partnership*
The Health Strategy speaks of the integral role of voluntary agencies in health care provision and of their ability to harness community support and to complement statutory services in an innovative and flexible manner. It states, however, that the direct funding of the voluntary agencies by the Department of Health impedes the proper co-ordination and development of services at local level. It proposes that a new

[33] see F. Lynch 'Health Funding and Expenditure in Ireland' in *A Healthier Future? Managing Healthcare in Ireland*, eds. E. McAuliffe and L. Joyce (Dublin, 1998), p. 107; there is increasing emphasis in healthcare literature on evidence-based medicine and cost-effective medicine in order to achieve the optimum outcome for given resources see, for example, J.A. Muir Gray *Evidence-Based Healthcare How To Make Health Policy and Management Decisions* (Churchill Livingstone, Edinburgh, 1997)

[34] *Shaping A Healthier Future A Strategy for Effective Healthcare in the 1990s* (Department of Health (1994)), pp 32–4

statutory framework would recognise the role and responsibilities of both parties and that the independent identity of the voluntary agencies would be fully respected under the new structure and that the voluntary agencies would retain their operational autonomy. The statement in the Health Strategy that these agencies 'will be fully accountable for the public funds which they will receive' signalled a change from the 'grant-in-aid model' of public funding for voluntary agencies towards the 'contract model'. Implied in this shift was that the measure of trust formerly reposed in voluntary agencies would become subject to more accountability and more direct control of expenditure.

The initial reaction of the directly-funded voluntary health agencies was to seek to maintain the status quo whereby they received their public funds from the Department of Health. As many of them were national agencies their focus was much wider than any local health board area and they feared a loss of their national impact on policy by becoming resource dependent on a local health body.

One important exploration of the policy occurred in relation to mental handicap services where about 85% of all such services are provided by voluntary agencies. It is useful to detail the proposed implementation of the policy in this area by way of contrast to what occurred in relation to public voluntary hospitals. The voluntary services in mental handicap services date from 1868 and have always been the major providers of mental handicap services.

In late 1995 the Department of Health acted on the Health Strategy in respect of services for persons with mental handicap by announcing the appointment of a Working Group to identify and advise the Minister on

- The arrangements for a national framework which should be put in place to ensure a smooth transfer of responsibility for funding of voluntary mental handicap agencies from the Department of Health to the health boards

- The process of transferring responsibility for funding from the Department of Health to the Mid-Western and Southern Health Boards of the relevant mental handicap agencies (it was proposed to begin in 1996 in those areas)

- The implications of these arrangements for other service-providers in the field of mental handicap (that is, in particular, those voluntary agencies already funded by the health boards under Section 65 of the Health Act, 1953).

The term 'national framework' was an important concession to the view of the Federation of Voluntary Bodies Providing Services for People with Mental Handicap: there were fourteen major voluntary bodies directly funded by the Department of Health.[35]

The development of 'partnership' obviously means different things to different individuals and organisations and it has become a 'buzz word' of political and social policy discourse in Ireland and in the health services.[36] The Federation of Voluntary Bodies, in the tripartite Working Group consisting of the Department of Health, the health boards and the Federation, sought and obtained 'Principles for Partnership in Services to Persons with a Mental Handicap' and it was agreed that Service Agreements would be based on these principles. In the *Enhancing the Partnership Report* there is outlined a structure to implement the principles with two levels: the national level whereby the Federation would be supported to continue to have an input into the overall development of policy at national level and the health board or regional level involving a Consultative Committee and a Development Committee. The Report seeks also to establish 'core principles' to underpin Service Agreements which include significantly 'arrangements for monitoring, review and resolution of difficulties' which was seen as vital to the effectiveness of the relationships being sought. Significantly another core principle underpinning Service Agreements is 'flexibility to take account of the unexpected or local circumstances'. It was agreed that Section 26 of the Health Act 1970 be the legal basis of the new arrangements rather than Section 65 of the Health Act 1953. It was considered by the Working Group that Section 26 of the 1970 Act, though not widely used, offered a better framework than Section 65 of the 1953 Act to support the kind of relationship to be expressed in service agreements between health boards and voluntary mental handicap agencies

During the process of preparing this significant Report the Health (Amendment) (No. 3) Act, 1996 was passed and it contained an important sub-section (2b) that health boards 'shall have regard to . . . the need for co-operation with voluntary bodies providing services

[35] see *Enhancing The Partnership Report of the Working Group on the Implementation of The Health Strategy in Relation to Persons with a Mental Handicap* (Department of Health, [1997] submitted December 1996), pp 2–3, p. 77

[36] for significant overview of 'partnership' in Irish governance see R. O'Donnell, D. Thomas 'Partnership and Policy-Making' in *Social Policy in Ireland Principles, Practice and Problems*, eds. S. Healy and B. Reynolds (Dublin, 1998), pp 117–146

similar or ancillary to services which the health board may provide, to people residing in the functional area of the health board'.

In addition to this legislative support statutory regulations are to be made under Section 72 of the Health Act 1970: these regulations will provide that any arrangement between a health board and a designated voluntary body for the provision of health services to people eligible under the Health Acts 1947 to 1996 will be made under Section 26 of the Health Act 1970 and will be subject to a Service Agreement whose form is to be set out in a schedule to the Regulations.

The effective tripartite relationships experienced in the Working Group were continued by the establishment of an Implementation Committee to deal with issues which might require clarification during the critical implementation stage. A formal procedure for the resolution of problems, providing for third party involvement, both during the implementation phase and the post-implementation phase was agreed as an 'insurance policy' for the voluntary service-providers.

Thus the voluntary services for mental handicap secured agreed structures to be supported by legislation which addressed their major concerns about undue interference in their operational autonomy and delayed cash flow from the funding authority (the health board). A basis has been laid in detailed discussions and agreements for 'enhancing the partnership.' In contrast public voluntary hospitals have simply been brought under the Health (Amendment) (No. 3) Act 1996 through the letter of determination process issued in December 1997 allocating funds for 1998. There has been no detailed discussion on operating principles nor has there been a relationship building process nor have securities been provided to allay concerns. The public voluntary hospitals have not formed a 'federation' to represent a coherent position on how the 'partnership' might be built with any new health authority or be continued with the Department of Health and Children. Individually such hospitals in Dublin have made submissions to The Task Force on the Eastern Regional Health Authority and a submission was jointly made by the five academic teaching hospitals in Dublin.[37]

The voluntary agencies concerned with mental handicap services were aware of the dangers inherent in the fact 'that the finance matters relating to the transfer of responsibility for funding were being consid-

---

[37] see *Interim Report of The Task Force on the Eastern Regional Health Authority June 1997* Appendix III

ered in isolation of the organisational and management structure and style necessary to define the interdependence between the policy role, strategic role and operations role of services to persons with a mental handicap'.[38] It is precisely this concern which has not been addressed in regard to services provided by voluntary hospitals.[39]

Significantly the voluntary agencies concerned with mental handicap services define 'voluntary' as follows:

> Voluntary organisations can be defined as formal organisations which are non-statutory, self-governing, non profit making, of benefit to the public and use volunteers to a greater or lesser extent. The voluntary sector encompasses a myriad of small and often loosely organised groups as well as large highly professional agencies. Some of the voluntary organisations are owned and operated by religious orders, others are incorporated by charter or statute.[40]

It is important also to note that the 'partners' in relation to mental handicap services have an agreed database upon which service agreements may be developed in The National Intellectual Disability Database. This Database 'will provide the best available description of the current level of service being provided by agencies'.[41] No such comparative database to provide a detailed activity profile of each hospital exists as yet which makes 'service planning' in relation to hospitals under the Letter of Determination in effect finance driven with cash limits or fiscal budgets being set upon a historical basis centrally by the Department of Health and Children.

Enhancing The Partnership recognised that 'new methodologies for costing services' are required for proper service planning and the development of service agreements.[42] This will be an even more substantive issue in relation to hospital service plans where such costing methods, devolved budgeting and clinical responsibility for budgets are in relatively early stages of development in Irish hospitals.

Above all the climate which is created for partnership is crucial as is the need for confidence building measures:

---

[38] *Enhancing The Partnership* op. cit., p. 20

[39] A 'Governance Initiative' from the Department of Health and Children initiated in mid-1998 has opened up issues concerning proper governance and management responsibilities in hospitals and this process being facilitated by the Office of Health Management but it is not a formal policy development forum

[40] *Enhancing the Partnership*, op. cit., p. 18

[41] ibid, p. 38

[42] *Enhancing The Partnership*, p. 50

The Working Group can hardly over emphasise the importance of fostering a climate of trust between the voluntary agencies and the health boards in relation to the proposed changes in the organisation, and funding of mental handicap services . . . The Minister and the Department were clearly aware of the sensitivities associated with the proposed change of funding when they established this Working Group. The acceptance of the Working Group's recommendations and their implementation by all parties will in itself be a major confidence building measure.

The Report stressed the importance of staff in each agency knowing each other in advance of discussing details concerning the transfer of funding.[43]

The process of 'enhancing the partnership' between voluntary and statutory agencies in health care requires very detailed consideration as indicated by the Report of the Working Group entitled *Enhancing the Partnership*. The process, however, is greatly hindered by the absence of an agreed national framework for voluntary and statutory relationships. As Pauline Faughnan has noted

> Despite the importance of the activities of the voluntary sector and the role it has traditionally played in Irish society, there is no policy at national level within which its contribution may be located. There is no clear statement of principles which underlie the relationship between the voluntary and statutory sectors in general. Neither is there agreement as to the relative spheres of competence and legitimacy or the balancing of functions between the voluntary and statutory sectors within the health arena.[44]

Therefore when the Department of Health and Children propose a 'partnership' with 'non-statutory' providers in the mission statement of the Department it quite unclear both as to what such a 'partnership' entails and what understanding of 'non-statutory' (or 'voluntary') is implied. The services in relation to mental handicap have struggled, not unsuccessfully, to define and agree a framework for 'partnership' in relation to their services but unless this is supported by a wider framework of understanding and a deep commitment based on under-standing of 'the relative spheres of competence and legitimacy' the implementation of what is set out in the Report must remain problem-atical.

[43] ibid, pp 67–8

[44] P. Faughnan 'A Healthy Voluntary Sector: Rhetoric or Reality?' in *Reflections on Health Commemorating Fifty Years of the Department of Health 1947–1977*, ed. J. Robins (Department of Health, Dublin, 1997), p. 238

(b)   *Service Planning as link between voluntary and statutory sectors*

Analysis of policy in respect of voluntary and statutory relationships in Irish health care reveals that there is no appropriate policy framework in place which addresses the legitimate requirements of both voluntary and statutory healthcare agencies in respect to public voluntary hospitals. There is a long-established 'policy line' within the Department of Health from 1986, or indeed much earlier, which explicitly seeks to exercise financial control and co-ordination of the hospital sector by bringing the public voluntary hospitals under health board ('authority') funding arrangements. The 'voluntary' hospitals are extremely vulnerable in respect of this consistent policy. As David McKevitt noted in 1990

> The 'cutback' phase in 1987 and 1988 demonstrated that the administrative centre had more control over the voluntary sector (by way of the direct budget relationship) than it enjoyed in the Health Board sector. As a direct result of the budgetary mechanism the Department of Health could close voluntary hospitals; legally, of course, the closure is a decision for the hospital board as the Department does not have jurisdiction in the actual closure decision. Evidence also suggests that the Department achieved some closures earlier than even they had planned. The 'rush' of events in 1987 overwhelmed the hospital segment and advantage was taken to achieve long-sought rationalisation proposals, e.g. Dr. Steeven's Hospital in Dublin.[45]

In the absence of an explicit theoretical and empirical basis for a policy, which might adequately take account of the distinctive 'spheres of competence and legitimacy' and might seek 'to balance' the functions of both statutory and voluntary agencies it was easy, given the financial control and 'means of influence' at the discretion of the Department to erode the voluntary hospital movement even while talking the language of 'partnership'. An adequate policy would require to have policy objectives which would be designed to promote and develop the distinctive contributions of 'voluntary' hospitals and against which outcomes of policy would be measured. No such policy has been developed.

The implications for governance and management of public 'voluntary' hospitals of the current policy approach of the Department of Health and Children are profound and wide-ranging.

---

[45] D. McKevitt *Health Care Policy in Ireland A Study in Control*, (Hibernian University Press [Cork 1990]), pp 151–2

The *Commission on Health Funding Report* of 1989 found that the principal difficulties in the general hospital sector lay not in funding but rather in organisation and administration. The Kennedy Reports of the Dublin Hospital Initiative Group in the early 1990s were very influential in recommending less involvement by the Department in the management of services and greater co-ordination between hospital and community based services. The Health Strategy of 1994, with an emphasis on the health status of the population being measured and evaluated, signposted a very significant long term move towards a more critical evaluation of outcomes as opposed to measuring activity volumes. For hospital management this shift implies more decision making and accountability at local and/or institutional levels. The policy, as set out, is for the Department to reduce its own involvement in the management of hospital services and to increase its role in the strategic development of services. This requires a devolution of responsibility and an improvement of the co-ordination of services at local level.

The 'service plan' as set out in the 1996 Health Act, referred to above, has become the lynch-pin for the future interaction between the Department of Health and Children and every health service providing agency including the public 'voluntary' hospitals. In effect this means that the Department through the letter of determination sets the fixed cash limits or budget and the agency is legally required to produce and operate a service plan within the budget. Section 6 of the Health (Amendment) Act, 1996 specifies that each Board must submit a Service Plan to the Minister on an annual basis. Service planning may be seen as part of the strategic planning ethos emphasised in the Government's Strategic Management Initiative and in the Health Strategy of 1994. Section 6.2 of the 1996 Act states that these plans should 'include a statement of the services to be provided by the Health Board and estimates of the income and expenditure of the Board for the period to which the plan relates and be consistent with the financial limits determined by the Minister'. It is hoped that service plans will identify priority areas—both unmet needs and changing patterns of needs—and eventually incorporate performance measures of health outcomes.

The 'service plan' as set out in the 1996 Act applies by statute to health boards but crucially it is also applied 'in an administrative way' by the Department of Health and Children to public voluntary hospitals which it directly funds. It is not clear what legal effect this 'administrative' application of the Act has but for all practical purposes public voluntary hospitals appear bound by the Act by the decision of the Minister and the Department.[46]

The Task Force Report on the Eastern Region and the subsequent Health (Eastern Regional Health Authority) Act, 1999 envisages that service planning will play a pivotal role in the funding arrangements between statutory and voluntary providers under the new Authority.[47] It is recommended that the major acute hospitals and the three Area Health Boards negotiate service agreements with the Eastern Regional Health Authority for a period of three to five years. It is hoped by the Task Force that the use of service planning will provide transparency, equity and fairness in respect of the funding of both statutory and voluntary services in the new arrangements under the Authority.

5. PARTNERSHIP AND SERVICE PLANNING: A LITERATURE BASED CRITIQUE

Partnership in public service has been a major theme of the voluntary sector literature which has examined the changing relationships between government and voluntary agencies.[48] In the construction of such partnerships it has been critical to understand how 'contracting' or 'service agreements' affect voluntary-statutory relationships.[49] 'Contract' is used here to include any significant departure from grant-in-aid funding (which has no obvious strings attached) and includes 'service planning' or 'agreements' which may technically not be contracts because they lack enforceability but which carry penalties in

[46] This was a major conclusion of the Deloitte & Touche Report to the Minister for Health and Children on *Management Reporting and Control, Service Planning, and the Financial Position of the Adelaide and Meath Hospital, Dublin, Incorporating The National Children's Hospital,* December 1998, p. 71, which will feature in the case study of this Hospital in chapter 5 below

[47] see *Interim Report of The Task Force on the Eastern Regional Health Authority,* June 1997 (no place of publication given), pp 27–8

[48] see in particular, L.M. Salamon 'Partners in Public Service: The Scope and Theory of Government—Nonprofit Relations' in *The Nonprofit Sector A Research Handbook* ed. W.W. Powell (Yale University Press, New Haven and London, 1987) pp 99–116 and L.M. Salamon *Partners in Public Service: Government—Nonprofit Relations in the Modern Welfare State* (Johns Hopkins University Press, Baltimore, MD, 1995)

[49] see R.M. Kramer 'Voluntary Agencies and the Contract Culture: 'Dream or Nightmare?' *Social Service Review,* Vol. 68, No. 1, March 1994, pp 33–60

respect of future funding possibilities. Such penalties are at the discretion of the funding authority. The concept of 'service planning' has been adopted and implemented in the Irish health system without detailed consideration by *both* voluntary and statutory agencies of what contribution to such an important public policy might have been made from experiences with 'the contract culture' in other countries.[50] One study of the lessons learned about contracting in the United States of America concluded in respect of the United Kingdom:

> The development of contracting is likely to change the nature of the voluntary sector—making it more like the private sector, increasing the size of big organisations, squeezing out many smaller organisations, reducing lobbying activity, increasing the influence of professionals and reducing the role of volunteers.[51]

There is in the literature a range of 'models' in the application of 'service planning' and it is important to assess the impact on the relationships of voluntary and statutory agencies of the various approaches.[52] Each 'model' will affect in different ways patterns of governance and management in voluntary organisations.[53]

The effects of the 'contract culture' on voluntary agencies may be considered under five key aspects bearing on the possible effects on voluntary organisations:

(i)   bureaucratization or formalisation of the organisation

(ii)   inappropriate regulations

(iii)   threats to autonomy and goal distortion

(iv)   financial insecurity

---

[50] One recent study uses some UK studies but not the extensive international literature available; see Anna Maria Meegan 'Management of Service Agreements between Voluntary and Statutory Sectors in Irish Health Service Provision', unpublished M.Sc. Health Services Management Thesis, Trinity College, Dublin, 1998

[51] R. Gutch *Contracting Lessons From the US* (NCVO Publications, London, 1992) p. 83

[52] The literature on such 'models' includes P.M. Kettner, L.L. Martin 'Purchase of Service Contracting: Two Models' *Administration in Social Work*, Vol. 14, No. 1, 1990, pp 15–30; R.H. DeHoog 'Competition, Negotiation or Cooperation Three Models for Service Contracting' *Administration & Society*, Vol. 22, No. 3, 1990, pp 317–340; J.M. Costan 'A Model and Typology of Government—NGO Relationships' *Nonprofit and Voluntary Sector Quarterly*, Vol. 27, No. 3, 1998, pp 358–382

[53] see J.R. Saidel, S.L. Harlan 'Contracting and Patterns of Nonprofit Governance' *Nonprofit Management and Leadership*, Vol. 3, No. 3, 1998, pp 243–259

(v)   erosion of the advantages, social and economic, which voluntary agencies claim to confer.[54]

There are a number of important studies concerning 'contracting' which address key issues based upon experiences in a range of countries.[55]

Services agreements or service plans are an innovative development in Irish health services. The way such agreements or plans are introduced and developed is of course decisive as to their effects on voluntary organisations. The rationale may be fiscal control as was strongly the case in the 1980s or it may be based on an explicit public policy to develop partnership and complementarity between voluntary and statutory agencies. The literature available is useful in identifying a range of possible advantages as well as a list of possible disadvantages of 'service planning'. The advantages which might be derived from using service agreements are many: such agreements may provide

- a means to integrate services provided by diverse agencies
- for full accountability
- a means for strategic planning of services
- for matching between funding and service provision
- a written plan to respond to user needs
- for 'value for money' assessments to be made
- for standards to be set
- more equity in service provision
- a more transparent funding arrangement
- a basis to assess service developments or improvements against the existing pattern of provision.

[54] see J. Kendall and M. Knapp *The Voluntary Sector in the UK* Johns Hopkins Nonprofit Sector Series 8 (Manchester University Press, Manchester, 1996), pp 227–237 where the evidence is marshalled for the UK experiences of contracts under these headings.

[55] see *The Contract Culture in Public Services Studies from Britain, Europe and the USA*, eds. Perri 6, J. Kendall (Arena, Aldershot, 1997) S.R. Smith, M. Lipsky *Nonprofits for Hire: The Welfare State in the Age of Contracting* (Harvard University Press, Cambridge, Mass, 1993); J. Lewis 'What Does Contracting Do to Voluntary Agencies?' and N. Deakin 'What does Contracting Do To Users' in *Voluntary Agencies Challenges of Organisation and Management* eds. D. Billis and M. Harris (London, 1996)

It is possible also that such agreements or plans may give a greater guarantee of continuity (by planning for three to five years, for example) and the actual negotiation of these plans may provide opportunities to build relationships between the voluntary and statutory agencies involved; in theory there is no reason why flexibility and negotiation for future changes in the course of the plan's implementation cannot be provided for in such agreements. Statutory agencies may come to have an increasing understanding of the work and philosophy of voluntary organisations; indeed the 'value base' of voluntary organisations could be outlined and honoured in such agreements thus providing greater clarity of the roles and responsibilities of voluntary organisations and of statutory authorities.

However, the application of service agreements or contracts may have a range of detrimental effects on voluntary organisations. Such effects include

- a focus on competition for statutory resources which may emphasise reduction of costs over quality of service or user outcomes

- imposition of certain service orientations on the mission of the voluntary organisation altering the objectives, processes and even the clientele served

- erosion of trust between voluntary and statutory agencies because of closer monitoring of services, and a reduction of the discretion required by providers who are closer to the 'coal face' of service provision

- the effects on management and on governance may be inconsistent with the values of voluntarism; participation by volunteers, staff and users in service developments may be not adequately be allowed for by the funding authorities

- voluntary support and funding may be reduced as the organisation may be perceived as a statutory service provider, as alternative rather than autonomous providers

- the shift of accountability of the voluntary organisation from their members and users of their services towards accountability to the funder

- the campaigning, lobbying and advocacy roles of voluntary organisations may be eroded as increasingly contract renewal and funding is dependent on the goodwill of those who might be the focus of such actions by voluntary bodies

- voluntary or other income may be diverted to meet deficits engendered by 'underfunding' of the agreed service levels.

There are very heavy 'transaction costs' in preparing, negotiating, and implementing complex 'service planning' arrangements which involve a range of providers and possibly of funders of services. The 'space' in which voluntary organisations traditionally flourish which allows for a range of intangible attributes—such as voluntary 'spirit' or 'ethos', innovation, flexibility, commitment to optimum care, user choice, and so forth—may be so shaped by 'service plans' that the very advantages of using voluntary service providers may be lost.

In brief, this overview of the advantages and disadvantages shows that 'service planning' may represent 'an enabling state' or a 'controlling state' and the fate of voluntary organisations depends greatly upon which approach is adopted by the state.

There are some key issues which ought to be considered in the Irish context. Firstly, what is meant by 'partnership'? Ideally partnership ought to refer to any agreed relationship based upon a set of linkages between two or more agencies as to the provision of public services which involves clarity about roles and responsibilities, a sharing of risks and uncertainties, the pursuit of joint objectives and in which the partners together formulate policy in respect of service provision. A useful distinction has been made between 'active partnerships' and 'dependent partnerships'

> Active partnerships are those built through ongoing processes of negotiation, debate, occasional conflict, and learning through trial and error. Risks are taken, and although roles and purposes are clear, they may change according to need and circumstance. Dependent partnerships, on the other hand, have a blueprint character and are constructed at the project-planning stage according to rigid assumptions about comparative advantage and individual agency interests, often linked to the availability of outside funding.[56]

It is clear that 'service planning', as applied so far in the Irish health services, involves 'dependent partnerships' with voluntary organisations being obliged to obtain their budgets, fixed by the Department of Health and Children, within a legal framework (The Health (Amendment) (No. 3) Act, 1996) designed for the statutory sector without debate or discussion with the voluntary sector and without

[56] D.J. Lewis 'Interagency Partnerships in Aid-Recipient Countries: Lessons from an Aquaculture Project in Bangladesh' *Nonprofit and Voluntary Sector Quarterly* Vol. 27, No. 3, 1998, p. 326

Table 3   Contrasting Characteristics of Active and Dependent Partnerships

Active Partnerships	Dependent Partnerships
Process	Blueprint, fixed term
Negotiated, changing roles	Rigid roles based on static assumptions about comparative advantage
Clear purposes, roles, and linkages but an openness to change as appropriate	Unclear purposes, roles, and linkages
Shared risks	Individual interests
Debate and dissent	Consensus
Learning and information exchange	Poor communication flows
Activity-based origins—emerging from practice	Resource-based origins—primarily to gain access to funds

SOURCE: D.J. Lewis 'Interagency Partnerships in Aid-Recipient Countries: Lessons from An Aquaculture Project in Bangladesh' *Nonprofit and Voluntary Sector Quarterly* Vol. 27, No. 3, 1998, p. 327

clarity in public policy about the respective roles of the voluntary and statutory sectors. As Lewis notes '. . . there is a world of difference between the effects of contracting on agencies who have no objection to contracting on the one hand, and on those who do object, but have little choice in the matter, on the other.'[57] In Ireland national policy has not made explicit the legitimacy of the voluntary sector: this means that voluntary agencies fear that the balance of power in the 'partnership' is permanently and detrimentally tilted against them in respect of their values, independence, mission, goals and advocacy role. Indeed the 'service planning' approach applied to date and the devolution of executive responsibility from the Department may be experienced as 'a decentralisation of blame' where the risks are not shared:[58] what exists in the Irish context is a Department (and/or an Authority) providing a determination (in effect a cash limit) to a dependent agency (the voluntary hospital, for example) and requiring and specifying (some of the elements of) a service plan for the amount determined. This

[57] J. Lewis 'What does Contracting Do to Voluntary Agencies' op. cit., p. 99

[58] for this in the UK context see R. Klein *The Politics of the National Health Service* 3rd Edition (Longman, Harlow, 1995)

inevitably creates a suspicion that what is central to Irish health policy is rationing of financial resources in the well established context of infinite demand and finite resources found in health care: since 'rationing decisions are by definition almost always unpopular, there is a marked tendency for responsibility to be transferred from one group of stakeholders to another'.[59]

There is no doubt that service planning is 'a basic reconfiguration' of 'power relationships and policies'.[60] The case history of the new Hospital in Tallaght described in Chapter 5 below will describe the stark effects upon the governance and management of a public voluntary hospital of the application of 'service planning' under the 'dependent partnership' model. However, there are other possible 'models' which would provide for much more positive relationships between voluntary and statutory agencies.

A growing body of literature has begun the task of examining contract implementation, including contracting procedures, decision-making processes, and organizational environments.[61] The 'competition model', with its origins in right wing political ideologies of the 1980s based on the 'market', has been criticised and compared to two alternative contracting models 'the negotiation and co-operation models'.[62] These alternative models may be much more appropriate to voluntary organisations. The 'negotiation' model 'involves relational contracting, in which a form of consensual and incremental decision making is the norm'.[63] In this model the government and the agency involved in the contract are on a more equal footing than in the competition model. The 'co-operation model' is typically characterized by only one contractor and 'the government and the contractor are relatively equal partners'.[64] The 'co-operation model' has been termed the 'partnership model':[65]

---

[59] see C. Ham 'Priority Setting: Political Issues' in *Fixing Health Budgets: Experience from Europe and North America* eds. F.W. Schwartz, H. Glennerster, R.B. Saltman (John Wiley, Chicester, 1996) p. 14

[60] *The Contract Culture in Public Services* eds. Perri 6, J. Kendall, op. cit., p. 2

[61] see R.H. DeHoog 'Competition, Negotiation, or Cooperation Three Models for Service Contracting' *Administration & Society* Vol 22, No. 3, 1990, pp 318–319

[62] ibid, p. 319; DeHoog describes each 'model' and their advantages and limitations

[63] ibid, p. 325

[64] ibid, p. 330

[65] see P.M. Kettner, L.L. Martin 'Purchase of Service contracting: Two Models' *Administration in Social Work* Vol. 14, No. 1, 1990, pp 15–30 for analysis of the 'partnership' and 'market' models

The system is quite decentralized and flexible, with discretion about many contracting decisions in the hands of program managers who often develop a personal relationship with the contractor. Both sides will share information, since each side has incentives to make adjustments and improvements as necessary. The contractor becomes a key actor in providing needs assessments, planning programs, and determining the methods and levels of service delivery. Both sides will try to anticipate implementation problems, yet knowing that they cannot write all possible contingencies into the contract . . . In sum, they will emphasize the program or services, clients, and outcomes in place of the proper process, procedures, and paperwork.[66]

As a result of their differing decision-making processes and control mechanisms, each of these three models has various advantages and disadvantages that must be carefully understood when adopting 'service planning' as a mechanism of public funding of services by diverse providers. Voluntary organisations may be particularly suitable for the negotiation or co-operative/partnership models.[67] A genuine partnership model would be defined as a set of policies and practices on the part of statutory and voluntary agencies based on the premise that both sectors 'should actually comprise one comprehensive human services system': in this model the contract is a mechanism for both sectors to join together as partners in joint ventures 'designed to maximise the outputs of a state or community human service system through collaborative action'.[68]

One study of the issue of public accountability versus autonomy in relation to contracts states that the 'threat that government funding poses for nonprofit autonomy depends on nonprofit behaviour as much as that of contracting governments . . . The extent to which government funding detracts from the autonomy of nonprofit organi-zations and encroaches on their uniqueness will depend on the behaviour of contracting governments as well as that of nonprofit organizations'.[69] In effect governments should recognise that 'excessive intrusions limit the advantages' of the voluntary sector while voluntary organisations need to be conscious of the implications of contracting

---

[66] DeHoog, op. cit., pp 330–1

[67] ibid, p. 336; see also J.M. Ferris and E. Graddy 'Contracting Out: For What? With Whom?' *Public Administration Review* Vol. 46, 1986, pp 332–344

[68] Kettner, Martin, op. cit., p. 16

[69] James M. Ferris 'The Double-Edged Sword of Social Service Contracting: Public Accountability Versus Nonprofit Autonomy' *Nonprofit Management & Leadership* Vol. 3, No. 4, Summer 1993, pp 363–376

for governance and management.[70] Managing the 'tangled' relationships between statutory and voluntary agencies is 'an increasingly urgent governance challenge'.[71] The various governance models available to voluntary hospitals and organisations in meeting this challenge will be discussed below in Chapter 4.

The pursuit of more co-operative relationships is inhibited by the absence of a firm theoretical basis for statutory—voluntary relationships and by lack of consideration of the options available for such relationships. Costan has presented a valuable generalised model and typology of relationship alternatives, in the context of development agencies, based upon eight types of government—non-governmental organisation relationships: repression, rivalry, competition, contracting, third-party government, co-operation, complementarity and collaboration. Each type is distinguished according to several variables

- the Government's resistance or acceptance of institutional pluralism

- the government—voluntary organisation 'linkages'[72]

- the relative power relationships

- the degree of formality

- the approach of government policy to voluntary organisation.[73]

---

[70] ibid, p. 363; see, in particular, J.R. Saidel, S.L. Harlan 'Contracting and patterns of nonprofit governance' *Nonprofit Management and Leadership* Vol. 8, No. 3, 1998, pp 243–259; see also the important examination of how funding relationships affect the management of nonprofit organizations by K.A. Gronbjerg 'Managing Grants and Contracts: The Case of Four Nonprofit Social Service Organizations' *Nonprofit and Voluntary Sector Quarterly* Vol. 20, No. 1, 1991, pp 5–24

[71] Saidel & Harlan, op. cit., p. 243; for a valuable analysis of the various strategies used by voluntary agencies to cope with their dependencies on government for funds see R.M. Kramer and B. Grossman 'Contracting for Social Services: Process Management and Resource Dependencies' *Social Service Review* Vol. 61, No. 1, 1987, pp 32–55

[72] Five levels of government linkage are described:

i) *autonomy:* no interaction or government control

ii) *low* linkage with little interaction

iii) *moderate* linkage with some but not regular interaction

iv) *high* linkage with much interaction but some reciprocity

v) *direction* with heavy interaction controlled by government see Costan op. cit., pp 361–2

[73] see J.M. Costan 'A Model and Typology of Government—NGO Relationships' *Nonprofit and Voluntary Sector Quarterly* Vol. 27, No. 3, 1998, pp 358–382

It is possible using Costan's typology to envisage voluntary-statutory relationships involving collaboration which would respect the integrity of the participating organisations and in which the respective organisations are able to maintain their autonomy, underlying value system, and mission. Such collaboration could only develop where there is a full acceptance of 'the relative spheres of competence and legitimacy and a balancing of functions between the voluntary and statutory sectors in health care'; as Faughnan has pointed out there is no 'agreement' in Irish health policy in this regard.[74] The next chapter examines the theories of voluntary action in society and outlines a legitimating political philosophy for such action based upon citizenship theory in a pluralist democracy. Without such an explicit philosophy neither public policy in respect of voluntary-statutory relationships nor governance and management within voluntary organisations can be satisfactorily addressed.

[74] P. Faughnan 'A Healthy Voluntary Sector: Rhetoric or Reality?' in *Reflections on Health Commemorating Fifty Years of the Department of Health 1947–1997* ed. J. Robins (Department of Health, Dublin, 1997) p. 238

CHAPTER 3

Theories of Voluntary Action in Society: Active Citizenship and Pluralist Democracy

"Theory cannot just be picked up; it has to be searched for, chiseled, shaped, pounded, reorganized, and reoriented. Creating coherence out of existing bits of theory is like getting an inside straight in poker. Theorising is a creative act. Whether one is asserting that a theory of a kind exists (how remarkable!) or inventing one that claims to be new (thus running afoul of the encapsulated wisdom of the ages—if new, not true; if true not new), one gets into trouble whichever way one goes."

AARON WILDAVSKY *Craftways On the Organisation of Scholarly Work*, (New Brunswick and London, 1989), p.29.

"We ask whether it is imaginable that citizens can realize political institutions that not only work but justify their commitment to them. What sort of citizens and institutions does it take to constitute a democratic society? How can such institutions and citizens be fostered?"

JAMES G. MARCH, JOHAN P. OLSEN *Democratic Governance* (The Free Press, New York, 1995), p. 47

"If citizens are to be competent, won't they need political and social institutions to help make them so? Unquestionably. Opportunities to gain an enlightened understanding of public matters are not just part of the definition of democracy. They are a requirement for democracy".

ROBERT A. DAHL *On Democracy* (Yale University Press, New Haven and London , 1998) p. 79

1. INTRODUCTION

In the search for a convincing philosophical justification for voluntary service provision this chapter reviews the normative roles ascribed to voluntary action in society by democratic theorists. It commences, however, with a brief summary of the explanatory theories which have been developed since the 1970s in the literature on the voluntary and nonprofit sector: these theories seek to explain the existence of the voluntary sector from empirical studies. Such theories help to answer the question why voluntary action occurs but normative theories are necessary to provide the basis for a fundamental philosophical and political argument as to the possible contributions of voluntary action in a democracy.

The normative theorists reviewed from Tocqueville's *Democracy in America* in the 1830s to Henry Tam's *Communitarianism* in the 1990s cohere around a central concept and context: active citizenship within a pluralist democracy.[1] This key concept of 'active citizenship' provides a convincing philosophical justification for voluntary action within the context of a pluralist democracy. Lest the search for such a philosophical rationale of voluntary action be thought somewhat distant from, and even unrelated to, voluntary and statutory relationships it is important to note that the Green Paper *Supporting Voluntary Activity* published by the Irish Government in 1997 identified, amongst a number of relevant developments to be considered in the context of a White Paper, 'issues relating to 'participative democracy' principles, under discussion in current sociological political science literature'; the Green Paper in an important section entitled 'Re-Thinking Our Vision' argued that there is a need 'to create a more participatory democracy where active citizenship is fostered. In such a society, the ability of the voluntary and community sector to provide channels for the active involvement and participation of citizens is fundamental'. The Green Paper saw the sector contributing to 'a democratic, pluralist society' and it drew upon the concept of a 'civil society', promoted by 'an enabling and open State which is engaged in dialogue and partnership and which allows bottom-up responses to emerge from voluntary and community groups'. The concept of 'active citizenship' becomes central to the new 'vision':

---

[1] See Alexis de Tocqueville *Democracy in America* ed. J.P. Mayer (Anchor Books edition, New York, 1969) and Henry Tam *Communitarianism A New Agenda For Politics and Citizenship* (Macmillan Press, London, 1998)

Active citizenship refers to the active role of people, communities and voluntary organisations in decision making which directly affect them. This extends the concept of formal citizenship and democratic society from one of basic civil, political, social and economic rights to one of direct democratic participation and responsibility. In this sense, citizenship is a political activity which gives citizens the opportunity to shape the society in which they live . . . Active citizenship is also about the strengthening of voluntary and community organisations. . .[2]

The purpose of this chapter is to contribute to the identification of the relative spheres of competence and legitimacy of the statutory and voluntary sectors in a democratic society through a better understanding of the place of voluntary action in democratic life. Previous chapters have identified the absence of an adequate public philosophy legitimating voluntary action in Irish society. The religious justification, based upon subsidiarity, while valuable and important, is insufficient to provide legitimacy in an increasingly secular society seeking to develop a public policy on the appropriate relationships between the state and voluntary organisations. This chapter articulates a public philosophy of voluntary action based upon citizenship theory drawing heavily from the civic republican tradition but not exclusively so as many currents in recent democratic theory converge around citizenship. The argument is that the active citizen involved in shaping civic life is at the core of a public philosophy which is particularly appropriate in a democratic Republic.

Given that such a convincing justification for voluntary action exists what are the general implications for governance and management of voluntary organisations? The chapter concludes with reflections upon suggested approaches or frameworks for democratic governance in both the statutory and voluntary sectors. The elements of governance consonant with the philosophy of voluntary action proposed should incorporate the norms of the citizenship theory proposed and in addition, allow for any insights from the empirical explanatory theories of voluntary action which are now briefly summarised.

2. CURRENT THEORIES OF VOLUNTARY ACTION

The major theories developed in recent decades to explain the voluntary or 'non-profit' sector in western societies have been

[2] see *Supporting Voluntary Activity: A Green Paper on the Community and Voluntary Sector and its Relationship with the State* (Stationery Office, Dublin [1997]) p. 2, pp 24 - 5

summarised recently by Helmut Anheier.[3] There are five theories which seek to explain why voluntary organisations exist. They may be briefly described as follows:

(i) *Public goods or heterogeneity theory*

Weisbrod, who might be seen as the founding father of nonprofit economics, suggests that voluntary organisations produce 'public goods' which cannot be provided through the market because they cannot be withheld from individuals who refuse to pay for them. A lighthouse is a good example of a 'public good' which either must be provided by government or on a voluntary basis. The public sector can and does provide public goods using taxation as a funding mechanism. Voluntary organisations, even where the public sector provides 'public goods' may augment them to cater for diverse or heterogeneous demands or choices which the government would find difficult to justify in taxation and public expenditure terms.[4]

(ii) *Trust or contract failure theory*

According to this theory, developed by Hansmann, Ben-Ner and Van Hoomissen, voluntary organisations exist because of instances of contract failure or need for trust: this is where consumers of a service find it difficult to assess what they purchase and where profit-making firms might have an incentive to increase profits at the expense of quality. If a voluntary agency is providing the service, such as education or health for 'non profit' motives, it is argued that it will be more trust-worthy: this emphasises the 'non-profit distribution' constraint and the fact that governance structures of voluntary agencies suggest 'trustwor-thiness'. This theory might explain voluntary organisations operating hospitals, schools, day care or homes for the elderly especially as often the consumer is not the same as the purchaser as for example, when a parent purchases schooling for a child at school.[5]

[3] see H.K. Anheier 'Voluntary Action Studies: What are the Issues' in *Voluntary Action in Ireland, North and South: Report of a Research Symposium* ed. A. Williamson (Association for Voluntary Action Research in Ireland, Centre for Voluntary Action Studies, University of Ulster, Coleraine, 1998) pp 41–52

[4] see B. Weisbrod *The Voluntary Nonprofit Sector* (Lexington, Mass., 1977) and *The Nonprofit Economy* (Harvard University Press, Cambridge, Mass., 1988)

[5] see H. Hansmann 'Economic theories of nonprofit organisations' in *The Nonprofit Sector: A Research Handbook* ed. W.W. Powell (New Haven and London, 1987) A. Ben-Ner and T. Van Hoomissen 'Nonprofit Organizations in the mixed economy: a demand and supply analysis' in *The Nonprofit Sector in the Mixed Economy* eds. A. Ben-Ner and B. Gui (University of Michigan Press, 1993) pp 27–58

(iii)   *The value-expressive or supply-side theory*
This theory, associated with Estelle James, suggests that those motivated by values or an ideology, such as religious bodies, use voluntary organisations to achieve their goals.[6] Accordingly the greater the ideological and religious competition in a country the larger the voluntary sector. James observes that 'universally, religious groups are the major founders of nonprofit service institutions' and she states

> This simple observation—that religious groups are the major founders of private schools and other NPOS (non profitmaking organisations)—has important implications for nonprofit theory. It explains why nonprofits are concentrated in areas such as education and health . . . their object was not to maximise profits but to maximise religious faith or religious adherents and schools are one of the most important institutions of taste formation and socialization. Similarly, hospitals are a service for which people will have an urgent periodic need; hence they constitute an effective way for religious groups to gain entrée and goodwill in a society.

James concludes that the religious motive for founding voluntary organisations 'provides a powerful supply-side explanation for where nonprofits are found, why the nonprofit form is used, which services are provided by nonprofits and how these institutions may compete effectively with a public or secular profit maximizing alternative'.[7]

The value-expressive character of voluntary organisations according to this view is what distinguishes them from business or government organisations. Thomas H. Jeavons has argued that 'what is most significant' in distinguishing between the different sectors 'is the initial and essential purposes of the organisations within them'. He sees voluntary organisations existing 'primarily to give expression to the social, philosophical, moral, or religious values of their founders and supporters'.[8]

(iv)   *Voluntary-state complementarity or interdependence theory*
Lester M. Salamon developed a 'new theory' that voluntary agencies were 'partners in public service' with governmental agencies because

[6] Estelle James 'The Nonprofit Sector in Comparative Perspective' in *The Nonprofit Sector: A Research Handbook* ed. W.W. Powell (New Haven and London, 1987); see also *The Nonprofit Sector in International Perspective*, ed. Estelle James (Oxford, 1989); see also S. Rose-Ackerman 'Altruism, nonprofits, and economic theory' *Journal of Economic Literature* Vol. 34, No. 2, 1996, pp 701–728

[7] James (1987) op. cit

[8] Thomas H. Jeavons 'When the Management Is the Message: Relating Values to Management Practice in Nonprofit Organisations' *Nonprofit Management & Leadership* Vol. 2, No. 4, Summer, 1992, p. 404

'the voluntary sector's weaknesses correspond well with government's strengths, and vice versa'.[9] It makes sense in this theoretical perspective to use voluntary agencies 'to carry out governmental purposes'. Widespread reliance upon the voluntary sector is 'not an anomaly but exactly what one would expect'. Salamon suggests that instead of demoting the voluntary sector to a derivative role it should be seen as 'the preferred mechanism' for providing collective goods, with government assuming the residual role.

Salamon usefully identifies four voluntary-sector failures which justifies government involvement

- 'philanthropic insufficiency'—which concerns the inability of the sector to generate sufficient income

- 'philanthropic particularism' which describes the tendency of voluntary organisations to focus on particular sub-groups

- 'philanthropic paternalism'—where those in control of resources can choose whom to serve

- 'philanthropic amateurism' which relate to professional service provision.

Salamon states

> Potentially, at least, government is in a position to generate a more reliable stream of resources, to set priorities on the basis of a democratic political process instead of the wishes of the wealthy, to offset part of the paternalism of the charitable system by making access to care a right instead of a privilege, and to improve the quality of care by instituting quality-control standards. By the same token, however, voluntary organisations can personalise the provision of services, operate on a smaller scale than government bureaucracies, reduce the scale of public institutions needed, adjust care to the needs of clients rather than to the structure of government agencies, and permit a degree of competition among service providers.[10]

[9] Lester M. Salamon 'Partners in Public Service: The Scope and Theory of Government-Nonprofit Relations' in *The Nonprofit Sector: A Research Handbook* ed. W.W. Powell (New Haven and London, 1987), p. 113

[10] Salamon, op. cit., p. 112; Salamon's contribution to theory inspired an important volume explicitly concerned with the relationship between voluntary organisations and government *Government and Voluntary Organisations A Relational Perspective* eds. S. Kuhnle, P. Selle, (Aldershot, Hants., 1992); Salamon has developed his thinking in L.M. Salamon *Partners in Public Service: Government—Nonprofit Relations in the Modern Welfare State* (Johns Hopkins University Press, Baltimore, 1995)

(v) *Social Origins theory*

This theory developed by Salamon and Anheier argues that the size, role and financing of the voluntary sector depends upon the type of welfare regime in a country. The sector is seen as part of a complex set of historical relationships among social classes, party politics, government regulations and the influence of interest groups. Such a theory is particularly interested in the cultural and political embeddedness of voluntary organisations in any particular society.[11]

Each of these theories offer important insights into why voluntary organisations exist in mixed economy based democratic societies. It is helpful to identify what are often seen as 'unique competencies' or 'roles' of voluntary organisations. Kramer has identified four such attributes or functions:

- *The vanguard role* whereby voluntary organisations innovate, pioneer or demonstrate programmes or services

- *The advocate role* whereby such organisations act as pressure groups to advance interests or views

- *The value-guardian role* which sees voluntary organisations promoting citizen participation, developing leadership and protecting minorities

- *The role of provider of services* which neither government nor businesses are able to assume directly or fully.[12]

While these attempts may describe what exists in the voluntary sector and why the sector exists we need to explore normative democratic theory in order to propose what ought to be the relationships between the state and voluntary organisations.[13]

[11] see L.M. Salamon, HK. Anheier 'Social Origins of Civil Society: explaining the nonprofit sector cross-nationally' *Voluntas: International Journal of Voluntary and Nonprofit Organisations* Vol. 9, No. 3, 1998, pp 213–248

[12] R. Kramer 'Voluntary agencies and the personal social services' in *The Nonprofit Sector: A Research Handbook* ed. W.W. Powell (Yale University Press, New Haven and London 1987) pp 240–257; Kendall and Knapp have identified five functions of voluntary organisations: the service-providing function, the mutual-aid function, the pressure-group function, the advocacy function, the resource and co-ordinating function see J. Kendall and M. Knapp 'A loose and baggy monster boundaries, definitions and typologies' in *An Introduction To The Voluntary Sector* eds. J. Davis Smith, C. Rochester, R. Hedley (London, 1995) pp 67–8

[13] see James Douglas 'Political Theories of Nonprofit Organisation' in *The Nonprofit Sector A Research Handbook* ed. W.W. Powell, op. cit., pp 43–54 for a pioneering attempt to suggest 'some normative hypotheses'

3. CLASSICAL THEORY: TOCQUEVILLE AND MILL

The origins of voluntaryism as a societal principle can be found in the liberalism of the eighteenth and nineteenth century, with its emphasis on individual action and its antipathy to state action. It is best expressed in the classic works of Alexis de Tocqueville and John Stuart Mill.

In the second part of his classic *Democracy in America* Alexis de Tocqueville has a key section entitled 'On the use which the Americans make of associations in civil life'. He observed 'the immense number of different types of association' and how Americans

> combine to give fêtes, found seminaries, build churches, distribute books, and send missionaries to the antipodes. Hospitals, prisons, and schools take shape in that way. Finally, if they want to proclaim a truth or propagate some feeling by the encouragement of a great example, they form an association . . . This the most democratic country in the world now is that in which men have in our time carried to the highest perfection the act of pursuing in common the objects of common desires and have applied this new technique to the greatest number of purposes.

Tocqueville warned about the dangers of government taking the place of associations as this would erode the willingness of people to form associations:

> The more government takes the place of associations, the more will individuals lose the idea of forming associations and need the government to come to their help. That is a vicious circle of cause and effect. Must the public administration cope with every industrial undertaking beyond the competence of one individual citizen? . . . The morals and intelligence of a democratic people would be in as much danger as its commerce and industry if ever a government wholly usurped the place of private associations. Feelings and ideas are renewed, the heart enlarged, and the understanding developed only by the reciprocal action of men one upon another.

Tocqueville believed that government, by itself, was 'incapable of refreshing the circulation of feelings and ideas among a great people'. He felt that once government left 'the sphere of politics to launch out on this new track, it will, even without intending this, exercise an intolerable tyranny. For a government can only dictate precise rules. It imposes the sentiments and ideas which it favours, and it is never easy to tell the difference between its advice and its commands'. Tocqueville was so convinced of the vital role of voluntary associations that he concluded this key section as follows:

In democratic countries knowledge of how to combine is the mother of all other forms of knowledge; on its progress depends that of all the others.

Among laws controlling human societies there is one more precise and clearer it seems to me, than all the others. If men are to remain civilized or to become civilized, the art of association must develop and improve among them at the same speed as equality of conditions spreads.

John Stuart Mill was heavily influenced throughout his writings by Tocqueville. He later noted how his thoughts

> moved more and more in the same channel, though the consequent modifications in my practical political creed were spread over many years, as would be shown by comparing my first review of *Democracy in America*, written and published in 1835, with the one in 1840 (reprinted in the *Dissertations*) and this last, with the *Considerations on Representative Government*.[14]

In his classic liberal manifesto *On Liberty* Mill is concerned with the distinction between genuine self-government and the tyranny of the majority about which he had learned much from Tocqueville. Following Tocqueville, Mill thought that the everyday understanding of democracy was insufficiently attentive to the difference between ruling oneself and being dominated by everyone else. For Mill self-government certainly embraced most of the goals that professed democrats sought, including a chance for the ordinary person to exercise an influence on government by way of the ballot box and by other devices; but for Mill self-government also had to embrace such character-improving devices as the requirement that everyone must play some part in actively managing the affairs of his or her own community, whether in jury service or serving on parish councils, or in other ways of voluntary service and action.

Mill particularly noted that the second part of *Democracy in America* explored 'a newer and more difficult subject of enquiry than the first' that is, the effects of democracy 'upon society in the widest sense; upon the relations of private life, upon intellect, morals, and the habits and modes of feeling which constitute national character'.[15] Both Mill and Tocqueville were keenly interested in how knowledge and intelligence were diffused throughout society particularly through voluntary associ-

[14] *The Autobiography of John Stuart Mill*, ed. A.O.J. Cockshut (Ryburn Library Edition, Halifax, 1992), pp 104–5

[15] J.S. Mill 'M. de Tocqueville on Democracy in America' *Edinburgh Review* LXXII, 1840 reprinted in *John Stuart Mill On Politics and Society*, selected and edited G.L. Williams (Fontana/Collins, Glasgow 1976) p. 189

ations of many kinds. Noting that 'the constituent elements of political importance' were 'property, intelligence, and the power of combination' , Mill observed 'one of the commonplaces of the age, that knowledge and intelligence are spreading, in a degree which was formerly thought impossible, to the lower, and down even to the lowest rank' and he went on

> And this is a fact, not accomplished, but in the mere dawn of its accomplishment and which has shown hitherto but a slight promise of its future fruits. It is easy to scoff at the kind of intelligence which is thus diffusing itself; but it is intelligence still. The knowledge which is power, is not the highest description of knowledge only: any knowledge which gives the habit of forming an opinion, and the capacity of expressing that opinion constitutes a political power; and if combined with the capacity and habit of acting in concert, a formidable one.[16]

Tocqueville, as Mill noted, saw the principal source and security of American freedom not in the formal elections by popular suffrage but 'in the administration of nearly all the business of society by the people themselves . . . which enlightens the people, which teaches them, by experience, how public affairs must be carried on'.[17] Mill concluded 'life is a problem not a theorem; that action can only be learned in action'.[18] Mill's classic *On Liberty* is dedicated by him to von Humboldt's dictum: 'The grand, leading principle, towards which every argument unfolded in these pages directly converges, is the absolute and essential importance of human development in its richest diversity.'

Mill's most important criterion of good government is that it should promote the capacities of the people, their 'virtue and intelligence'. He dreaded any societal arrangement that would 'dwarf' human beings. Both Mill and Tocqueville, in promoting what Mill calls 'civil or social liberty', believed in the educative effects of participation in public affairs.[19] Mill in his review of *Democracy in America* quotes Tocqueville extensively on this:

> Not what is done by a democratic government, but what is done under a democratic government by private agency, is really great. Democracy does not confer the most skilful kind of government upon the people, but it produces that which the most skilful governments are frequently unable to

[16] ibid, p. 200

[17] ibid, p. 204

[18] ibid, p. 205

[19] quotations from *On Liberty* are taken from J.S. Mill *On Liberty* ed. with introduction by G. Himmelfarb (Penguin classics edition, London, 1985)

awaken, namely, an all-pervading and restless activity—a superabundant force—an energy which is never seen elsewhere, and which may, under favourable circumstances, beget the most amazing benefits. These are the true advantages of democracy.[20]

Mill describes 'the appropriate region of human liberty' as follows, concluding with the liberty 'of combination among individuals':

> It comprises, first, the inward domain of consciousness, demanding liberty of conscience in the most comprehensive sense . . . secondly, the principle requires liberty of tastes and pursuits, of framing the plan of our life to suit our own character . . . thirdly, from this liberty of each individual follows the liberty, within the same limits [i.e. 'so long as what we do does not harm others'] of combination among individuals; freedom to unite for any purpose not involving harm to others; the persons combining being supposed to be of full age and not forced or deceived.[21]

Later Mill emphasised the importance of 'different experiments of living' so 'that free scope should be given to varieties of character, short of injury to others; and that the worth of different modes of life should be proved practically, when anyone thinks fit to try them.' Mill sought 'the free development of individuality' and scope must be given for 'spontaneity' in order for human beings to flourish fully.[22] As Isaiah Berlin has observed

> Mill believes that man is spontaneous, that he has freedom of choice, that he moulds his own character, that as a result of the interplay of men with nature and with other men something novel continually arises, and that this novelty is precisely what is most characteristic and most human in men.[23]

In his final section entitled 'Applications' Mill deals with the issue of restricting government activity designed for the public benefit. He makes three arguments

(i)   People themselves generally are in the best position to conduct any activity which affects them directly

(ii) Even if people would not be as effective as 'officers of government' it is nevertheless desirable that it should be done by them voluntarily 'as a means to their own mental education—a mode of

[20] Tocqueville, *Democracy in America*, Vol. 2, Ch. 2, quoted by Mill in his review 'M. de Tocqueville on Democracy in America', op. cit., pp 208–9

[21] *On Liberty*, op. cit., p. 71

[22] *On Liberty*, op. cit., pp 120 ff

[23] Isaiah Berlin 'John Stuart Mill and the Ends of Life' in J.S. Mill *On Liberty in Focus*, ed. J. Gray and G.W. Smith, (London, 1991), p. 136

strengthening their active faculties, exercising their judgment, and giving them a familiar knowledge of the subjects with which they are thus left to deal'. Mill states 'This a principal, though not the sole, recommendation of jury trial (in cases not political); of free and popular local and municipal institutions; of the conduct of industrial and philanthropic enterprises by voluntary associations.' Mill goes on to 'the practical part of the political education of a free people' played by the people taking responsibility for their own affairs:

> Without these habits and powers, a free constitution can neither be worked nor preserved, as it exemplified by the too often transitory nature of political freedom in countries where it does not rest upon a sufficient basis of local liberties . . . Government operations tend to be everywhere alike. With individuals and voluntary associations, on the contrary, there are varied experiments and endless diversity of experience. What the State can usefully do is to make itself a central depository, and active circulator and diffuser, of the experience resulting from many trials. Its business is to enable each experimentalist to benefit by the experiment of others, instead of tolerating no experiments but its own.

(iii) The third and 'most cogent reason' for restricting the interference of government is 'the great evil of adding unnecessarily to is power'. Mill feared that the extension of the functions of government 'causes its influence over hopes and fears to be more widely diffused, and converts more and more, the active and ambitious part of the public into hangers-on of the government, or of some party which aims at becoming the government'. Mill observed that 'where everything is done through the bureaucracy, nothing to which the bureaucracy is really averse can be done at all'.

Mill desired to see 'the greatest dissemination of power consistent with efficiency; but the greatest possible centralization of information and diffusion of it from the centre'. His final sentiments are worth quoting

> The mischief begins, when, instead of calling forth the activity and powers of individuals and bodies [the government] substitutes its own activity for theirs; when, instead of informing, advising, and upon occasion, denouncing, it makes them work in fetters, or bids them stand aside and does their work instead of them . . . a State which dwarfs its men, in order that they may be more docile instruments in its hands even for beneficial purposes—will find that with small men no great thing can really be accomplished;'[24]

[24] *On Liberty*, op. cit., pp 180–187

Mill in his *Autobiography* noted the benefit he derived from Tocqueville's study of the fundamental question of centralization

> The powerful philosophic analysis which he applied to America and to French experience led him to attach the utmost importance to the performance of as much of the collective business of society, as can safely be so performed, by the people themselves, without any intervention of the executive government, either to supersede their agency, or to dictate the manner of its exercise. He viewed this practical political activity of the individual citizen, not only as one of the most effectual means of training the social feelings and practical intelligence of the people, so important in themselves and so indispensable to good government, but also as the specific counteractive to some of the characteristic infirmities of democracy, and a necessary protection against its degenerating into the only despotism of which in the modern world there is real danger—the absolute rule of the head of the executive over a congregation of isolated individuals, all equals but all slaves[25]

Alan Ryan's re-assessment of Mill helpfully brings us to consider more recent democratic theories:

> Mill was in several senses of the term a 'communitarian liberal'. He thought social philosophy should begin by contemplating human beings not in a state of nature or behind a veil of ignorance, but immersed in their social setting . . . Mill had no doubt that it was an important truth that we grow up in communities of different kinds, and form our ideas and ideals in the course of learning to live with others. He thought that most of us find it difficult to imagine ourselves outside the social setting in which we move; and he wanted to create a society of liberals, not a collection of liberal monads.[26]

4. RECENT DEMOCRATIC THEORY: COMMUNITARIANISM, CIVIL SOCIETY AND 'THIRD WAY' POLITICS

Voluntary organisations have gained an increasingly significant place in recent democratic political theories especially those associated with what is known as 'the liberal-communitarian debate', and with proponents of 'civil society' and of 'the third way'.[27]

[25] J.S. Mill, *Autobiography*, op. cit., p. 105

[26] Alan Ryan 'Mill in a liberal landscape' in *The Cambridge Companion to Mill* ed. John Skorupski (Cambridge, 1998) p. 530

[27] For overviews of these theories see M. Festenstein 'Contemporary Liberalism' and E. Frazer 'Communitarianism' in *New Political Thought An Introduction*, ed. A. Lent (London, 1998); for 'civil society' see J. Keane *Civil Society Old Images, New Visions* (Cambridge, 1998) and 'third way' see A. Giddens *The Third Way The Renewal of Social Democracy* (Cambridge, 1998)

In the last twenty years communitarianism as a distinctive theoretical position has emerged from critiques of certain aspects of recent liberal theories. In general communitarians emphasise the social nature of individuals, relationships and institutions. According to Amitai Etzioni, a leading communitarian theorist, communitarianism 'entails a combination of social order and autonomy . . . a virtuous equilibrium, the golden rule.'[28]

Etzioni has had a long interest in the issues concerning voluntary action in society; he wrote a pioneering sociological study entitled *The Active Society A Theory of Societal and Political Processes* (New York, 1968) which sought to outline 'the components of the active orientation' which he noted had 'three major components':

> A self-conscious and knowing actor, one or more goals he is committed to realise, and access to levers (or power) that allow resetting of the social code. (We repeat that the active self as a rule is not an individual, since one man is generally unable to transform collectivities, but a combination of persons who jointly activate their social grouping and thus alter their collective life and their individual selves).[29]

This major study focused upon 'the transition from modern to post-modern society and the conditions for the rise of an active society'. The 'active society' for Etzioni 'is a society whose values are more fully realized than those of less active ones' through the participation of all the significant groups in public life

> This is because many values are inherently dependent on an active society in that they either assume community-wide participation as part of their very definition (political democracy, for example), or such participation is a prerequisite for their realization (as in the case of distributive justice)[30]

Etzioni observes that values which are 'not mediated through concrete social structures tend to become tenuous, frail, and, in the long run, insupportable. Although verbal formulations may remain, authentic commitment is gradually eroded'. The key question, therefore, is which structures will best realise values in society. Hence, Etzioni provides a rationale for voluntary action in society: 'not only do more people gain a share in the society, thereby reconstituting its structure, but the

---

[28] A. Etzioni *The New Golden Rule Community and Morality in a Democratic Society* (London, 1997), p. xix

[29] A. Etzioni, *The Active Society A Theory of Societal and Political Processes*, (New York, 1968), pp 4–5

[30] ibid, pp 6, 12

members themselves are also transformed; they advance along with the society that they are changing'. Etzioni's perspective is

that of a social self as an object of transformation (a common sociological tradition) and as a subject who maintains an active orientation (an important tradition of political science). Our study systematically combines these two perspectives: it is the exploration of a society that knows itself, is committed to moving toward a fuller realisation of its values, that commands the levers such transformation requires, and is able to set limits on its capacity for self-alteration—lest it become self-mutilation. This would be an active society.[31]

Etzioni's two more recent works *The Spirit of Community*, published in 1993, and *The New Golden Rule*, published in 1996, have been influential in setting out a positive vision and manifesto for communitarian politics and have helped also to shape the renewal of social democratic politics known as 'the third way'. Communitarian themes have also connected with conceptions of 'civil society' which have developed rapidly in political thought since the late 1980s.[32] Etzioni states:

The communitarian quest . . . is to seek a way to blend elements of tradition (order based on virtues) with elements of modernity (well-protected autonomy) . . . I shall argue that a new golden rule should read: respect and uphold society's moral order as you have society respect and uphold your autonomy'.[33]

Communitarians, such as Etzioni, accept liberalism as an essentially progressive political philosophy but wish to balance 'the me-istic forces with a fair measure of resumed we-ness'. They see the individual as embedded in social existence and membership of 'community' as 'the most important sustaining source of moral voices other than the inner self'.[34] In the wake of the extreme individualism associated with the 'new right' of the Thatcher and Reagan years political theorists have been exploring the possibility of rediscovering or reinventing a public civic polity which would emphasise public and collective responsibilities, ethical, moral and social virtues as well as social cohesion. In

[31] ibid, pp 14–16
[32] A. Etzioni, *The Spirit of Community Rights, Responsibilities and the Communitarian Agenda* (first published in the USA, 1993, London, 1995); *The New Golden Rule Community and Morality in a Democratic Society* first published in the USA, 1996, London, 1997); for example of the direct influence of 'community' and 'civil society' on political leaders see Tony Blair *The Third Way New Politics for the New Century*, (The Fabian Society, London, 1998)
[33] *The New Golden Rule*, op. cit., p.xviii
[34] *The Spirit of Community*, op. cit., p. 26, 38

addition against the background of concern that the modern welfare state has become 'overloaded' and ineffective 'community' may represent in this context a more effective means of delivering public benefit and services in society.

In such theories voluntary organisations receive much attention: they are bound to receive a significant place in any theory which emphasises that an individual's identity, values and understandings are socially constructed and expressed. In addition, communitarianism is attentive to the historical and cultural contexts of the virtues associated with liberty and order and, of course, many voluntary organisations are rooted in the particular histories and cultures of the groups which participate in them. Etzioni argues that '*a good society requires an order that is aligned with the moral commitments of the members*'; his communitarian order is 'largely voluntary' as it is based upon members' voluntary compliance. To establish such an order Etzioni places heavy reliance upon 'normative means (education, leadership, consensus, peer pressure, pointing out role models, exhortation and, above all, the moral voices of communities). In this sense, the social order of good societies is a moral order'.[35]

Etzioni focuses upon families, schools and 'community' as the key sites for these 'normative means' of moral suasion. He has some reservations about the efficacy of voluntary organisations which he believes have 'meagre bonding power' in contrast to communities 'with their much stronger inter personal attachments'; Etzioni notes that voluntary organisations provide 'some bonding but not much of a moral culture'.[36] There are, however, two key points to note in relation to Etzioni's apparent dismissive approach to voluntary organisations. First he appears to have 'chess clubs', 'bowling alleys' and 'choirs' in mind when he makes these observations which, of course, ignores the very strong attachments and moral commitments found in religious voluntary organisations, for example, as well as in other significant voluntary bodies of various kinds. Indeed later, as shall be seen, Etzioni is more positive about the importance of voluntary organisations as 'sub-communities'. Secondly Etzioni and other communitarian theorists do not have a well worked out conception of 'community'.

[35] *The New Golden Rule*, op. cit., pp 12–13
[36] *The New Golden Rule*, p. 27, p. 96

For some communitarians 'community' stands for a set of relations between persons (based upon trust, mutual respect, generosity, mutual understanding, shared values, reciprocity and so forth). Etzioni states at one point: 'community is a set of attributes, not a concrete place'. For others 'community' is conceived of as an entity, with boundaries and a particular location but there is an ambivalence about community as locality and an emphasis on community surrogates such as voluntary organisations that people construct in response to the atomism, alienation and anonymity of urban life. Yet again, at other times 'community' is conceived of as a thinking subject as when Etzioni speaks of 'the moral voice of the community'.[38] This conceptual confusion about what is meant by 'community' presents a major theoretical weakness in communitarianism and obscures the central role of voluntary organisations as means of expressing the values communitarianisms espouse. As Crawford has pointed out when reviewing *The Spirit of Community*

> . . .there is slippage between 'tradition' and 'community': between 'community' as a sense of something lost and 'community' as a focus for building modern democratic institutions which address the problems of social integration and mutual empowerment in an increasingly differentiated and individualized world.[39]

Henry Tam's critical synthesis of communitarianism argues for what he describes as 'inclusive communities' which may exist in the state, business or 'third sector' and Tam states

> People live in overlapping communities, with varying degrees of emotive ties and subject to different power relations. These communities may range from an extended family, a school, a neighbourhood, a research society, a professional group, a co-operative or a business enterprise, to a region, a country, an international association or a global network.

For Tam it is the 'operative power relations' in such entities in all sectors of society which determines whether they are 'inclusive communities': in order to build such communities in every sphere and at every level of social existence

> Communitarian politics requires the development of citizens who can take part in co-operative enquiries determining a wide range of issues; who

[37] ibid, p. 6

[38] *The Spirit of Community*, p. 54

[39] A. Crawford 'Review Article *The Spirit of Community Rights, Responsibilities, and the Communitarian Agenda*' *Journal of Law and Society*, Vol. 23, No. 2, June 1996, p. 252

recognise that they share a respect for values and accept the responsibilities these values imply; and who actively support the transformation of power relations for the common good.[40]

It is this argument within communitarianism for the significance of collectives, institutions, human relations and that ethical values are not simply located in the individual but are rather to be found expressed in the social relationships of individuals in associations that is profoundly important in respect of the role of voluntary organisations. Theories of social constructionism are very important in discovering the role of voluntary organisations in society; other significant theorists have accorded more attention to such organisations than has Etzioni within democracy.[41]

Communitarian theories have been greatly influenced by the philosophy of Alasdair MacIntyre whose thesis is that conceptions of justice and practical reason emerge from particular types of social order—particular communities—and are developed as rational conceptions by particular socially embodied traditions. In MacIntyre's view rational evaluation of conceptions of justice can only be carried through from the standpoint of some particular tradition.[42] This approach leads to a renewed valuation of reciprocity, solidarity, trust, mutuality, tradition and so on—values which have tended to be neglected in individualist philosophies. There is also an important methodological point: communitarians argue that the way to discover values and ethical principles is to interpret and refine values that already exist in the ways of life of actual living groups, associations or communities rather than to try to deduce and apply universally valid fundamental principles. MacIntyre writes '. . . the self has to find its moral identity in and through its membership in communities, such as those of the family, the neighbourhood, the city and tribe . . .'[43] and he argues 'what matters at this stage is the construction of local forms of community within which civility and the intellectual and moral life can be sustained through the dark ages which are already upon us'.[44]

[40] see Henry Tam *Communitarianism A New Agenda for Politics and Citizenship* (Macmillan Press, London, 1998) pp 7–8

[41] see, for example, Robert Putnam, *Making Democracy Work: Civic Traditions in Modern Italy*, (Princeton, N.J., 1993)

[42] see A. MacIntyre *After Virtue A Study in Moral Theory*, (London, 1981) and *Whose Justice? Which Rationality?*, (London, 1988)

[43] *After Virtue*, op. cit., p. 221

[44] ibid., p. 245

Whatever about MacIntyre's bleak assessment of modern civilisation the point is fundamentally important in respect of voluntary organisations. As Etzioni states there are no 'freestanding individuals' because 'people are socially constituted and continually penetrated by culture, by social and moral influences, and by one another'. Etzioni argues that autonomy cannot be characterised ' as merely an individual virtue of persons who cherish freedom and who conduct themselves in ways that sustain that virtue'; rather autonomy is 'a societal attribute' and is 'socially constructed'. It is 'an attribute of a society that provides structured opportunities and legitimisation for individual and subgroup expression of their particular values, needs, and preferences'. In other words 'the social fabric sustains, nourishes and enables individuality rather than diminishes it'.[45]

It is, therefore, obvious that communitarians will take issue with an idea that has been so powerful in modern societies that the individual stands in a direct, straightforward relationship with the state and with society. They dispute the place of the market as the key social institution and they focus upon a variety of institutions and traditional ways of doing things which characterise the relationships between the individual and the state such as corporations, voluntary organisations, occupational groups, families and religious institutions.[46]

Communitarianism relies upon voluntarism in society: the absence of coercive power means that people are free to choose whether to engage in certain activities, hold certain views or even whether to continue to be a community member. Despite the glaring lack of rigour in the definition of 'community' communitarians provide a normative perspective and offer insights into how public policies ought to operate in western democracies in respect of voluntary action.[47] Implied clearly is a shift of theoretical focus towards voluntary social relationships and away from state intervention as a means both of distributing public goods and benefits and of regenerating moral values and commitments providing an alternative to more state regulation and enforced codes. Etzioni states

[45] *The New Golden Rule*, op. cit., pp 21–26

[46] M. Walzer, for example, in *Spheres of Justice*, (Oxford, 1983) emphasises the place and meaning of a good (for example healthcare) in a culture before we can say how it ought to be distributed.

[47] Crawford astutely notes "an assertion of 'community' identity at a local level can be beautifully conciliatory and socially constructive but it can also be parochial, intolerant and punitive" see *Review Article: The Spirit of Community*, op. cit., p. 260

A major sociological function of the community, as a building block of the moral infrastructure, is to reinforce the character of individuals . . . The significance of voluntary associations in this context has often been highlighted as protecting individuals from the state (a protection they would not have if they faced the state as isolated or 'atomized' individuals) and as intermediating bodies that aggregate, transmit, and underwrite individual signals to the state. In terms of the moral infrastructure, the very same voluntary associations often fulfil a rather different function: they serve as social spaces in which members of communities reinforce their social webs and articulate their moral voice. That is, they often constitute sub communities within more encompassing communities.[48]

Etzioni speaks of the need to 'rearrange' the 'intellectual-political map' by leapfrogging 'the old debate between left-wing and right-wing thinking' suggesting 'a third social philosophy'.[49] Related to communitarian thought in recent years have been new political theories which have been concerned with 'civil society' and 'the third way'.

'Civil society', as the self-organisation of strong and autonomous groups that are separate from and balance the state have acquired renewed significance in recent years. The concept has very significant theoretical importance for the role of voluntary organisations. As Powell and Guerin have noted, 'civil society' is presented by its advocates as a democratic movement based upon the concept of active citizenship, as distinct from the dependent status imposed by the entitled citizenship of the welfare state. The emphasis of active citizenship is on participation in the decision-making process, leading to the empowerment of the citizen.[50] A commitment to active citizenship based upon a vibrant voluntary sector has been identified by many theorists to be a key ingredient of civil society.[51] John A Hall notes that

[48] *The New Golden Rule,* op. cit., p. 187

[49] ibid, p. 7

[50] F. Powell and D. Guerin *Civil Society and Active Citizenship: the role of the voluntary sector* (Association for Voluntary Action Research in Ireland, Centre for Voluntary Action Studies, University of Ulster, Coleraine, 1999) p. 14

[51] see *Supporting Activity A Green Paper on the Community and Voluntary Sector and its Relationship with the State* (Stationery Office, Dublin, [1997] p. 24 which defines 'civil society' as follows: 'The term 'civil society' refers to those areas of social life organized through private or voluntary arrangements outside of the direct control of the State. There term applies particularly to those self-governing social communities and movements, representing divergent views and opinions and discharging public functions such as provision of social and other services, campaigning, self-regulation of professions and sports etc., which act as a counterweight to the power of the State and corporate business sectors. Central to the concept is a view of members of society governing and providing for themselves though co-operation and participation in voluntary organisations'.

civil society 'is a particular form of society, appreciating social diversity and able to limit the depredations of political power, that was born in Europe; it may, with luck, skill and imagination spread to some other regions of the world'.[52] Václav Havel has been a most influential theorist and practitioner of the concept: his continuing stress on both responsible citizenship and a pluralist civil society can be seen as central to the commitment to democracy embedded in his thought.[53] Havel's most important contribution to recent democratic theory is his focus on the cultural and social context of politics and in particular his willingness to assert the importance of ethical values. Havel stresses the value of voluntary associations: 'The whole country will be crisscrossed by a network of local, regional, state-wide clubs, organisations and associations with a wide variety of aims'.[54] April Carter writes

> One connecting theme between Havel's writings in the 1970s and the 1990s can be summed up in the phrase 'civil society'. This is not a term Havel himself usually used in his opposition period—his preferred concept then was anti-political politics—but it was widely used by East European intellectuals in the 1980s and taken up in the West to denote a distinction between state power and the creative possibilities inherent in a plurality of groups and organisations developing autonomously from below. In liberal democracies civil society is envisaged as a network of associations creating social ties between individuals and fostering organisational and political skills. It is therefore both a source for political initiatives and a check on State oppression.[55]

Havel's concept of civil society suggests the value of plural spheres in society as opposed to an overriding commitment to a single public sphere of politics. Carter notes the similarity, though arrived at quite independently and in different contexts, of Havel's thought with that of Tocqueville:

> who also celebrated decentralisation of power to local government, valued a network of voluntary associations fostering variety and initiative and had a view of responsible citizenship which required a degree of participation.

[52] J.A. Hall 'In Search of Civil Society' in *Civil Society Theory History Comparison*, ed. J.A. Hall (Cambridge, 1995), p. 25

[53] see A. Carter 'Václav Havel: Civil Society, Citizenship and Democracy' in *Liberal Democracy and its Critics*, eds., A. Carter and G. Stokes, (Cambridge, 1998), pp 58–76; see V. Havel *Letters to Olga* (London 1988) and *Disturbing The Peace* (London 1990)

[54] Havel, *Summer Meditations*, quoted in Carter, op. cit., p. 69

[55] A. Carter 'Václav Havel: Civil Society, Citizenship and Democracy', op. cit., pp 69–70

They also share a sense of the interrelations between the character of a society and its culture and the character of its politics. Finally, there are parallels with de Tocqueville in Havel's criticism of mass society.[56]

Other writers have also resuscitated Tocquevillean prescriptions to restore integrity and public spirit and responsible citizenship.[57]

According to Anthony Giddens the 'third way' refers to 'a framework of thinking and policy making that seeks to adapt social democracy to a world which has changed fundamentally over the past two or three decades. It is a third way in the sense that it is an attempt to transcend both old-style social democracy and neo-liberalism.'[58] 'Third way' thinking is very positive about the role of the voluntary sector; in contrast as Giddens observes '. . . old-style social democrats were inclined to be suspicious of voluntary associations'.[59]

Tony Blair, the most prominent 'third way' political leader, now proclaims that 'governments must be acutely sensitive not to stifle worthwhile activity by local communities and the voluntary sector. The grievous 20th century error of the fundamentalist Left was the belief that the state could replace civil society and thereby advance freedom'. Blair states that a ' key challenge of progressive politics is to use the state as an enabling force, protecting effective communities and voluntary organisations and encouraging their growth to tackle new needs, in partnership as appropriate'. He emphasises the need for a 'strong civil society; as 'a complement to (but not a replacement for) modern government':

> The Third Way recognises the limits of government in the social sphere, but also the need for government, within those limits to forge new partnerships with the voluntary sector. Whether in education, health, social work, crime prevention or the care for children, 'enabling' government strengthens civil society rather than weakening it, and helps families and communities improve their own performance. Volunteering; school governorships; fostering and adoption; public health; young offender programmes—all demonstrate the state, voluntary sector, and individuals working together.

[56] ibid, p. 71

[57] see, for example, J.B. Elshtain, *Democracy on Trial*, (New York, 1995); R.D. Putnam *Making Democracy Work: Civil Traditions in Modern Italy*, (Princeton, N.J., 1993) M. Walzer 'The Civil Society Argument' in *Dimensions of Radical Democracy*, ed. C. Mouffe, (London, 1992)

[58] A. Giddens *The Third Way The Renewal of Social Democracy*, (Cambridge, 1998), p. 26

[59] ibid, p. 9

New Labour's task is to strengthen the range and quality of such partnerships.[60]

Giddens also emphasises the partnership which should exist between government and 'agencies in civil society to foster community renewal and development' and he writes

> The fostering of an active civil society is a basic part of the politics of the third way . . . civic decline is real and visible in many sectors of contemporary societies . . . Government can and must play a major part in renewing civic culture. State and civil society should act in partnership, each to facilitate, but also to act as a control upon, the other . . . An increasingly reflexive society is also one marked by high levels of self-organisation.

Giddens points to research evidence which indicates

> A burgeoning civil sphere, at least in some areas and contexts; . . . that activity in the voluntary sector has expanded but government should help 'repair the civil order' amongst social groups where it is weak through encouraging local voluntary initiative and social entrepreneurship. Voluntary organisations are perceived in 'third way' thought as vital social capital.[61]

5. SUMMARY: ROLES OF VOLUNTARY ORGANISATIONS IN DEMOCRATIC THEORIES

This review of classical and recent democratic theories has indicated the very significant roles accorded to voluntary action by key theorists. As expressed by Tocqueville and Mill voluntary associations help secure freedom, limit the government's power and influence over citizen's freedom, educate citizens and develop character. Such organisations release energies in society and because of the diverse interests they express are sources of originality and social progress. They are 'civilising' agents assisting people to take responsibility for their own affairs. Accordingly in Tocqueville's and Mill's view voluntary associations are not simply desirable features in democratic societies: they are necessary and essential to the health of democratic society.

The recent democratic theorists reviewed have sought to recover these key insights into the role of voluntary associations in democratic society. There is a greater stress in recent theories on the value-expressive character of 'active societies' which is produced by voluntary associ-

---

[60] Tony Blair *The Third Way New Politics for the New Century*, (The Fabian Society, London, 1998), p. 4, p. 14

[61] A. Giddens, *The Third Way*, op. cit., p. 69, pp 78–84

ations of all kinds. The development of the moral responsibilities of citizens is achieved through their social relationships: there is considerable concern expressed about the decline in morality and the moral order of liberal democratic societies. Enabling and enhancing voluntary action is perceived to be an important means of addressing such a decline. In addition voluntary organisations are seen as key actors in 'civil society', not only helping to articulate a 'moral voice' but as a more effective means to deliver public benefits and services than are the governmental agents of the Welfare State. Voluntary organisations are seen as partners for an 'enabling' state. They are effective expressions of the pluralist nature of society and are an essential balance to the uniformity of State action and thereby they help combat popular disillusion and disengagement from politics. In order to develop these crucial normative insights into a legitimating public philosophy for voluntary action in a democratic Republic—for Ireland in particular—the next section explores civic republicanism and active citizenship in a pluralist democracy.

6.   CIVIC REPUBLICANISM: ACTIVE CITIZENSHIP IN A PLURALIST
DEMOCRACY

There has been a great renewal of interest in the concept of citizenship among political theorists in the 1990s.[62] Governments have taken initiatives to promote citizenship realising that the health of a democracy depends upon the qualities and attitudes of its citizens.[63] Increased attention is being paid to the development of the necessary civic virtues.[64] It is important to note that 'active citizenship' was promoted

[62] see W. Kymlicka and W. Norman 'Return of the Citizen: A Survey of Recent Work on Citizenship Theory' *Ethics* Vol. 104 (January 1994) pp 352–381; two more recent studies are central to the development of citizenship theory Thomas Janoski *Citizenship and Civil Society A Framework of Rights and Obligations in Liberal, Traditional and Social Democratic Regimes* (Cambridge University Press, Cambridge 1998) and Will Kymlicka *Multicultural Citizenship A Liberal Theory of Minority Rights* (Clarendon Press, Oxford, 1995); on the key question of balancing rights and obligations in citizenship see the influential work by David Selbourne *The Principle of Duty An Essay on the Foundations of the Civic Order*, first published 1994, Abacus Book edition with revisions London, 1997)

[63] see Britain's Commission on Citizenship *Encouraging Citizenship* [1990]; Senate of Australia *Active Citizenship Revisited* [1991]; Senate of Canada *Canadian Citizenship: Sharing the Responsibility* [1993] noted in Kymlicka and Norman, op. cit., p. 353

[64] see the important contribution by Richard Dagger *Civic Virtues Rights, Citizenship and Republican Liberalism* (Oxford University Press, New York, 1997)

by the 'new right' before it became more central to social democratic theory: there has been a rekindling of interest in the notion of citizenship across the political spectrum with varying motivations and expectations.[65] There are growing fears that the civility and public-spiritedness of citizens in liberal democracies may be in serious decline. The question has arisen in recent theory: where do citizens learn the civic virtues?

The modern civic republican tradition provides a theoretical basis for a developed form of participatory democracy: civic republicans emphasise the intrinsic value of political participation for the participants themselves as 'the highest form of living-together that most individuals can aspire to'.[66] This presents a challenge to the very privatised and impoverished view of what it means to be a citizen long accepted and still current in democratic societies; civic republican insights may be associated with 'civil society' theorists who argue that it is in the voluntary organisations of civil society that citizens learn the virtues of mutual obligation.[67] Mary Ann Glendon has claimed that civil society is the 'seedbed of civic virtue'.[68]

Liberal theorists have done important work identifying the virtues required for responsible citizenship. Galston, for example, divides them into four groups

(i)   general virtues: courage, law-abidingness, loyalty

(ii) social virtues: independence, open-mindedness

(iii) economic virtues: work ethic, capacity to delay self-gratification, adaptability to economic and technological change

---

[65] see two important discussions Susan J. Smith 'Society, Space and Citizenship: a human geography for the 'new times'?' *Transactions Institute of British Geographers* New Series, Vol. 14, No. 2, 1989, pp 144–156 and Adrian J. Kearns 'Active Citizenship and Urban Governance' *Transactions of the Institute of British Geographers* New Series, Vol. 17, No. 1, 1992, pp 20–34

[66] Adrian Oldfield *Citizenship and Community Civic Republicanism and the Modern World* (Routledge, London and New York, 1990) p. 6

[67] Michael Walzer states that 'the civility that makes democratic politics possible can only be learned in the associational networks' of civil society see M. Walzer 'The Civil Society Argument' in *Dimensions of Radical Democracy: Pluralism, Citizenship and Community* ed. C. Mouffe (London 1992) p. 104

[68] Mary Ann Glendon *Rights Talk: The Impoverishment of Political Discourse* (The Free Press, New York, 1991) p. 109

(iv) political virtues: capacity to discern and respect the rights of others, willingness to demand only what can be paid for, ability to evaluate the performance of those in office, willingness to engage in public discourse.[69]

There is increasing support from different democratic political traditions and theories 'that citizenship must play an independent normative role in any plausible political theory and that promotion of responsible citizenship is an urgent aim of public policy'.[70] One important instrument of such a policy would be to promote voluntary organisations for public benefit enabling citizens to identify with the *res publica*.

The search for a public philosophy which encompasses the fullest possible scope for voluntary action in a democracy by embracing active citizenship ultimately requires a fresh expression of republicanism. There has been a recent and very marked increase in scholarly attention to the possibilities inherent in republican ideas or concepts.[71] This has also been reflected to a more limited extent in Irish political discourse.[72] The dynamic open-ended possibilities of republicanism allow for the fullest development and expression of citizenship. As Fontana concludes 'The true heritage of the bourgeois liberal republic

---

[69] see William Galston *Liberal Purposes: Goods, Virtues, and Duties in the Liberal State* (Cambridge University Press, Cambridge, 1991) pp 221–24

[70] Kymlicka and Norman, op. cit., p. 368; see also Eamonn Callan *Creating Citizens Political Education and Liberal Democracy* (Clarendon Press, Oxford, 1997)

[71] it is significant that republicanism was included as a new chapter only in the second edition of David Held's very valuable book *Models of Democracy*, (first published in 1987, second edition, Polity Press, Cambridge, 1996), the new chapter entitled 'Republicanism: Liberty, Self-Government and the Active Citizen' is a brilliant brief survey of republican democracy; see also *The Invention of the Modern Republic* ed. B. Fontana (Cambridge University Press, Cambridge, 1994); P. Pettit *Republicanism A Theory of Freedom and Government* (Clarendon Press, Oxford, 1997); R. Dagger *Civic Virtues Rights, Citizenship, and Republican Liberalism* (Oxford University Press, New York and Oxford, 1997) and A. Oldfield *Citizenship and Community Civic Republicanism and the Modern World* (Routledge, London, 1990)

[72] see Richard Kearney *Postnationalist Ireland Politics, Culture Philosophy* (Routledge, London and New York, 1997) especially Ch. 2 'Ideas of a Republic and Ch. 3 'Genealogy of the Republic' which are valuable contributions; see also *The Republican Ideal Current Perspectives* ed. Norman Porter (Blackstaff Press, Belfast, 1998) especially the valuable introduction by Porter and the essay 'Republicanism revisited' by A. Kilmurry and M. McWilliams for introduction of civic republican ideas; for historical treatment of Protestant eighteenth-century civic republicanism see Ian McBride *Scripture Politics: Ulster Presbyterians and Irish Radicalism in the late eighteenth century* (Oxford, 1998)

is not so much what it has achieved, but the chances it leaves open'.[73] Increasingly it is seen that the republican state 'must connect with a form of civil society in which republican values are firmly entrenched'.[74] As Richard Kearney has observed there 'is a battle to be fought over the meaning of the term 'republicanism' for Irish citizens in the emerging Europe' and in exploring classical and renaissance republicanism he asks a question very relevant to a secular Ireland: 'how is one to institute a meaningful mode of civic being—a republican polis—in a secular time independent of transcendent meaning?'[75] A republic is founded upon a constitutional order of equal citizens

> The republic sought to found its authority on *lex* rather than *rex*, and *prudentia* rather than *providentia*. It called for a theory investing humans with the ability to inaugurate new orders in the realm of secular history. This ability became identified with the Latin term, *virtus*, a reworking of the Greek term, *arete*, meaning the power by which persons act effectively in a civic context. It is a form of civic action, largely influenced by the Aristotelian conviction that political and social association are natural to human beings . . . In short, virtue is acknowledged as a moral and political relationship of citizenship, a relationship in which each citizen agrees to rule and be ruled in such a way that one's own civic virtue is intimately bound up with that of one's fellow citizens.[76]

There is, therefore, a distinctive republican conception of society which is based upon active citizenship: in a republic 'citizen participation is so indispensable to the conduct of politics that society should be structured to ensure its effective possibility'.[77] The community and voluntary sector provides the effective possibility of widespread citizen involvement, participation and development. As Norman Porter observes

> In the old language of a civic republicanism whose roots can be traced to Aristotle . . . political participation involves the cultivation of civic virtues among citizens. As the North American political philosopher Michael Sandel puts it 'republican politics cannot be neutral towards the values and ends its citizens espouse'; rather, what is required is 'a formative politics, a politics that cultivates in citizens the qualities of character self-government requires.[78]

[73] *The Invention of the Modern Republic* op. cit., p. 5
[74] Pettit, *Republicanism* op. cit., p. 13
[75] Kearney *Postnationalist Ireland* op. cit., p. 37 and p. 43
[76] ibid, pp 44–5
[77] Norman Porter, *The Republican Ideal* op. cit., p. 29
[78] op. cit., p. 31 quoting M. Sandel *Democracy's Discontent: America in Search of a Public Philosophy* (Harvard University Press, Cambridge, Mass., 1996) p. 6

Richard Dagger has shown that liberalism and republicanism may be blended successfully and that the republican-liberal conception of citizenship 'links our enduring concern for self to the public life of a deliberative citizen'.[79] Dagger argues 'that the republican-liberal citizen is someone who respects individual rights, values autonomy, tolerates different opinions and beliefs, plays fair, cherishes civic memory, and takes an active part in the life of the community'.[80] The nature of these virtues indicate that much of the cultivation must take place in families, neighbourhoods, churches, the workplace and in voluntary associations of many kinds—in brief in what has come to be called 'civil society'; as Dagger observes 'republican liberals will want a thriving civil society'.[81] It is important, therefore, to increase the number and enhance the power of voluntary associations that connect the private and public aspects of life. Dagger concludes

> Civil society can indeed promote the public good by serving as a buffer between the individual and the state. But this is not all that it can or should do. Civil society must also be civil in two senses of the word. First, it must promote civility in the sense of a decent regard for the rights and interests of others, including their right of and interest in autonomy. Second, civil society must promote civility in the sense of civic responsibility—of citizens working together for their common good. In both ways, civil society teaches the civic virtues.[82]

Recent political theory has evolved in the context of rapid political change notably since the 1989 revolutions of Eastern Europe. It has emerged also with a consciousness of the failure of statism in the 20th century. Thus, for example, Tony Blair speaks of the need to 'reinvent government' and to end the 'divorce' between democratic socialism and liberalism which, he believes, weakened progressive politics in the 20th century.[83]

The rediscovery of the virtues of citizenship is profoundly important for a public philosophy that legitimises voluntary action in society. The ideas associated with *citizen virtue* have to be developed,

---

[79] Dagger *Civic Virtues, Rights, Citizenship and Republican Liberalism* p. 195 quoting S. Burtt 'The Politics of Virtue Today: A Critique and a Proposal' *American Political Science Review* Vol. 87, 1993, pp 360–368

[80] Dagger *Civic Virtues* op. cit., p. 196

[81] op. cit., p. 198

[82] op. cit., p. 200

[83] see Tony Blair *The Third Way New Politics for the New Century*, op. cit., p. 3, p. 15

however, for complex and rapidly changing societies. The twentieth century saw the arrival of universal franchise in liberal democracies. In the twenty first century the challenge will be to translate this 'formal' citizenship into an active citizenship based upon an ideal of civic participation which integrates and involves ordinary people: in a democratic Republic it is the people who should govern all aspects of their society which directly concern them. Participatory democracy requires to be developed to supplement formal representative democracy. As Charles Leadbetter has stated 'civic spirit' is 'the big idea for a new political era'.[84] The values cherished by people in society are fostered and preserved not simply through formal institutional arrangements (such as free elections between competing parties) but through the exercise of *virtue*, civic spirit—a willingness to set the good of others above one's private desires or individualistic interests—and the exercise of such virtue can only be done in co-operation with others.[85] This is at the heart of classical civic republicanism: the common business (*res publica*) of the citizens should be conducted *by them* for the common good. Civic republicanism developed from the belief, originating in the sixteenth century, but drawing inspiration from the ancient world, that the state should be an integral part of a free, flourishing society by acting in the interests of all and being guided by the active participation of its citizens. Voluntary organisations are vital for the development of the kind of political culture which is able to sustain a free public life through active citizenship.

Thomas Janoski divides civil society into four interactive components: the state sphere, the private sphere, the market sphere and the public sphere: '*civil society represents a sphere of dynamic and responsive public discourse between the state, the public sphere consisting of voluntary organizations, and the market sphere concerning private firms and unions*'.[86] Janoski identifies five types of voluntary associations operating in the public sphere: political parties, interest groups, welfare associations,

[84] see Charles Leadbetter *Civic Spirit The Big Idea for a New Political Era*, (Demos, London, 1997)

[85] Important 'virtue-based' liberal works insisting upon a high degree of democratic participation through active citizenship are B. Barber *Strong Democracy: Participatory Politics for a New Age*, (Berkeley CA, 1984) and W. Galston *Liberal Purposes: Goods, Virtues and Diversity in the Liberal State* (Cambridge, 1991)

[86] T. Janoski *Citizenship and Civil Society a Framework of Rights and Obligations in Liberal, Traditional and Social Democratic Regimes* (Cambridge University Press, Cambridge, 1998) pp 12–13

social movements and religious bodies.[87] He compares liberal, communitarian and social democratic theories to show how conceptions of citizenship and civil society in these theories fit 'the structuring of citizenship' in various types of regimes found in welfare states: these regime types are 'social democratic', 'traditional', 'liberal' and 'mixed'. Janoski categorises Ireland as a 'mixed' regime type: it has elements of the 'social democratic', 'traditional' and 'liberal' regime types.[88] As a 'mixed' regime Ireland displays some of the characteristics associated with each of the three main regimes ('liberal', 'social democratic' and 'traditional') based upon three political philosophies, liberalism, social democracy and communitarianism which are explored in detail by Janoski. The future course of development in a 'mixed' regime in respect of citizenship and voluntary action will be at once more difficult to predict and perhaps more problematic to chart. This may help to explain why it has been so difficult to formulate and implement a clear public philosophy and policy in the more ambiguous Irish context. Janoski is pursuing a more developed theory of citizenship for reasons such as comparative research and to explain aspects of civil society and social organisation but also because

> A theory of citizenship provides a means to understand the solidarity that holds societies together. Citizenship presumes some determinate community or civil society with some connections and networks between people and groups, and some norms and values that provide meaning to their lives[89]

Janoski's identification of the 'social capital' involved when citizens engage in exchanges which build solidarity may be associated with recent important work on 'social capital' understood as 'the propensity of individuals to associate together on a regular basis to trust one another and to engage in community affairs'.[90] Associational life has

[87] ibid, p. 14

[88] Janoski, op. cit., pp 22–23; he also ranks the United Kingdom and New Zealand as a 'mixed' type of regime; the Scandinavian countries are 'social democratic', the United States, Canada, Australia are 'liberal' and Austria, Belgium, France, Germany and Italy are 'traditional' according to the regime type variables used by Janoski

[89] ibid, p. 24

[90] Peter A. Hall 'Social Capital in Britain' *British Journal of Political Science* Vol. 29, No. 3, July 1999, p. 418; see also Derek Bacon 'Social Capital and Civil Society: the contribution of voluntary action' unpublished presentation to the AVARI/CVAS Research Forum, 2 June 1999, (Centre for Voluntary Action Studies, University of Ulster, Coleraine)

become a key indicator for examining the rate or destruction of social capital.[91] Voluntary participation and action is conceived of as a prime builder of the more desirable forms of social capital.[92] Janoski has developed the concept of 'responsible patriotism' that embodies fuller conceptions of citizen obligations and he explores the effects of two kinds of citizen 'exchanges' in respect of organising rights and obligations:

> Generalized exchange promotes solidarity and long-term focus on societal benefits, while restricted exchange operates in the short term with a focus on individual social mobility . . . The restricted exchange approach (for every right there is an immediate and expected obligation) tends to result in immediate and sometimes greedy responses. Where generalized exchange exists (rights and obligations are more loosely but still ultimately coupled), rights and obligations filter through society in diverse ways in a system that requires high amounts of trust.[93]

These exchanges operate in 'the web of voluntary associations that makes up civil society'.[94] Janoski points out that legitimacy 'rests on a widespread belief that some aspect of a generalized exchange system is working (whether direct generalized exchange or the trickle down results of restricted exchange), while illegitimacy consists of rampant beliefs that only self-interest through restricted exchange works without wider benefits'.[95]

It is important to note that both Hall and Janoski observe that the actions and policies of the state have a great bearing on the development or otherwise of social capital and an active citizenship based

---

[91] Hall, op. cit., pp 420–425 analyses the membership in voluntary associations in Britain from the 1950s to 1990s as this is part of the core definition of social capital

[92] see the important local study of the churches in this context Derek Bacon 'Splendid and Disappointing' Churches Voluntary Action and Social Capital in Northern Ireland (Centre for Voluntary Action Studies, University of Ulster, 1998)

[93] Janoski, op. cit., p. 26; see also chapter 3 'Reconstructing Obligations and Patriotism: Limitations, Sanctions, and Exchange in a System of Rights' and chapter 4 'Citizen-Selves in Restricted and Generalized Exchange'; Hall, op. cit., p. 457, in exploring the levels of social trust that exists in Britain distinguishes between value-systems according to a dimension that can be labelled 'other-regarding' versus 'self-regarding'

[94] Janoski, op. cit., p. 26

[95] Janoski, op. cit., pp 133–136; Janoski analyses voluntary association membership and participation in the different regimes types, pp 134–5

upon generalized exchange.[96] Janoski provides a typology of citizens—incorporated, active, deferential, privatized, and marginal—that encompasses varying degrees of these two types of exchange.[97] The state is not a neutral force concerning the type or development of citizenship:

> The active citizen participates in the activities of the polity, has concern for the people in the group, and exhibits a large degree of generalized exchange behaviour. However, the active citizen is often engaged in conflict with established elites and most often approaches problems from a grassroots level . . . The active citizen tends towards generalized exchange because this person believes that much can be done altruistically (i.e. for 'the people' or 'the country').[98]

The approach of the state, 'the structure of state processes' has a determining role to play in such citizenship development.[99] These include 'the social mechanisms to create citizenship' such as the educational process (which may include civic education oriented toward rights and obligations)[100] and the scope provided for in social policy for voluntary action. The state may control the development of the institutional processes of society (that is the 'patterned interactions set up and controlled by formal and informal norms') which are important in regard to

- the structuring of organizational forms creating norms of group behaviour and organisational identity such as (political structures, democratic norms, and participation in voluntary associations)

- the 'macro-structuring of large domains' of society including the family, education, media, medicine, legal system, economy and polity (how are organizations, groups and the public tied together in functioning networks)

---

[96] Janoski, pp 140–141; Hall, op. cit., pp 440–443; Hall notes that British governments have made substantial efforts 'to ensure that voluntary activity flourishes'

[97] Janoski, op. cit., p. 26; pp 95–101

[98] ibid, pp 96–7

[99] This section is based upon Janoski, op. cit., especially pp 107–8 on 'institutions and exchange'

[100] on role of citizenship education see N. Pearce, S. Spencer 'Reports and Surveys Education for Citizenship: The Crick Report' *The Political Quarterly*, Vol. 70, No. 2, April–June 1999, pp 219–224

Within these types of institutions 'a complex web of norms and positions are constructed' and they may be based upon highly restricted exchanges or upon more generalised forms of exchange in the different sectors such as education or health care. As Janoski notes to use 'an ideal type, societies can build institutions that promote diverse aims of quality of life, or institutions that primarily benefit some people more than others'.

Janoski's study assists in the reflection on 'the quality of discourse in civil society' and he notes that voluntary associations in liberal regimes 'are often buried in the details of fund-raising and distributing goods and services to the needy:

> These activities are particularly prone to co-optation by elites and the state due to their control of private and public funding, and voluntary associations tend to avoid controversy for fear of alienating donors—voluntary associations in social democratic regimes have the ability to be much more independent and engaged in critical discourse. Although the social democratic regime state may provide much of the funds for voluntary associations, they are not reduced to fund-raising efforts and are surprisingly critical of state policies. Voluntary associations, especially those operating in the welfare sector, that are dependent on uncertain and discretionary funding from a wide range of donors will not want to alienate potential supporters by critical or political positions.[101]

The impoverished public discourse observed in Irish society may be explained in part by such resource dependencies of voluntary bodies.[102]

Janoski's account of civil society assists in the understanding of the creation of civic virtue; if civil society protects democracy then it is important to show how this is done by various groups in different societies and how 'citizen-selves' are created in relation to the state. This leads to a focus on how voluntary associations operate in civil society to develop certain types of citizenship and on how citizens view state and voluntary relationships. In particular how voluntary organisations are governed and managed will be determinative of their

---

[101] Janoski, op. cit., p. 133

[102] see Chapter 1 above; it is noteworthy that two recent well informed commentators on Irish society have identified a need to shift from 'a community of believers' to 'a community of equal citizens' see Fintan O'Toole 'Replacing a community of believers with one of citizens' *The Irish Times*, 16 July 1999 and Chrystel Hug *The Politics of Sexual Morality in Ireland* (Macmillan Press, 1999) which notes that the 'débats de sociéte' which have characterised recent public discourse in Ireland involves a clash between a Catholic ideology of social order and 'a new citizen-based order', pp 1–2

facilitation of active citizenship development. State policies and citizen action over a longer time horizon can lead either to a society of citizens 'that works together' or 'one of greedy citizens who act like hungry and wide-eyed children in a candy store'.[103] In brief Janoski argues that voluntary means of maximising participation by citizens 'are a way to carry societies toward reconnection'.[104] The state and the voluntary sector must interact positively to develop 'active citizenship in a dynamic and responsive public discourse'.

The central importance of voluntary associations to this view of citizenship has been prefigured in two important social philosophers John Macmurray (1891–1975) and Hannah Arendt (1906–1975) whose contributions are of growing importance to democratic theories which are still at an embryonic stage in respect of how the depletion of social capital in respect of citizenship might be restored.

Tony Blair's political outlook owes a great deal to the philosophy of Macmurray. Blair states that Macmurray 'confronted what will be the critical political question of the twenty first century: the relationship between individual and society'.[105] Macmurray was the chief British representative of the philosophy of personalism which has as its central affirmation the existence of free and creative persons. Emmanuel Mournier, the leading French exponent of personalism, has written

> The name was born of a response to the expression of the totalitarian drive, against this drive, in order to stress the defence of the person against the tyranny of apparatus. From this aspect there was a risk of lining up with all the old reactionary individualism . . . From the beginning, therefore, we were careful to associate with it the word 'communal'

The adult only finds himself 'in his relationship to others, and to things, in work and comradeship, in friendship and in love, in action and encounter and not in his relationship to himself'.[106]

Macmurray placed the individual within a social setting: knowledge was something gained through experience in action as action necessarily involves the element of thought, and a degree of conscious intention;

---

[103] Janoski, op. cit., p. 232
[104] ibid, p. 233
[105] see *The Personal World John Macmurray on Self and Society*, selected and introduced by Philip Conford (Edinburgh, 1996); see Foreword by Tony Blair, p. 10
[106] Emmanuel Mournier *Be Not Afraid* (London, 1951), p. 119 quoted in *The Personal World*, op. cit., p. 19

furthermore we act in a world of other people. Hence we owe our identity and very being to the existence of others. As persons it is our nature to communicate and reciprocate as we share in a common life:

> In fact, it is the sharing of a common life which constitutes individual personality. We become persons in community, in virtue of our relations to others. Human life is *inherently* a common life. Our ability to form individual purposes is itself a function of this common life.[107]

Macmurray's philosophic approach is central to the revival of the vital sense of social obligation and community life which lies at the heart of the vision of active citizenship.[108]

Macmurray's view of 'the self-realisation of persons in relation' is foundational for theories of communitarianism but also for building theories of active and committed citizenship. Macmurray observed that 'the crisis of the personal is the crisis of liberalism' and he combatted the Cartesian mode of philosophy which saw the individual as no more than a detached consciousness.[109] Knowledge was gained through experience in action which involves a degree of conscious intention.[110] Macmurray insists that personal life is not a mere matter of fact—of response to stimulus or of inevitable process—but is a matter of *intention*. He writes

> We are not organisms, but persons. The nexus of relations which unites us in a human society is not organic but personal. Human behaviour cannot be understood, but only caricatured, if it is represented as an adaptation to environment; and there is no such process as social evolution but, instead,

[107] John Macmurray *Conditions of Freedom* (London, 1950), p. 56 quoted in *The Personal World*, op. cit., p. 165

[108] On the malaise in this regard in Western democratic societies see David Smail *The Origins of Unhappiness*, (London, 1993); Martin Rowley *The Private Future: Causes and Consequences of Community Collapse in the West*, (London, 1973); Michael Sandel *Democracy's Discontents: America in Search of a Public Philosophy*, (Cambridge, Mass., 1996)

[109] Macmurray's philosophical work culminated in the publication of his Gifford Lectures, *The Form of the Personal* in two volumes *The Self as Agent*, 1957 and *Persons in Relation* (1961); quotation from *The Self As Agent* from *The Personal World*, op. cit., p. 55

[110] This relates closely to the work of Michael Polanyi (1891–1976) the scientist and social philosopher who in his major work *Personal Knowledge Towards a Post-Critical Philosophy* (2nd Edition, London, 1962) coined the term 'personal knowledge' affirming that all knowing of reality involves the personal commitment of the knower as a whole person and Polanyi emphasises the tradition in which one lives for discovery of knowledge which require 'structures of conviviality'

a history which reveals a precarious development and possibilities both of progress and of retrogression.[111]

Hannah Arendt, another social philosopher who, like Mill, was aware of the novel and spontaneous possibilities inherent in voluntary action, also saw politics as a peculiarly open-ended and unpredictable activity.[112] Arendt favoured what she usually spoke of as 'public freedom': the direct participation in politics by ordinary citizens. Arendt as Canovan observes,

> 'rethinks politics itself, focusing attention on the plural and spontaneous nature of action . . . she stresses the openness of the future, the capacity of political actors to make new beginnings and do the unexpected. She had faith in the permanent possibility of action by those who choose to accept their responsibility as citizens. She was aware that even when the outcomes of political action are desirable, they are also contingent and fragile, dependent on the continuing action of those who care about the political realm'.

Arendt's work is important for a revitalised concept of active citizenship because she recognised 'that it is plurality—the fact that we are all the same precisely in being *different*, and that each of us is capable of acting spontaneously and of thinking our own thoughts—that is at the heart of being human, and that finds its clearest expression in politics.'[113]

Plural viewpoints and plural initiatives are at the heart of politics and this Arendt felt had been ignored by political philosophers and in political theory. As Canovan states in the Arendtian view the ability to act, inherent in human beings, is the key to politics:

> When we act, we reveal that we are free beings, as Rosa Parks and Martin Luther King did in the America South, and as Lech Walesa and his comrades in Solidarity did in Poland. So utterly unpredictable are such

[111] *Persons in Relation* quoted in *The Personal World*, op. cit., p. 113

[112] For detailed treatment of Arendt's political philosophy see Maurizio Passerin d'Entrèves *The Political Philosophy of Hannah Arendt* (Routledge, London and New York, 1994) especially in this context Ch. 4 'Hannah Arendt's conception of citizenship'; Margaret Canovan *Hannah Arendt A Reinterpretation of Her Political Thought* (Cambridge University Press, Cambridge, 1992) especially in this context Ch. 6 'A new republicanism'; for Arendt's philosophy in the context of her life see Elizabeth Young-Bruehl *Hannah Arendt For Love of the World* (Yale University Press, New Haven and London, 1982)

[113] see Margaret Canovan 'Hannah Arendt: Republicanism and Democracy' in *Liberal Democracy and its Critics*, eds. A. Carter and G. Stokes (Cambridge, 1998), pp 39–40; Arendt's major works include *The Origins of Totalitarianism* (1951), *The Human Condition*, (1958), *On Revolution*, (1963), *Between Past and Future*, (1968), *Men in Dark Times*, (1968); *On Violence*, (1969), *Crises of the Republic*, (1972)

actions that Arendt describes the capacity to act as 'the one miracle-working faculty of man'. As the place of action, politics is also the arena in which freedom in this characteristically Arendtian sense of beginning something new can be most fully displayed and enjoyed.[114]

This action is always *interaction*: we take initiatives that need the co-operation of others and Arendt's work directs us to rediscover the possibilities of action amongst citizens.

> Arendt's message is therefore that ordinary citizens can be free and powerful; not by waiting for someone in authority to give them power, but by having the courage to act in concert and create their own public space. Such spaces do not need pre-existing institutions, but come into existence among those who act together.[115]

This vision of public-spirited citizens and their creative function is fundamental to a flourishing democratic society and has tended to be ignored until recently in mainstream democracy theory. Arendt's contribution is to provide an historically informed philosophical under-pinning to the vital role played by voluntary action in society. She sees such action as lying in the capacity that belongs to all individuals for starting something that had never existed before and so to realise both power and freedom: her stress on spontaneity and calling the new into existence is crucial and distinctive to the citizen's role in Arendt's version of republican freedom. As Jeffrey Isaac has noted there are many similarities between her conception of civic engagement and that of Havel.[116] Arendt believes that citizens have the capacity not just to choose between prescribed alternatives, as in representative democratic systems, but in co-operation and solidarity with others to call entirely new possibilities into existence: they have the role of *initiative* rather than simply the role of *choice*, in this she clearly recalls the Tocquevillean view of democracy. Politics, for Arendt, is something that happens in between human beings. Canovan has noted

> One of the implicit conditions for freedom in Arendt's sense is that human spontaneity and the great power generated by co-operation should be exercised within the bounds of what, quoting Melville, she calls 'lasting institutions', within a public space guarded by constitutional arrangements upheld by the public commitments of citizens.[117]

[114] Canovan, op. cit., pp 43–4

[115] Canovan, op. cit., p. 45

[116] see J.C. Isaac 'Oases in the desert: Hannah Arendt on democratic politics' *American Political Science Review*, 88; 1 (March, 1994), pp 156–68

[117] M. Canovan *Hannah Arendt A Reinterpretation of Her Political Thought* (Cambridge University Press, Cambridge, 1992) p. 216

Arendt's insights into citizenship development through civic engagement provides a basis for considering the normative role of voluntary organisations in democracy. As described by Isaac voluntary organisations are 'oases of civic initiative' invigorating representative democracy and complementing it.[118] Such organisations are essential in any society which values the principles of freedom, plurality, equality, and solidarity.

7. DEMOCRATIC GOVERNANCE

The range and power of normative political theory which may be marshalled to legitimise voluntary action as an expression of active citizenship in democratic society is impressive. The focus of this study is the relationship between voluntary and statutory bodies: it is clear that this vision of active citizenship implies changes in all societal institutions not just in the 'third sector'. This conclusion reflects upon overall approaches or frameworks for democratic governance which would facilitate active citizenship through voluntary action in Ireland.

Irish society is constituted as a 'democracy in a Republic'.[119] The challenge is 'to perfect and deepen' Irish democracy to use Dahl's phrase:

> Democracy, it appears, is a bit chancy. But its chances also depend on what we do ourselves. Even if we cannot count on benign historical forces to favor democracy, we are not mere victims of blind forces over which we have no control. With adequate understanding of what democracy requires and the will to meet its requirements, we can act to preserve, and what is more, to advance democratic ideas and practices.[120]

Active citizenship in the first instance requires 'the recovery of civism in public administration'.[121] As Frederickson observes the effective public administration of the future 'should be intimately tied to citizenship, the citizenry generally, and to the effectiveness of public managers who work directly with the citizenry'.[122] Those involved in statutory bodies need to understand their central role in facilitating the conditions of citizenship

[118] Isaac, op. cit., p. 165

[119] The phrase is that of Abraham Lincoln, quoted in R.A. Dahl *On Democracy* (Yale University Press, New Haven & London, 1998) p. 4

[120] ibid, p. 2, p. 25

[121] see H. George Frederickson 'The Recovery of Civism in Public Administration' *Public Administration Review* Vol. 42, No. 2, November/December 1982, pp 501 - 8

[122] ibid, pp 501–2

For public administration both in practice and in education, this will mean a return to an emphasis on the *public* aspects of the field and to the basic issues of democratic theory. If public administration is to be effective, persons who practice it must be increasingly familiar with issues of both representational and direct democracy, with citizen participation, with principles of justice, and principles of individual freedom.[123]

The requirements of democracy's political institutions such as associational autonomy, inclusive citizenship, freedom of information and expression together with free and fair elections are all heavily reliant upon voluntary organisation and action together with citizen competence.[124] Dahl, for example, notes that independent associations are 'a source of civic education and enlightenment. They provide citizens not only with information but also with opportunities for discussion, deliberation, and the acquisition of political skills'.[125]

Dahl states that

> One of the imperative needs of democratic countries is to improve citizens' capacities to engage intelligently in political life . . . these older institutions will need to be enhanced by new means of civic education, political participation, information and deliberation that draw creatively on the array of techniques and technologies available in the twenty-first century.[126]

Voluntary organisations which have public purposes are one key means of civic education for citizenship and participatory politics. It is recognised that they need to be supplemented by other forms of civic education and development.[127]

Tocqueville had the crucial insight that *administrative* centralization 'which would restrict the self-regulation of free associations' would frustrate 'the competences and responsibilities of citizens who participate in these associations'.[128] He saw the role of the state as that of protecting public order, ensuring respect for laws and achieving a stable order and he added significantly

[123] ibid, p. 503

[124] Dahl, op. cit., pp 83–99

[125] ibid, p. 98

[126] ibid, pp 187–8; see also the work of Amy Gutmann *Democratic Education* (Princeton, N.J., 1987)

[127] see Benjamin R. Barber *Strong Democracy Participatory Politics for a New Age* (University of California Press, Berkeley and Los Angeles, California, 1984) pp 233–244

[128] see H.E.S. Woldring 'State and Civil Society in the Political Philosophy of Alexis de Tocqueville' *Voluntas: International Journal of Voluntary and Nonprofit Organizations* Vol. 9, No. 4, 1998, p. 364

The first duty imposed on those who now direct society is to educate democracy; to put, if possible, new life into its beliefs, to purify its mores; to control its actions; gradually to substitute understanding of statecraft for present inexperience and knowledge of its true interests for blind instincts; to adapt government to the needs of time and place; and to modify it as men and circumstances require.

A new political science is needed for a world itself quite new.[129]

Tocqueville's concept of the role of the state in facilitating active citizenship is echoed in Oldfield's work on civic republicanism in respect of the need for appropriate constitutional settings for the practice of citizenship:

> There have to be arenas where potentially everyone can take part, where everyone can do something. In the modern state, this means the decentralization of political tasks and functions . . . What is to be sought is the creation and widening of opportunities for responsible self-government by citizens . . . Self-government can refer to any public tasks and activities that a community wishes to engage in.[130]

A range of conditions need to be met for the practice of citizenship; these are summarised by Oldfield:

> These conditions are that individuals need resources: they need empowering—in terms of knowledge, skills, information, time and well-being—to become effective agents in the world. They need opportunities—in terms of the decentralization of both political and economic power—in which they can be effective agents, that is citizens. Finally, they need to be provided with the required motivation to take the practice of citizenship seriously, in terms of performing the duties which they owe to the political community of which they are members.[131]

Two major contributions have been made in the 1990s to new conceptions of democratic governance. These concern 'associational democracy' as described by Paul Hirst and 'institutional perspectives' on democratic governance as presented by March and Olsen.

Paul Hirst has revived associationalist doctrines in his critique of representative democracy and outlined how they might contribute 'to the reform of democratic governance and to the organisation of economic affairs and welfare services in western societies'.[132]

---

[129] A. de Tocqueville *Democracy in America* ed J.P. Mayer (Anchor Books edition, New York, 1969) p. 12

[130] Adrian Oldfield *Citizenship and Community Civic Republicanism and the Modern World* (Routledge, London and New York, 1990) p. 28

[131] ibid, p. 145

[132] see P. Hirst 'Associational Democracy' in *Prospects for Democracy North, South, East, West* ed. D. Held (Polity Press, Cambridge, 1993) p. 112

Associationalism may be loosely defined as a normative theory of society the central claim of which is that human welfare and liberty are both best served when as many of the affairs of society as possible are managed by voluntary and democratically self-governing associations.[133] Hirst seeks to supplement and extend rather than replace representative democracy through a growth in the scope of governance through associations:

> Associational governance would lessen the tasks of central government to such an extent that greater accountability of both the public power and of the devolved associational agencies would be possible. The main political objective of modern associationalism is to decentralize and devolve as much of the affairs of society as possible to publicly funded but voluntary and self-governing associations.[134]

Voluntary organisations, or associations are now widely regarded in many streams of democratic theory as the social foundation for plural political interests, as the cement of the 'civil society' that sustains the state and as providers of the 'social capital' which is essential for the future development of societies. Hirst, indeed, argues that such self-governing voluntary bodies should not be seen as 'secondary associations' but 'as the primary means of organizing social life': For associationalists

> . . . a self-governing civil society becomes primary, and the state becomes a secondary (if vitally necessary) public power that ensures peace between associations, protects the rights of individuals and provides the mechanisms of public finance whereby a substantial part of the activities of associations are funded . . . large areas of governance of social affairs come to depend either on associations directly or on processes of co-ordination and collaboration between associations. In this way what the state does becomes more readily accountable. As its work is increasingly regulatory, so the legislature and judiciary rise in importance relative to the executive, reversing the strong trends in the other direction. . .[135]

Hirst outlines the role of the state as one of inspection and overseeing associations ensuring 'their compliance with democratic norms in their internal governance and their conformity to commonly agreed community standards of service provision'.[136] Most political theorists

[133] ibid; see also P. Hirst *Associative Democracy New Forms of Economic and Social Governance* (Polity Press, Cambridge, 1994)
[134] Hirst, 1993, op. cit., pp 116–117
[135] Hirst, 1993, op. cit., p. 117
[136] Hirst, 1993, op. cit., p. 117

see the state as the central political community whereas associationalists believe voluntary self-governing associations to be the primary means of democratic governance involving two processes

> First, that the state should cede functions to such associations, and create the mechanisms of public finance whereby they can undertake them. Second, that the means to the creation of an associative order in civil society are built up, such as alternative sources of mutual finance for associative economic enterprises, agencies that aid voluntary bodies and their personnel to conduct their affairs effectively, and so on. This is not intended to be a once-and-for-all change, but a gradual process of supplementation, proceeding as fast as the commitment to change by political forces and the capacity to accept tasks by voluntary associations allows.[137]

An associationalist reform strategy would require both voluntary action and state co-operation.[138]

Another major contribution has been made by March and Olsen to 'a framework for thinking about democratic governance'.[139] They argue that 'exchange perspectives', that is, the language which has traditionally been used in democracies emphasising 'exchanges' among 'rational self-interested citizens' provides an 'incomplete' basis for 'thinking about governance'

> From an institutional perspective a democratic polity is constituted by its basic practices and rules, as well as by individual purposes and intentions. Political action is organized through the interdependent obligations of political identities. Governance involves affecting the frameworks within which citizens and officials act and politics occurs, and which shape the identities and institutions of civil society.[140]

March and Olsen ask how organisations in a democratic society 'are structured, how they work, how they change, how they are governed, and how governance might be made honorable, just, and effective'; organisations are required which 'sustain and elaborate democratic values, beliefs, and identities' and which make politics 'civil, account-

---

[137] P. Hirst *Associative Democracy New Forms of Economic and Social Governance* op. cit., p. 21

[138] ibid, pp 40–43; Hirst sees associationalism 'not as a social system complete in itself, but as an axial principle of social organization. That is, a pattern of organizing social relations that can be generalized across sectors and domains of social activity. In this it resembles the market and bureaucratic administration', ibid, p. 42

[139] see James G. March, Johan P. Olsen *Democratic Governance* (The Free Press, New York, 1995)

[140] ibid, p. 6

able, capable, and transformative'.[141] Modern theories of rational exchange 'do not imagine a shared preference function or common will as a basis for action within a collectivity . . . they assume that there is a conflict of interest among individual actors and that collective action stems from the coercion of mutual self-interest, not from shared values or preferences'.[142] In contrast 'an institutional perspective' on governance 'involves creating capable political actors who understand how political institutions work and are able to deal effectively with them':

> The core notion is that life is organized by sets of shared meanings and practices that come to be taken as given. Political actors act and organize themselves in accordance with rules and practices that are socially constructed, publicly known, anticipated and accepted. Actions of individuals and collectivities occur within these shared meanings and practices, which can be called identities and institutions. Institutions and identities constitute and legitimize political actors and provide them with consistent behavioural rules, conceptions of reality, standards of assessment, affective ties, and endowments, and thereby with a capacity for purposeful action.[143]

Exchange traditions 'downplay the significant, or meaning of the common good and doubt the relevance of social investment in citizenship' while 'institutional theories of politics give importance to the idea of community. Humans (or their institutions) are seen as able to share a common life and identity and to have concern for others'.[144] The active citizen who is able to exercise civic virtues is essential to a polity in order to check the pursuit of selfish interests and to recognise a standard of obligation towards others:

> . . . citizenship or membership in the polity is the most important and inclusive identity. It is the highest form of association, responsible for the common good of society. Being a citizen and holding public office are constitutive belongings integrating and shaping other allegiances and particular identities derived from social affiliations like the family, voluntary associations, class, or one's market position. Citizens and office-holders are presumed to act according to norms associated with their roles rather than in pursuit of personal advantage and interests . . . the hope of governance is to encourage ordinary people, with their usual mix of identities and interests, to attend to the obligations of citizenship.[145]

[141] ibid, p. 6
[142] ibid, p. 9
[143] ibid, p. 28, p. 30
[144] ibid, p. 36
[145] ibid, pp 37–8

According to March and Olsen 'the craft of governance' from an institutional perspective is organised around four tasks

- *developing identities of citizens* and groups

- *developing capabilities* appropriate to action

- *developing accounts* of political events (i.e. the meaning of history, the options and possibilities for action)

- *developing an adaptive political system* which copes with changing demands and environments.[146]

Active citizenship involving democratic governance implies changes in the state sector, the business sector and the 'third sector'.[147] Each sector must embrace new sets of responsibilities which require to be clearly delineated and based upon an agreed vision of active citizenship in a developing democratic Republic. It is significant that the Compact between Government and the voluntary and community sector in Northern Ireland embraces 'shared values' including 'active citizenship' (participation of people in society through volunteering, community involvement, and self help initiatives), 'pluralism' (upholding the rich diversity of cultures, identities and interest within Northern Ireland), 'democracy' (a society that enables all its citizens to participate, to share rights and responsibilities, and which incorporates an independent voluntary and community sector).[148] What has been discovered in this exploration of democratic theories is that if people

> are fundamentally constrained to do only what state institutions command
> them to do, or they are motivated solely by personal gains in a market
> system, then civic order itself would inevitably suffer as fewer and fewer
> citizens volunteer their time and resources to pursue their common
> values.[149]

[146] ibid, pp 45–6

[147] see Henry Tam *Communitarianism A New Agenda For Politics and Citizenship* (Macmillan Press, London, 1998) chapters 6–8 outlining the required changes in each sector from a 'communitarian' perspective

[148] see *Building Real Partnership Compact Between the Government and The Voluntary and Community Sector in Northern Ireland* (Northern Ireland Office, December 1998) p. 11

[149] Tam, op. cit., p. 196; see the important article by James M. Ferris 'Coprovision: Citizen Time and Money Donations in Public Service Provision' *Public Administration Review* Vol. 44, No. 4, July/August, 1984, pp 324–333; 'coprovision' is defined by Ferris as 'the voluntary involvement of citizens in the *provision* of publicly provided goods and services or close substitutes, p. 326

Voluntary organisations, whose legitimacy derives from active citizenship in a pluralist democracy, will be required to enable citizens to experience taking responsibility for pursuing values that go beyond themselves (helping to define and realise the common good); they will also be required to enable citizens to work together to achieve common purposes and they will be required to provide a balance in relation to the activities of the state and business sectors by being active in their own right and not simply as mere agents to deliver state programmes. If voluntary organisations are to fulfil these roles in building 'civil society' there will be a great need for effective organisational development. Governance of such organisations will require an appreciation of democratic power relations and a recognition of how the specific activities of each voluntary organisation relate to the wider strategies affecting the communities served.[150] Genuine citizenship based partnerships will require to be developed in the service of the common good. These normative standards provide a critical perspective for the detailed examination of voluntary and statutory relationships and their implications for governance and management in the Irish hospital sector which follows in Part II.

---

[150] See the important analysis of 'governance' as 'self-organizing interorganizational networks' by R. A. W. Rhodes 'The New Governance: Governing without Government' *Political Studies* Vol XLIV, 1996 pp 652-667; for a valuable exploration of the Irish experience see M. Adshead and B. Quinn 'The Move from Government to Governance: Irish development policy's paradigm shift' *Policy & Politics* Vol 26 No 2, April 1998 pp 209-225.

Part I: Summary and Preliminary Analysis

In Part I 'The Changing Context' major implications emerged in respect of governance and management of voluntary organisations and in particular public voluntary hospitals, relating to philosophy, legitimacy, power relationships and values.

A. *Philosophy and Legitimacy*

It has been argued in the previous chapter that there exists a convincing legitimating political philosophy which underpins the roles of voluntary organisations in a democratic society. This philosophy is based upon active citizenship in civil society which locates a vital and essential contribution of the 'voluntary citizen' to democratic society through voluntary association for public purposes. Such voluntary participation has an essential 'values expressive' function in a pluralist and democratic society. The particular insight that there is a crucial relationship between the 'method of government' in voluntary organisations and the flourishing of 'voluntary citizenship' is of major importance in respect of the design and operation of governance and management. Beveridge's claim that the functioning of effective voluntary organisations is a 'distinguishing mark of a free society' and that such organisations must have 'independence from public control' and 'have a will and a life' of their own has been found to have been well made in the light of the normative theory concerning 'active citizenship' in a democratic republic.

It is important therefore, to assess whether particular governance and management arrangements embrace or allow for this particular philosophic stance. Secondly it is necessary to find, in Beveridge's words, ways 'of fruitful co-operation between public authorities and voluntary agencies'.[1] There are profound and wide ranging implications in respect of governance and management pertaining to any 'partnership' arrangements between voluntary and statutory agencies and in particular to the concept of 'contracting' or 'service agreements' which were discussed in Chapter 2 above.

[1] see discussion of Beveridge above, Chapter 1, pp 20-1

B. *Dynamic power relationships and values*

The analysis in Part I has demonstrated the changing and dynamic relationships which have existed over time between voluntary hospitals and the State. Such relationships are best understood through the dynamics centred upon resource allocation, control mechanisms and policy direction. The insight of Melissa Middleton that the board—environment relationship is central to our understanding of nonprofit boards is very important.[2] Boards

> 'are special boundary-spanning and control units that keep organizations connected to parts of their environment while also differentiating them from external elements. The major functions boards perform in this capacity include the following:
>
> • They develop exchange relationships with external parties to ensure the flow of resources into and out of the organization .
>
> • They process information gained from these exchanges to make the internal organizational adjustments necessary to meet environmental demands.
>
> • They buffer the organization from the environment and thus protect it from external interference.
>
> • They reduce environmental constraints by influencing external conditions to the organization's advantage.'[3]

This board—environment linkage is perhaps best understood as attempts to manage power relations and Emerson's power-dependence theory is particularly helpful in this context.[4] In brief Emerson's power-dependence theory notes that the power between two organisations will be governed by the degree of dependency of each organization on the other and by the availability of alternative sources of each organization's requirements and these factors will result in four possible dependency positions: low (mild needs, many alternatives) moderate (mild needs, few alternatives) moderate (strong needs, many alternatives)

---

[2] M. Middleton 'Nonprofit Boards of Directors: Beyond The Governance Function' in *The Nonprofit Sector A Research Handbook*, ed. W.W. Powell, (Yale University Press, New Haven and London, 1987), pp 141–153; see also the very important James D. Thompson *Organisations in Action*, (New York, 1967) for analysis of the 'task environment' i.e. those parts of the environment which are relevant or potentially relevant to goal setting and goal attainment of an organisation and for the insight concerning each organisation's 'domain' or 'territory' which automatically creates dependence on others.

[3] ibid, p. 143

[4] see Richard M. Emerson 'Power-Dependence Relations' *American Sociological Review*, Vol. 27, No. 1, 1962, pp 31–41

high (strong needs, few alternatives). These positions of relative power and dependence may be 'managed' or 'manipulated' and various strategies to gain power may be employed.

The decisive determinant of the scope of public voluntary hospitals in the current Irish context is their high dependency position vis a vis the State (The Department of Health and Children). The essence of the governance and management issue, then, is how to manage this dependence upon a statutory agency so that the characteristics which ought to pertain to a voluntary board are retained and are allowed to flourish.

The hypothesis noted in the Introduction to this study put forward by the Secretary-General of the Department of Health and Children that voluntary hospitals and statutory hospitals will develop governance and management 'along similar lines' has to withstand the crucial test of relating to the legitimating philosophy of active citizenship and the values and attributes of voluntary organisations' governance and management.[5] As Jeavons has noted the 'values-expressive character' of voluntary organisations is what distinguishes them from either business or government organisations: this distinctive character of voluntary organisations creates a special context for their governance and management.[6] Jeavons states that voluntary organisations established for public benefit 'usually have come into being and exist primarily to give expression to the social, philosophical, moral, or religious values of their founders and supporters'.[7] Jeavons posits that business organisations revolve around wealth, statutory agencies around power and the voluntary sector around values. The claim of voluntary or philanthropic organisations on resources (economic goods and institutional legitimacy) is based 'on their embodying moral commitments' according to Jeavons. If this is so, then it means 'that the quality of these organization's values-expressive character and behaviour is crucial, for it is the demonstration of these moral commitments that then legitimates and strengthens their claims'.[8] Jeavons notes that as a result of their historical development and of their contemporary roles voluntary

---

[5] see statement by Secretary-General in the Introduction above p. 4

[6] T. H. Jeavons 'When the Management is the Message: Relating Values To Management Practice in Nonprofit Organizations' *Nonprofit Management & Leadership*, Vol. 2, No. 4, Summer 1992, pp 403–417

[7] ibid, p. 404

[8] Jeavons, op. cit., p. 406

organisations 'carry much of the burden of mediating civic, moral, and spiritual values in the public realm and from one generation to the next'.[9]

The implications for governance and management of voluntary organisations of this understanding of their key attributes become clear: 'What distinguishes the context for management in a values-expressive organisation is that how the organization goes about setting and attaining specific goals becomes as important as the goals themselves'. Jeavons warns that 'the process of institutionalization' may be particularly dangerous for 'value-expressive' organizations because this process is one 'through which organisations tend to become self-serving, and if these organizations were created to serve others and the common good, and if that is the basis on which they sell themselves, then institutionalization brings with it a fundamental and often visible discontinuity between espoused purposes and values and operative purposes and values'.[10]

Those responsible for governance and management in voluntary organizations, according to the argument presented by Jeavons, need to be particularly attentive to three concerns: the ethical integrity of the organisation, the degree to which the organization's performance actually serves the public good and the degree to which the treatment of staff and volunteers honours the moral and social values that the organization intends to project in its service work.

In Part II the implications for governance and management of public voluntary hospitals of the changing context analysed in Part I will be explored in detail.

[9] ibid, p. 409
[10] ibid, pp 410–411

PART II

The Implications of Context and Theory
for Governance and Management
of Public Voluntary Hospitals

CHAPTER 4

Hospital Governance and Management: models and 'usable theory'

'Effective governance by the board of a nonprofit organization is a rare and unnatural act'

B.E. TAYLOR, R.P. CHAIT, AND T.P. HOLLAND, 'The New Work of the Nonprofit Board', Harvard Business Review, September–October 1996, p. 36

'In a pluralist society, boards of trustees are inevitably an arena for playing out different visions, expectations, and values'

P.D. HALL, *Inventing the Nonprofit Sector and other Essays on Philanthropy, Voluntarism, and Nonprofit Organizations,* (John Hopkins University Press, Baltimore, MD, 1992), p. 206

'The governing board is a nonprofit organization's most important volunteer entity'

T.P. HOLLAND 'Strengthening Board Performance' in *Skills for Effective Management of Nonprofit Organizations,* eds. R.L. Edwards, J.A. Yankey, M.A. Altpeter (National Association of Social Workers, Washington, Dc, 1998), p. 425

1. INTRODUCTION

This chapter explores the literature on board governance drawing particularly upon that concerned with board governance in the context of voluntary organisations and of hospitals. The purpose is to assess the available models of board governance and management in the light of the implications which arose in Part I concerning philosophy, legitimacy, statutory and voluntary relationships and the values associated with voluntary organisations. The consideration here is whether there are specific governance and management models which are designed to secure and foster the distinctive characteristics of voluntary action such as active citizenship and the values that may be expressed most effectively by voluntary organisations. It is appropriate to consider any such models in designing governance structures for public voluntary hospitals.

Having reviewed the prescriptive literature in relation to board governance and drawn upon insights from organisation theory in relation to the operation of voluntary organisations the chapter concludes by suggesting a 'usable theory' of governance and management in voluntary organisations in the Irish context. Such a theory seeks to account for the normative philosophy of active citizenship in a pluralist democracy (which legitimates voluntary action) and to account for the power relationships and resource dependent-relationships of public voluntary hospitals (and of many Irish voluntary organisations) so that the essential roles and values of voluntary action may be preserved and fostered as these relationships are experienced and developed.

2. THE NORMATIVE ROLES OF THE BOARD IN A VOLUNTARY CONTEXT

In the last ten years a number of key texts on governance and management in voluntary boards and in hospitals have been produced.[1] With

[1] These include C.O. Houle *Governing Boards Their Nature and Nurture* (Josey-Bass Publishers, San Francisco, 1989); John Carver *Boards That Make a Difference A New Design for Leadership in Nonprofit and Public Organizations* first published 1990, Second Edition (Jossey-Bass Publishers, San Francisco, 1997); Christopher R.M. Wilson *New On Board Essentials of Governance for Hospital Trustees* (Canadian Hospital Association Press, Ottawa 1991); Diane J. Duca *Nonprofit Boards: Roles, Responsibilities and Performance* (John Wiley & Sons, New York, 1996); T.P. Holland, R.A. Ritro, A.R. Kovner *Improving Board Effectiveness Practical Lessons for Nonprofit Health Care Organizations* (American Hospital Publishing, Inc., Chicago, 1997); R.C. Andringa, T.W. Engstrom *Nonprofit Board Answer Book Practical Guidelines for Board Members and Chief Executives* (National Center for Nonprofit Boards, Washington, D.C., 1997)

respect to hospital boards in particular it is important to note that in Canada in 1990 accreditation standards for the governing bodies were put in place and are required for use by all accredited Canadian health-care organizations and these standards are widely accepted by such organizations.[2] Similar standards are very likely to be developed and applied in Ireland in order to improve board governance. In Ireland the Department of Health and Children through the Office for Health Management promoted in 1998 a 'Governance Initiative' with the objective of providing 'a forum for discussion which would help Boards to agree a system of good governance values, structures and practice, against which they may audit their present state of fitness and implement any appropriate programme of improvement'.[3] A significant reform of the Board of St. James's Hospital took place in 1998: the significance derives from the fact that the 'model' introduced for St. James's Hospital, which is governed by a Statutory Order under the Health (Corporate Bodies) Act 1961, is likely to apply to other public hospitals governed under this Act.[4] The Department of Health and Children has been closely involved in this reform which provides a statutory 'new model' which may be used to compare any 'model' which is suggested as being appropriate for voluntary hospitals.[5]

The major texts and initiatives noted above are concerned to strengthen board performance; they offer very little commentary in respect of the board's role in preserving and developing the legitimacy of voluntary organisations through active citizenship and the particular values associated with voluntary organisations. Houle in a small 'afterword' entitled 'The Living Proof of Democracy' states

> There is much talk of a social power structure, and boards are clearly a part of the pattern of organized authority. But the members of boards tend to think of them instead as responsibility structures that help bear the weight of organized society. They represent diversity and variety and are

[2] Letter from Elma G. Heidemann, Executive director, Canadian Council on Health Services Accreditation, to author, 12 July 1999; these standards are published as Appendix 2 in Wilson *New On Board Essentials of Governance for Hospital Trustees*, op. cit., pp 109–188 and reproduced below as an Appendix

[3] see *Governance & Hospital Boards Discussion Document* (Department of Health & Children, June 1999)

[4] see St. James's Hospital Board (Establishment) Order, 1971 (Amendment) Order, 1998, Statutory Instrument S.I. No. 538 of 1998

[5] The new Board of St. James's Hospital is described in greater detail in Chapter 6 where it is compared to a 'new model' suggested for voluntary hospitals see pp 244-251 below

the chief means by which private citizens learn how to carry the burdens of governance. Boards do not talk very much about democracy. They do not need to do so. They are the living proof of it.[6]

Wilson has an important chapter entitled 'The Wisdom of Lay Governance' which identifies four of the key contributions of lay citizens on boards (as opposed to a reliance on professional experts as the ultimate authority in a hospital) when boards are engaged in making 'social choices, or choices on behalf of society':

(i) lay governors are 'representative of the community' in the sense of being 'in place of the thousands in the community who are not at the board table to oversee an enterprise that both belongs to the people and has the obligation to care for them'.

(ii) lay governors 'bring with them and demonstrate a general *life competence* in their consideration of the hospital's business'

(iii) lay governors are 'concerned with fairness' when deciding upon issues

'. . . the trustees' respect for the competence of the professional will always be tempered by their concern for fairness to the individual whether it be the patient, the staff member, a local merchant or an unpopular physician . . . This concern for fairness is important because the hospital, with its size, purchasing power and scientific sophistication could be seen as a monster to those dependent on it, its patients, suppliers, and staff'

(iv) lay governors are trustees 'a trustee of a public resource, and what good board members bring to this aspect of their role is *a sense of proportion*'. This involves good judgement in the use of resources in the interests of those served by the organisation rather than the professional ambitions of any particular member or members of staff.[7]

The 'Governance Initiative' in Ireland has not focussed upon the particular requirements of voluntary hospital boards but on the features of good governance generally in all hospitals. However, the Discussion Document states

There is no one best way of providing good governance. A fundamental principle in the design of governance structures and processes is that they should be carefully crafted to suit the needs of an individual hospital. Nonetheless, there are principles of good governance which should be observed irrespective of context.[8]

[6] Houle *Governing Boards their Nature and Nurture*, op. cit., p. 183

[7] Wilson *New on Board: Essentials of Governance for Hospital Trustees*, op. cit., pp 13–23

[8] *Governance & Hospital Boards Discussion Document* (Department of Health and Children, June 1999) p. 1

If the context is that of a public voluntary hospital how should the governance structures and processes be crafted? Margaret Harris has posed a basic question in the context of the rapidly changing environment 'do we need voluntary governing bodies?[9] Gwen Jaffro has shown that the prescriptive literature on boards which sets out the normative roles and functions for governing boards is not reflected in the reality of the Irish voluntary organisations she surveyed.[10] There often exists confusion about the role and responsibilities of the board and the board and staff 'tend to be involved in both governance and management, and in some cases the board only acts as a 'rubber stamp' to decisions made by the staff'.[11] In an age of contracting when professional staff negotiate and are held to be accountable for the contract or service plan by the statutory funding authority it is particularly important to question the role of voluntary governing bodies.[12] Harris has pointed out that in the growing body of research literature, voluntary governing bodies are given insufficient attention.[13]

Voluntary agencies since the 1980s, as Harris points out, have had to adapt to changes in their environment such as

- New assumptions that they will expand their role in service provision

- Expectations that they will be sympathetic to the public policy agenda of government funders

- Pressures to become more publicly accountable

- Exhortations to adopt more business-like methods and market orientations

- Discontinuities and increased uncertainty in funding

- Pressure to enter into contracts as service providers with statutory authorities in their purchaser role.[14]

---

[9] Margaret Harris 'Do We Need Voluntary Governing Bodies?' in *Voluntary Agencies Challenges of Organization and Management*, eds. D. Billis and M. Harris, (London, 1996), pp 149–165

[10] G. Jaffro 'Insights into the Boards of Irish Voluntary Agencies' *Administration*, Vol. 46, No. 3 (Autumn 1998), pp 60–91

[11] ibid, pp 86–89

[12] Harris, op. cit., pp 150–1

[13] Margaret Harris 'Voluntary Management Committees: The Impact of Contracting in the UK' in *The Contract Culture in Public Services Studies from Britain , Europe and the USA*, eds. Perri 6, J. Kendall, (Arena, Aldershot, Hants., 1997), p. 69

[14] ibid, pp 70–4

Given the 'value expressive' role of voluntary organisations the impact of contracting on governing board members is worrying from the five case studies reported by Harris

> '. . . those who served because they were committed to the 'idea' of their agency, or in order to represent the interests of service consumers were often indifferent to or alienated by the contracting process. Others were angry about what they saw as a threat to their autonomy, their rights and ability to identify and meet needs in their own way'.[15]

On the other hand negotiations over contracts 'had forced some management committees to re-examine their roles and responsibilities'; some 'had become more aware of their role as guardians of the organisation's mission'; others 'had become more aware of their legal and financial obligations by trying to find out more 'about what's going on, on a daily basis' in their agencies, or by trying to raise independent funding'.[16]

Voluntary organisations are 'value-led': they are established and managed by people 'who believe that changes are needed, and they want to do something about it themselves'.[17] Peter Drucker observes that 'the product' of 'non-profit' organisations 'is a *changed human being*. The nonprofit institutions are human-change agents. Their product is a cured patient, a child that learns, a young man or woman grown into a self-respecting adult; a changed human life altogether'.[18] Given these fundamental normative attributes 'management cannot be imported unchanged and imposed on value-led organizations. Subtle and critical differences that are rooted in the different ethos that underlies these organisations have to be understood'.[19] Critical issues must be addressed differently in voluntary organizations as compared with for profit organizations: 'The third sector needs its own management theories adopted and adapted to suit its own needs'.[20] As Charles

---

[15] ibid, p. 75; the threat to the 'active citizen' based boards in voluntary organisations from changes in public policy is underlined by Harris in 'Instruments of Government? Voluntary sector boards in a changing public policy environment' *Policy & Politics* Vol 26 No. 2, April 1998 pp 177-188

[16] Harris, 1997 op.cit., p. 76

[17] M. Hudson, *Managing Without Profit The Art of Managing Third-Sector Organizations*, (London, 1995); Hudson states that 'the ethos which unites' all third sector organizations is that they are 'value-led', p. 11

[18] Peter F. Drucker, *Managing the Non-Profit Organization Practices and Principles*, (London, 1992), p. x

[19] Hudson, op. cit., p. 13, pp 33–39

[20] ibid, p. 14

Handy has asked: 'Is there lurking in the voluntary world a better theory of organizing?'[21]

This is an especially important question to ask in the context of voluntary organizations which are major service providers, such as hospitals, which are so closely dependent upon, and interlinked with statutory authorities in terms of resources and regulations. As Handy says

> If you join something because you believe in its cause and its values, because you want to, you are not about to submit yourself to some anonymous authority, to subject yourself to bureaucratic whims or to do, automatically, what someone else tells you to do.[22]

3. MODELS AND METAPHORS

Houle defines a board as 'an organized group of people with the authority collectively to control and foster an institution that is usually administered by a qualified executive and staff'.[23] The various models of governance and management that have emerged in the prescriptive literature require analysis in respect of the roles and functions of voluntary organizations in a rapidly changing context. The governance models available include

(i) *The tripartite system*
    This is a conventional model whereby the responsibilities for running the organisation are combined into a three-part interactive system comprised of a board of directors, an executive (CEO) and staff; this might be known also as a 'stewardship' model as the board exercises overall 'stewardship'.

(ii) *The philanthropic system*
    This is a traditional model often found in charitable voluntary organisations such as voluntary hospitals which have large boards often with a close involvement in the management of the organisation and a strong commitment to a particular set of values.

(iii) *The corporate system*
    This is drawn from the way boards function in the private sector often with a small board which includes active participation by management on the board, financial compensation for board membership and strong emphasis on financial outcomes.

[21] C. Handy *Understanding Voluntary Organizations*, (London, 1988), p. 1
[22] Handy, *Understanding Voluntary Organizations*, op. cit., p. 3
[23] C.O. Houle, *Governing Boards: Their Nature and Nurture*, (Jossey-Bass Publishers, San Francisco, 1989), p. 6

(iv) *The Carver policy governance system*
This is a system developed in 1990 by John Carver requiring the Board to focus above all on policy matters, providing policy-focussed leadership for the organisation.

(v) *The 'new work' system*
Associated with Taylor, Chait and Holland this system focuses upon four characteristics of Board work—it is concerned with crucial, 'do or die' issues central to the organisations success, it is driven by results linked to defined timetables; it has clear measures of success and it requires the engagement of internal and external constituencies of the organisation.

(vi) *The 'cyclical board' system*
This system recognises that boards of directors tend to behave in a certain way depending on board's stage of development, as well as that of the organisation. Boards assume different roles during a cycle of stages in the life and operation of their organisation. The merit of this system is that it is focussed upon board behaviour and change as opposed to simply offering principles of board governance.[24]

The governing boards of voluntary organisations have historically embraced the values of philanthropy, voluntarism, and independence so as to advocate and provide for services that meet client needs and to secure resources necessary for these services. Such boards have served as 'the collective conscience of their organizations', ensuring that the basic mission and underpinning values of voluntary activity are sustained.[25] However, as voluntary organisations have come under intense financial pressure and increasing State regulation there have been regular calls for the adoption of management and governance practices from the private sector: they must, it is argued become more businesslike in form, structure, practice and philosophy.

---

[24] see Diane J. Duca, *Nonprofit Boards: Roles, Responsibilities, and Performance*, (John Wiley, New York, 1996), Chapter One 'Models of Governance and Leadership' for brief outline of some current models, pp 3–16 and see Houle Governing Boards op. cit, pp 5–15; Carver *Boards that Make a Difference* op. cit.,; B.E. Taylor, R.P. Chait and T.P. Holland 'The New Work of the Nonprofit Board' *Harvard Business Review* Sept.–Oct. 1996, pp 36–46; M.M. Wood 'Is Governing Board Behaviour Cyclical?' *Nonprofit Management and Leadership* Vol. 3, No. 2, 1992, pp 143–50. The Department of Health and Children's *Governance & Hospital Boards Discussion Document* (June 1999) just refers to 'the tripartite system' and 'the policy driven system' and to the changing nature of the challenges facing organisations at different stages of development, pp 1 - 2

[25] J.A. Alexander, B.J. Weiner 'The Adoption of the Corporate Governance Model by Nonprofit Organizations' *Nonprofit Management & Leadership*, Vol. 8, No. 3, Spring 1998, pp 223–242; and T.H. Jeavons 'Stewardship Revisited: Secular and Sacred Views of Governance and Management' *Nonprofit and Voluntary Sector Quarterly*, Vol. 23, No. 2, 1994, pp 107–122

The 1990s have been marked by a resurgence of interest in questions of corporate governance in both public and private settings. Within the public sector in both Ireland and the United Kingdom there has been a rising level of concern about the failures of corporate governance and expressions of the need for more effective delivery of services and for more accountability.[26] In both countries there have been major shifts in management approaches within the public service. The emergence of what is known as New Public Management (NPM) in the 1980s was an attempt to remodel the public sector using private sector role models.[27] Central to NPM has been an attempt to shift power from providers to consumers of services by breaking up monopoly providers or where this has not been possible to bring in new forms of regulations such as the setting of service standards. In this context the reforms of the governance systems of public agencies (such as occurred in the National Health Service in the UK) are intended to produce governing boards that are expected to display more strategic forms of behaviour and to be more challenging of executive management.[28] In an assessment of the post-1990 corporate governance systems in the NHS the role of underlying values and beliefs was found to have been 'rarely discussed overtly at board meetings but lay beneath the surface'; yet the question of values is critical in health care

> Certain dilemmas facing NHS boards may be resolved only by a recourse to a debate about ultimate values rather than management means. Management in the NHS cannot be regarded as a 'neutral', technical activity but involves making judgements between perhaps contradictory priorities. Examples of these value laden dilemmas for NHS boards include: should a trust board seek to expand facilities for private patients? Should a purchasing authority place more emphasis on patient choice or

---

[26] In the Irish health service the failures of the Blood Transfusion Service Board has been the subject of a major *Report of The Tribunal of Inquiry into The Blood Transfusion Service Board* (Stationery Office, Dublin, 1997); in the United Kingdom there has been a range of Reports and Codes of Conduct and Accountability issued in respect of the National Health Service, see, for example, *Taken On Board Corporate Governance in the NHS: Developing The Role of Non-Executive Directors*, Audit Commission Management Paper, (HMSO Publications, 1995)

[27] see C. Hood 'A Public Management For All Seasons?', *Public Administration*, Vol. 69, Spring 1991, pp 3–19

[28] see E. Ferlie, L. Ashburner, L. Fitzgerald 'Corporate Governance and the Public Sector: Some Issues and Evidence from the NHS' *Public Administration*, Vol. 73, Autumn 1995, p. 375; see also J. Deffenbaugh 'Understanding the Roles of NHS Trust Board Members' *Journal of Management in Medicine*, Vol. 10, No. 2, 1996, pp 54–61

on social justice . . . Should it seek to develop a more explicit rationing process? What are the relative claims of prevention, treatment and care?[29]

Alexander and Weiner have examined this 'corporate governance' approach in relation to nonprofit hospitals in the United States seeking to understand the conditions under which voluntary (or nonprofit) organizations actually undertake significant changes in its governance structure and practices. Some healthcare experts contend that traditional methods of hospital governance have become anachronistic in light of new conditions;[30] it is argued that boards must adopt a more active, critical role in strategy formulation, environmental adaptation, and monitoring of hospital management. Hence governance as practised in large profit based corporations is viewed as a model worthy of emulation in voluntary hospitals: 'Indeed, the health care literature over the past decade has drawn sharp distinctions between the corporate governance model and the philanthropic governance model traditionally associated with nonprofit hospitals'.[31] Table 4 sets out some of the key differentiating characteristics of the philanthropic and corporate governance models.

A rapidly changing health care environment necessarily raises issues of governance and management. Shortell states that 'the effectiveness of hospital boards in the future will depend on their ability to:

1) Manage a diverse group of stakeholders

2) Involve physicians in the management and governance process

3) Meet the governance needs of multi-institutional systems and hospital restructuring

4) Meet the challenges of diversification and vertical integration

5) Understand strategy formulation and implementation as interdependent and interrelated processes'[32]

Shortell explores the appropriate metaphors for hospital governance. For example he notes the 'stewardship model' which emphasises the

[29] Ferlie, Ashburner Fitzgerald, op. cit., p. 381

[30] see, Alexander, Weiner, op. cit., and for example, S.M. Shortell 'New Directions in Hospital Governance' *Hospital and Health Services Administration*, Vol. 34, No. 1, 1989, pp 7–23

[31] Alexander, Weiner 'The Adoption of the Corporate Governance Model by Nonprofit Organizations, op. cit., pp 224–5

[32] S.M. Shortell 'New Directions in Hospital Governance' *Hospital & Health Services Administration*, Vol. 34, No. 1, Spring 1989, p. 7

Table 4 Differentiating Characteristics of Philanthropic and Corporate Governance Models

Philanthropic Model		Corporate Model	
1.	Large board size	1.	Small board size
2.	Wide range of perspectives/ backgrounds	2.	Narrow, more focussed perspectives/backgrounds
3.	Small numbers of inside directors	3.	Large number of inside directors
4.	Separation of management and governance	4.	Active management participation on board
5.	Informal management accountability to board	5.	Formal management accountability to board
6.	No limit to consecutive terms	6.	Limit on consecutive terms for board members
7.	No compensation for board service	7.	Compensation for board service
8.	Emphasis on asset and mission preservation	8.	Emphasis on strategic and entrepreneurial activity

SOURCE: J.A. Alexander, L. Morlock, B. Gifford 'The Efforts of Corporate Restructuring on Hospital Policymaking', *Health Services Research*, Vol. 23, No. 2, 1988, pp 311 - 327

board's role in protecting and safeguarding the hospital's assets and which situates governance as part of 'the proverbial three-legged stool'. This refers to striking a balance of power and appropriate responsibilities among the board, management and the medical staff; frequently 'this has taken the form of the board making policy, management implementing policy, and both board and management keeping the medical staff happy'.[33] Shortell argues this model or metaphor of the past must be replaced by new models or metaphors.

A vital role for the board of a hospital in terms of governance is to position the institution for the future. Shortell notes here that

---

[33] ibid, p. 9; for description and analysis of this 'model' in Irish public hospitals based upon consultant and management interviews, see P. Brown and G. Chadwick 'Management and the Health Professional' in *Reflections on Health Commemorating Fifty Years of The Department of Health 1947–1997*, ed. J. Robins (Department of Health, Dublin, 1997), pp 189 - 209

Success will depend on (1) the ability to shape the institution's culture and values for strategic advantage (2) the ability to govern a wide range of interorganizational relationships (3) the ability to maintain trust and institutional legitimacy; and (4) the ability to understand that future success will involve balancing social and economic criteria in learning to compete on both price and quality.[34]

Until recently governance was primarily hospital focussed and internally oriented. In the future it will be health care focussed and externally oriented. Governing boards will find themselves involved in a myriad of interorganizational relationships involving various systems, alliances and networks. The board will govern complex interdependencies.[35] John Carver in his influential book *Boards That Make A Difference: A New Design for Leadership in Nonprofit and Public Organizations* first published in 1990 (second revised edition 1997) set out a new vision for governing boards. Carver reviewed the literature on boards which essentially confirms that boards do not function effectively:

> Though possessed of ultimate organizational power, the governing board is understudied and underdeveloped. Here we confront a flagrant irony in management literature: *Where opportunity for leadership is greatest, job design for leadership is poorest.*[36]

He proposed a 'new governance' design:

> A model of governance is a framework within which to organize the thoughts, activities, structure, and relationships of governing boards. A designed model yields a new nature of governance, quite unlike a collection of even wise responses to specific governance problems. What should we expect from a model?[37]

Carver says that we have a right to expect a good model of governance to

1. 'Cradle' vision
2. Explicitly address fundamental values
3. Force an external focus
4. Enable an outcome-driven organizing system
5. Separate large issues from small

---

[34] Shortell, op. cit., p. 20

[35] ibid, p. 20

[36] J. Carver *Boards That Make a Difference A New Design for Leadership in Nonprofit and Public Organizations*, Second Edition, (Jossey-Bass, San Francisco, 1997), p. 8; emphasis in original.

[37] ibid, p. 17

6. Force forward thinking
7. Enable proactivity
8. Facilitate diversity and unity
9. Describe relationships to relevant constituencies
10. Define a common basis for discipline
11. Delineate the board's role in common topics
12. Determine what information is needed
13. Balance over control and under control
14. Use board time efficiently.[38]

Carver sets out a model to overcome the 'awkward gap between the sophistication of management and the sophistication of the board. Although public and nonprofit management is not known for its rigor, it has advanced considerably in the past two decades. Governance, on the other hand, has scarcely moved at all'.[39] Locating the essence of any organization 'in what it believes, what it stands for, and what and how it values' Carver proposes that the board govern through written policies as expressions of values and perspectives.[40] The board provides policy-focussed leadership and this is the 'hallmark of governance'. This ensures for the board

- Leverage and efficiency

- Proper use of the board's capabilities

- That the fundamentals are addressed

- Opportunity to provide vision and inspiration[41]

Carver states that written values and perspectives are called policies and they occur in four catergories for the purpose of governance.[42]

1)   ENDS or 'Mission-Related Policies': policies that prescribe what benefits will occur for which people at what cost; mission and priorities are included; what good is to be done for which people at what cost?

---

[38] ibid, pp 17–18; for a similar list in the Irish context see Sean Conroy 'Governance— Where The Dream Starts and the Buck Stops' in *A Healthier Future? Managing Healthcare in Ireland*. Eds. E. McAuliffe and L. Joyce, (IPA, Dublin, 1998), pp 68–9

[39] ibid, p. 21

[40] ibid, p. 22

[41] ibid, pp 25 - 6

[42] ibid, pp 34–5

2) EXECUTIVE LIMITATIONS or 'administrative parameters': policies that describe the prudence and ethics boundaries on acceptable staff acts, practices and circumstances.

3) BOARD PROCESS: policies that clarify the board's own job and rules including how it represents the 'ownership' and provides strategic leadership to the organisation.

4) BOARD-EXECUTIVE LINKAGE: policies that describe the delegation and accountability linkage through the CEO to the executive machinery.

Carver notes that the last three are relatively stable which enables most of the board's time may be spent on 'Ends' or 'mission-related' policies. Carver argues that 'one outcome of a good governance system is that the governors are free to concentrate on the mission and on those in whose behalf the mission is pursued'.[43]

Taylor, Chait and Holland argue that the key to improving the performance of nonprofit boards is what they call 'the new work' of the board:

> The new work has four basic characteristics. First, it concerns itself with crucial, do-or-die issues central to the institution's success. Second, it is driven by results that are linked to defined timetables. Third, it has clear measures of success. Finally, it requires the engagement of the organization's internal and external constituencies.[44]

They argue that 'the new work requires new rules of engagement and unorthodox ways of fulfilling a board's responsibilities'.[45] According to their formulation the CEO and the management work with the board to agree on the institution's priorities and strategic direction annually and to structure the board's work in task forces to reflect these priorities. The board must be made 'vulnerable to constituents' and should consult experts and have expertise on the board. Together the board and management should identify 10 to 12 critical indicators of success:

---

[43] ibid, p. 180; the Carver 'policy governance model' is advocated in the Irish context by Sean Conroy 'Governance–Where the Dream Starts and the Buck Stops' in *A Healthier Future? Managing Healthcare in Ireland*, ed. E. McAuliffe and L. Joyce, (IPA, Dublin, 1998), pp 64–74

[44] B.E. Taylor, R.P. Chait and T.P. Holland 'The New Work of the Nonprofit Board', *Harvard Business Review*, September-October 1996, pp 36–46

[45] ibid, pp 36–7

In the world of the old work, the lines were clearly drawn: the board remained on the policy-setting side of the net, management on the implementation side, and so the game of governance was played. In the new work, the board and management are on the same side of the net as partners in both roles. The question is not, Is this an issue of policy or implementation? Rather the question is, Is the issue at hand important or unimportant, central or peripheral?

Taylor, Chait and Holland state that few nonprofit organizations 'can risk barring the CEO from policy development or divorcing the board from policy implementation'. Contrary to the Carver policy gover-

Table 5   Teaching an Old Board New Work

	Old Work		New Work
1.	Management defines problems, assesses options, and proposes solutions. Board listens, learns, approves, and monitors.	1.	Board and management discover issues that matter, mutually determine the agenda, and solve problems together.
2.	Board sets policy, which management implements. Respective territories are sharply defined; there is little or no border traffic. Domains are decided by organization chart.	2.	Board and management both set policy and implement it. Lines are blurred, borders open. Domains are decided by nature of issue at hand.
3.	Structure of standing committees parallels administrative functions. Premium is on permanent structure, established routines. Members occupy functional niches. Board maintains busywork.	3.	Structure of board mirrors institution's strategic priorities. Premium is on flexibility, ad hoc arrangements. Members occupy functional intersections. Board creates centers of action.
4.	Board meetings are process driven. Protocol doesn't vary. Function follows form. Emphasis is on transmission of information and reports.	4.	Board meetings are goal driven. Protocol varies with circumstances. Form follows function. Emphasis is on participation and action.
5.	Board is a collection of stars. It recruits people with an eye to expertise and status. The CEO cultivates individual relationships and exploits each trustee's talents.	5.	Board is a constellation. It recruits team members with an eye to personality and overall chemistry. Boards cultivates group norms and collective capabilities of trustees.

SOURCE: Taylor, Chait and Holland 'The New Work of the Nonprofit Board', *Harvard Business Review*, September–October 1996, p. 41

nance model they argue that 'most important matters cannot be subdivided neatly into policy or administration'.[46]

The models reviewed briefly above are described in terms of attributes that both characterise and differentiate them as ideal types.[47] Each model reflects distinctly different values and organising principles, for example, the philanthropic model stresses the values of community participation, due process and stewardship while the corporate model stresses the values of strategy development, risk taking, and competitive positioning.

These different value orientations 'are supported and reinforced by configurations of governance attributes that cohere into stable, integrated patterns, or *gestalts*'.[48] For example, the larger size, diverse membership, and absence of term limits found in the philanthropic model both support and reinforce the inclusion of a broad range of perspectives and continuity of institutional values and traditions. By contrast, the smaller size, narrower membership, and use of term limits found in the corporate model both support and reinforce a streamlined, focussed strategic decision-making process. 'Thus each model displays logical and functional interdependencies that cannot be adequately captured by focussing on a single feature of governance (for example, insider representation) or even by looking at multiple governance attributes independently of one another'.[49]

As Alexander and Weiner point out adopting the corporate governance model is not as simple as appointing a new board member or making minor adjustments to the organisation's by-laws. To fully realise the alleged advantages of the corporate governance model, many simultaneous changes would have to occur in the nonprofit board's composition, structure and activity: although 'hybrid governance configurations may be possible, logical and functional interdependencies pose problems for selectively borrowing and mixing corporate and philanthropic governance attributes'.[50]

---

[46] ibid, pp 37–40

[47] This section is based upon J.A. Alexander, B.J. Weiner 'The Adoption of the Corporate Governance Model by Nonprofit Organisations' *Nonprofit Management & Leadership*, Vol. 8, No. 3, Spring 1998, p. 225

[48] ibid, 225

[49] ibid, p. 225

[50] ibid, p. 226

Alexander and Weiner found from their analysis of 2,038 nonprofit community hospitals in USA between 1985 to 1989 'that the corporate and philanthropic models of governance are ideal types, because most hospitals exhibit hybrid combinations of the two models. What this means is less clear—On the one hand, hospitals exhibiting hybrid configurations may be attempting to strike a balance between the competing demands of the market and regulation and the community. On the other hand, hybrid governance configurations may simply reflect a transitional state between the two ideal types'.[51]

Hospital affiliation within a larger health care system may expose the hospital to corporate governance practices by virtue of its participation with a corporate-style organisation; this may facilitate the adoption of a 'corporate system' because of the importance of that system for the accountable authority and this reduces the importance of the community and its representatives.[52]

Alexander and Weiner conclude by noting that future research might examine whether nonprofit organisations that embrace the corporate governance model exhibit greater emphasis on efficiency, greater responsiveness to changing environmental conditions, or greater propensity to initiate profound organisational changes—that is, core changes in the organisations' stated goals, forms of authority, business strategies, and control systems. Such research, they note might attend to the potentially negative consequences of corporate governance practices, including the loss of community support when philanthropic values are abandoned and how quality of care and other patient-based performance standards change.

4. ORGANISATION THEORY AND THE VOLUNTARY BOARD

The various models of governance reviewed above require to be placed in the context of insights drawn from organisation theory. It is important to have an understanding of the organisational context of voluntary organisations in their wider environment before suggesting a 'usable' theoretical model for public voluntary hospitals in the Irish context. There are key insights into the context of voluntary organisations to be drawn from open systems theory, resource dependence

---

[51] ibid, p. 237

[52] ibid, p. 238

theory and institutional theory in particular.[53] Each of these theories address problems associated with the relationships between organisations and their environments. The context of Irish voluntary organisations, and in particular of public voluntary hospitals, as outlined in Part I, demonstrates the importance of the changing environment for, and the resource dependent situation of, public voluntary hospitals.

W. Richard Scott's 'open systems' definition of organisations is particularly appropriate to public voluntary hospitals in Ireland:

> Organizations are systems of interdependent activities linking shifting coalitions of participants; the systems are embedded in—dependent on continuing exchanges with and constituted by—the environment in which they operate.[54]

Since J.D. Thompson's classic work *Organisations in Action* published in 1967 it has been recognised that the design of organisations, and in particular the function of governance for organisations should be effectively aligned with environmental constraints and possibilities. The board in particular has a 'boundary spanning' function buffering the technical work and services of the organisation from uncertainties in the environment. Organisations are not self-directed and autonomous. They need resources, including money, materials, personnel and information, and to get these they must interact with others who control these resources. Interdependence may be established between organisations which have mutual dependence on each other for resources and dependence is defined by the importance of a resource controlled by one organisation for any other particular organisation. Pfeffer and Salancik identified three conditions which define how dependent an organisation is

(i) the importance of a resource to it in terms of its magnitude and 'criticality' which is best revealed by how severe the consequences would be if it were not available

(ii) how much discretion those who control a resource have over its allocation and use; if the controllers have access to it and can make the rules about it, then an organisation which needs it can be put in a highly dependent position

---

[53] see William M. Evan *Organisation Theory Research and Design* (Macmillan Publishing Co., New York, 1993) especially the overview of organisation theories, pp 1–26

[54] W. Richard Scott *Organisations Rational, Natural and Open Systems* Third Edition (Prentice-Hall, Inc., Englewood Cliffs, N.J. 1992) p. 25

(iii) how far those who control a resource have a monopoly of it or can an organisation which needs it find an alternative source or substitute?[55]

A key insight of institutional theory is that organisations are more likely to survive if they obtain legitimacy and social support from their institutional environment in which they are embedded; therefore attention should be paid to the set of norms and values which obtain in these environments.[56] The social process of interaction by which actions are repeated and given meaning by those involved is defined as the process of *institutionalization*. A particularly valuable insight of institutional theory concerns *rationalized myths*: these are widely held beliefs that cannot be objectively tested but they are true because they are believed; in other words the effect of the myths inhere, not in the fact that individuals believe them, but in the fact that they 'know' everyone else does and thus for all practical purposes the myths are true. They are *rationalized* because they take the form of rules specifying procedures necessary to accomplish a given end. These institutional belief systems powerfully shape organizational forms.[57]

J.D. Thompson's crucial insight is that it is at the *institutional* level (rather than at the *technical* or *management* levels of the organisation)— that part of the organization that relates the organization to its wider environment, determines its domain, establishes its boundaries and secures its legitimacy—that at this level the organisation must be open to its environment.[58] The Board represents the apex of this institutional level and it becomes the focus of power and legitimacy of the organisation: it is the arena within which all the competing values, interests, and perspectives are articulated, examined, and resolved into directions for the future of the organisation. In the place of lists of the formal duties of boards which are often found in the prescriptive literature on boards it is more valuable to pay attention to the key dimensions of the governance structure within which the board is the focal unit: the

[55] see J. Pfeffer and G.R. Salancik *The External Control of Organisations A Resource Dependence Perspective* (Harper & Row, New York, 1978)

[56] see brief overview of institutional theory in Evan *Organisational Theory* op. cit., pp 11–14

[57] this brief description is based upon that given in W. Richard Scott *Organizations Rational, Natural and Open Systems*, op. cit., pp 117–8

[58] see J.D. Thompson *Organisations in Action* op. cit., pp 10–13

contextual, educational, interpersonal, analytical, political and strategic dimensions have been identified.[59]

Starkweather summarises the formal functions of hospital boards derived from the 'corporate model' of organisational governance. These function or duties are similar to those attributed to boards of private business corporations:—

1. establish institutional goals and major policies

2. ensure that plans and programmes are developed to meet corporate goals

3. provide for long-range financial well-being of the hospital

4. establish and maintain a qualified and functioning medical staff

5. appoint a chief executive officer and periodically evaluate his/her performance

6. review and approve the overall organisation and the delegations of authorities within it

7. ensure that the community is well-informed concerning the hospital's goals and performance

8. establish and maintain good procedures for conducting the affairs of the board, including periodic evaluation of board performance.[60]

Starkweather notes that these are 'passive' duties with the exception of the appointment of the CEO which occurs quite infrequently: in assuming 'this passive behaviour the basic capacity of hospital boards to wield power is seldom known, tested, or exercised'.[61] This raises the question of where power lies in the hospital context. Starkweather reviews several models drawn from economics and sociology which stress some sort of hospital power coalition. These better explain the dynamics of decision making and authority than does the traditional corporate model. While these coalition type models seem to explain hospital power better in general they remain vague concerning the organisational influences of hospital boards. It is clear that hospital

[59] see T.P. Holland 'Strengthening Board Performance' in *Skills For Effective Management of Nonprofit Organizations* eds. R.L. Edwards, J.A. Yankey, M.A. Altpeter, (National Association of Social Workers, Washington, DC, 1998), pp 425–452

[60] D. Starkweather 'Hospital Board Power', *Health Services Management Research*, Vol. 1, No. 2, July 1988, p. 74; similar lists for Boards generally are found in Houle, *Governing Boards* op. cit., pp 89–94 and in *Governance & Hospital Boards Discussion Document* (Department of Health and Children, June 1999) under 'central responsibilities' pp 2 - 3

[61] ibid, p. 75

decision-making is derived from 'some sort of multi-power construct': the hospital is a 'turf' upon which separate groups or individuals play out their distinct goals and aspirations. Theory must take account of 'some sort of exchange or coalition behaviour between parties, each of which possesses some degree of organisational power'.[62] An example is Perrow's classic study of the evolution of physician-administrator-trustee influence in one hospital over a period of several decades. In an early explication of resource dependency theory, Perrow explained the changes in each group's influence in terms of the group's position relative to organisational needs: if the group controlled scarce and needed resources it rose in power. Over time the rise and fall of organisational power among sub-groups of the hospital coalition could be explained by changes in organisational levels relative to environmental resources.[63]

Mintzberg in his major study *Power In and Around Organisations* draws a major distinction between 'internal coalitions' and 'external coalitions': his work has an important focus on boards of directors. He reviews the traditional list of board functions outlined in the corporate model and systematically dismisses those 'internal coalition' functions associated with organisational policy, management and evaluation.[64] Having dismissed most of the 'corporate model' functions of boards Mintzberg offers four functions of boards that constitute a 'service role'

(i)   co-opting external influencers

(ii) establishing contacts

(iii) enhancing the organisation's reputation—to legitimise it

(iv) giving advice to the organisation

This service role of the board is seen by Mintzberg as the main function of the board which is a tool of the organisation rather than a vehicle by which power is gained over the organisation. There is a power relationship but it goes in the opposite direction than envisioned in the

---

[62] Starkweather, op. cit., p. 76

[63] see C. Perrow 'Goals and Power Structures' in *The Hospital in Modern Society*, ed. E. Freidson (The Free Press of Glencoe, New York, 1963); Barocci documents the passage of 'primary control' in the hospital coalition from trustees to physicians to professionally trained managers see T.A. Barocci *Non-Profit Hospitals: Their Structure. Human Resources, and Economic Impact*, (Boston, 1981)

[64] H. Mintzberg *Power In and Around Organizations* (Englewood Cliffs, N.J., 1983) see especially Chapter 6 'The Board of Directors', pp 67–95

corporate model of board control. The board's chief function aside from giving advice to top management, is to be used by the organisation in its various exchange needs relative to the environment.

Starkweather argues that hospital board power is an 'agreeable fiction'—agreeable 'because it is comfortable for all key organisational elements to assert.' In fact lay board members do not have the qualifications to *do* anything

> They are ostensibly in charge of very complex and often very big institutions, yet most trustees feel insecure in their roles. It is no wonder; they have little or no expertise or preparation for their positions. They are 'in charge' of corporations that deliver enormous amounts and varieties of medical care, yet they know virtually nothing about the way medical care is practised—especially clinically but also organisationally. This situation seriously erodes the real power of these directors while also giving rise to an agreeable and convenient fiction.[65]

Starkweather argues that at best hospital boards hold limited veto power. This 'agreeable fiction' of board power better explains the behaviour of boards and other key groups than do the list of official functions or responsibilities emphasised in the corporate model. Indeed, 'it could explain why these lists often seem irrelevant'.[66] However Starkweather questions 'the future of hospitals that operate on this convenient myth in the face of new and harsher circumstances' such as when funding methods place hospitals at risk for their own efficiency and effectiveness. He concludes

> Fundamentally, the amount and nature of board power is a function of the organisation's relation to its environment. If hospitals are relatively autonomous, independent or even controlling of their environment, they can 'afford' boards whose 'power' is primarily one of organisation convenience. If the organisation is strongly resource dependent then the service and linking roles of boards become important. If the environment is one that requires organisational performance then the control and evaluation functions of boards will rise.[67]

5. CONCLUSION: 'USABLE THEORY' FOR PUBLIC VOLUNTARY HOSPITALS

The essential elements of an appropriate theoretical framework for governance and management of voluntary organizations, and in particular for public voluntary hospitals, were signposted in the analysis of

---

[65] Starkweather, op. cit., p. 82

[66] ibid, p. 83

[67] ibid, p. 84

the changing context of Irish voluntary healthcare agencies in Part I. The significant conclusions in the previous chapters were

(i) that there is a lack of clarity in Irish health policy as to the definition and constitution of voluntary organisations (Chapters 1 and 2
above)

(ii) that there is no generally accepted secular public philosophy concerning either the legitimacy of voluntary action or the contribution and
role of voluntary organisations in democratic society and their
relationships with statutory bodies (Chapters 1 and 2 above; Chapter 3
sought to outline an appropriate philosophy for voluntary action
based upon active citizenship)

(iii) that this lack of clarity and the absence of an accepted philosophy as
indicated in (i) and (ii) above has resulted in the resources
exchanged between voluntary and statutory organisations being
managed through a 'dependent partnership' model and through a
'fiscal control' approach to service planning which has negative
effects on the voluntary character of the organisations involved
(Chapter 2 above)

This chapter has indicated that voluntary organisations require a
different model of governance and management than those taken
simplicitor from statutory or private sector organisations.

It has surveyed the prescriptive literature on governance and
management in order to provide a sound theoretical basis for governance and management of public voluntary hospitals in the Irish
context. In brief a 'usable theory' of governance and management
needs to account for the legitimating philosophy of voluntary organisations and to indicate how the power relationships and resource
dependent relationships in which they are necessarily involved may be
developed so as to preserve the validity of active citizenship and the
'values expressive' function of voluntary organisations. Such a theory
should also facilitate improved voluntary and statutory relationships
through more positive models and approaches based upon 'active
partnerships' as described in Chapter 2 above. The phrase 'corporate
governance' must encapsulate all the structures and processes associated with decision-making and control within an organization.
Governance is about governing and the exercise of the board's legal
right to exercise its authority over an organization; however, how a
board goes about exercising its authority—its system or process for

managing the board's affairs—is only perhaps part of what is meant by governance. The importance of power relationships in this context has become clear. Starkey has noted

> We need to understand the roots of current debates on governance in earlier debates about power—for example, in the works of Machiavelli, Hobbes, Locke, and Rousseau—and about what makes a good society/organization'.[68]

We discover that 'the essential governance question concerns the nature of power, its 'ownership', exercise and limits'.[69] It is about who should control the organization, how, and for the pursuit of what goals.[70] This question 'directs our attention to the study of behaviour at the strategic apex of organizations, in particular the roles, pattern of relationships and distribution of power and influence at board level'.[71]

W. Richard Scott brings the questions of goal setting and power together when he asks who sets the goals in organizations?[72] The most satisfactory answer is that organizational goals are set 'by a negotiation process that occurs among members of *dominant coalitions*'.[73] Goals, of course, have varying uses such as

- Serving as bases of attachment for both organizational participants and external publics

- Providing criteria for generating and selecting among alternative courses of action

- Acquiring legitimacy, allies, resources and personnel from 'organisational audiences: publics, clients, taxpayers, regulators'

- Providing a basis for evaluating the behaviour of participants or of entire organizations

[68] K. Starkey 'Opening Up Corporate Governance' *Human Relations*, Vol. 48, No. 8, 1995, p. 838

[69] ibid, pp 838–9

[70] The work of Henry Mintzberg is particularly helpful in addressing the issues relating to the determination of organizational goals, see H. Mintzberg, *Power In and Around Organizations*, op. cit., especially Part III 'Organizational Goals', pp 243 - 290

[71] E. Ferlie, L. Ashburner, L. Fitzgerald 'Corporate Governance and the Public Sector: Some Issues and Evidence from the NHS' *Public Administration*, Vol. 73, Autumn 1995, p. 375

[72] W. Richard Scott *Organizations, Rational, Natural, and Open Systems* Third Edition, (Prentice-Hall, Inc., Englewood Cliffs, N.J., 1992) Chapter II 'Goals, Power and Control', pp 284–315

[73] ibid, p. 288; this section is largely based on Scott

Goals which serve these different uses may emanate from different sources in the organization: 'Symbolic goals are likely to be promulgated at the institutional level of the organization, which seeks to legitimate organizational purposes by stressing their larger social functions'.[74] It is amongst the dominant coalition in an organisation that such 'symbolic goals' or 'strategy' is set. Scott uses 'strategy' to mean 'the determination of the basic long-range goals and objectives of an enterprise, and the adoption of courses of action and the allocation of resources necessary for carrying out these goals' where the primary focus is on external concerns: the linkage of the organization to its environment. All the groups whose interests must be taken into account and who help define these goals or strategy for the organization are members of the dominant coalition. There is a constant dynamic at work and the size and composition of the dominant coalition may vary within the same organization from time to time. In Pfeffer and Salancik's words organizations are 'settings in which groups and individuals with varying interests and preferences come together and engage in exchanges'.[75] The factors which Scott identifies as affecting the dominant coalition are based upon the different sources of power; 'as environmental conditions vary we may expect power to shift within an organization from one group to another'.[76] The concept of a dominant coalition as the agent by which organizational goals are selected and imposed highlights the linkage of power and goal setting.

A hospital is a focus for a range of relationships with other bodies which have different degrees of power over its functioning and services. As a result it becomes evident that the most appropriate metaphors for governance and management of a voluntary hospital should be drawn from seeing organisations as political systems—that what is fundamentally involved is the management of power relationships.[77] This is consistent with the shift required from operational management to strategic direction as the focus of the work of the hospital board in the future as identified by Shortell: 'the emphasis needs to be on more rapid decision making, innovation, the ability to compete, strategic direction, external focus, vision, expertise, and accountability.[78]

[74] ibid, p. 286

[75] Pfeffer and Salancik. op. cit., p. 26

[76] Scott, op. cit., p. 294

[77] see G. Morgan *Images of Organization* 2nd Edition (Sage Publications, London, 1997) especially Chapter 6 'Interests, Conflict and Power—organizations as political systems'

[78] Shortell, op. cit., p. 10

Table 6   Power Relationships at Work in Hospitals

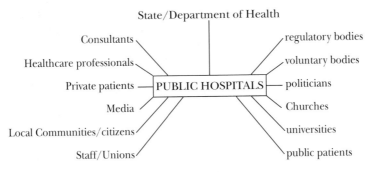

State/Department of Health

Consultants

Healthcare professionals

Private patients —— PUBLIC HOSPITALS —— politicians

Media

Local Communities/citizens

Staff/Unions

regulatory bodies

voluntary bodies

Churches

universities

public patients

To understand hospital organisations as political organisations involving a great diversity of interests (as indicated in Table 6 which shows the hospital as a 'turf' or focus for a range of groups with power over the organisation) is important in the context of developing a theory or framework for governance and management. As Morgan notes 'organisations are coalitions and are made up of coalitions, and coalition building is an important dimension of almost all organizational life'.[79] This is particularly true of public hospitals. Morgan observes that 'power is the medium through which conflicts of interest are ultimately resolved. Power influences who gets what, when, and how'.[80] Account needs to be taken of how 'outsiders' try to control the behaviour of organizations, how ideologies develop in organizations, how politics develops in organizations, how organizations reconcile conflicting goals and who wants to control the organization, why and how. Mintzberg is particularly helpful in understanding the 'external' and 'internal' coalitions which form in the attempt to exercise power and how 'configurations' of power emerge from the behaviour of these coalitions. As Mintzberg states 'If we are to improve the functioning of our organizations from within, and to gain control of them from without to ensure that they act in our best interests, then we must understand the power relationships that surround and infuse them'.[81]

[79] G. Morgan *Images of Organization*, 2nd Edition (Sage Publications, London, 1997), p. 166

[80] ibid, p. 70; Mintzberg defines power as 'the capacity to effect (or affect) organizational outcomes' *Power In and Around Organizations*, op. cit., p. 4

[81] ibid, pp 1–2

The pioneering work of Pfeffer and Salancik on the external control of organizations is especially relevant to the context in which voluntary organisations operate. Pfeffer in particular has studied hospital boards of directors in relation to their resource dependency and has found that those 'that did not structure their board consistent with their requirements for integration with the social context were less effective than those who did'.[82]

Mintzberg seeks to answer a number of fundamental questions:[83]

(i) How does the organization deal with multiple goals, or conflicting pressures?

(ii) Is the organization the *instrument* of some group-owners, society, another group—which imposes goals on it, or is the organization a *political arena* in which individuals vie for power? Or is perhaps a *system* unto itself, with its own intrinsic goals?

(iii) Has an organization a 'collective intent' or individual actors with intentions which get translated into organizational actions?

(iv) How do all the personal goals, values, intentions, needs, and expectations of the individual actors, get translated into organizational decisions and actions? How are the needs and power of the individual actors linked to organizational actions.

In simple terms Mintzberg sees organizational behaviour as 'a power game' in which various actors, 'influencers', seek to control the organization's decisions and actions; how they succeed determines what configuration of organizational power emerges. Thus to understand the behaviour of, say a hospital, it is necessary to understand which 'influencers' are present, what needs each seeks to fulfil in the hospital, and how each is able to exercise power to fulfil them. Essentially 'the influencer' requires some source or basis of power, a commitment to use it and skill in using it.

The general bases of power reflects some *dependency* that the organization has: an 'influencer' may control a resource, a technical skill or a body of knowledge which may be critical to the organization. An 'influencer' may have a basis of power stemming from legal prerogatives—exclusive rights or privileges to impose choices or may have access to those with a basis of power which may allow for favours to be traded on a *reciprocal* basis.

---

[82] see J. Pfeffer and G.R. Salancik, *The External Control of Organizations A Resource Dependence Perspective*, (Harper & Row, New York, 1978), p. 174

[83] Mintzberg, op. cit., pp 20–21

Given that governance of voluntary organizations concerns the exercise of power by 'active citizens' and the expression of values a 'usable theory' for board governance must take account of both these crucial aspects and the fundamental questions posed by Mintzberg. A generally accepted public philosophy and a clear public policy concerning the legitimacy of voluntary organisations in the provision of public services is essential to create an appropriate voluntarist context in which answers might be provided to Mintzberg's questions and in which 'influencers' operate to shape the organisation. A promising route into how such governance theory might be conceptualised for voluntary citizens who serve on boards is the argument of Jeavons that those responsible for governance in voluntary organizations should pay attention to 'the original meaning of stewardship'.[84] The service of board members and indeed the managers of such organizations needs to be marked by a quality of 'servanthood'—the application of the philosophy of service in the practice of leadership—as indicated in Robert K. Greenleaf's pioneering work on leadership in the 1970s and 1980s.[85] With these concepts of 'stewardship' and 'servanthood' the board of a voluntary organization will have as its first concern the welfare of others—those their organizations serve and those who serve in them. The second concern of the board will be for all aspects of the organization's life and mission: both boards members and staff 'must be concerned that the values central to their organization's mission are reflected in every facet of its operation'.[86] Boards of voluntary organisations need to reconceptualise their functions in terms of their service roles especially as vehicles for effective exchanges with the changing environment in which their organisations must now function.

A 'usable theory' of governance and management in Irish public voluntary hospitals will be built upon a number of key elements in particular the realities of power relationships and the resource dependent environmental context in which they operate as described above. It will be necessary 'to talk about democracy' contrary to Houle's remark quoted above; voluntary boards may be 'the living

---

[84] T.H. Jeavons 'Stewardship Revisited: Secular and Sacred Views of Governance and Management', *Nonprofit and Voluntary Sector Quarterly*, Vol. 23, No. 2, Summer 1994, p. 108

[85] see R.K. Greenleaf, *The Power of Servant Leadership*, ed. L.C. Spears (Barrett-Koehler Publishers, San Francisco, 1998) and *Reflections on Leadership How Robert K Greenleaf's Theory of Servant-Leadership Influenced Today's Top Management Thinkers*, ed. L.C. Spears (John Wiley, New York, 1995)

[86] Jeavons, 1994, op. cit., p. 120

proof of democracy' as Houle noted, but the future of such boards in the Irish context will depend upon the articulation and acceptability of a new legitimacy based upon the concept of the active citizen fulfilling social obligations in a pluralist democracy. This may be perceived as a 'rationalised myth', as described above, but such beliefs are profoundly important for civil society. The work of a voluntary board is in effect a service: the carrying out of responsible community ownership by committed, active voluntary citizenship and through such participation diverse values may be expressed and supported. The theoretical perspective must recognise that hospitals operate in an increasingly complex and demanding environment and that the 'lay wisdom' which citizens bring to governance will be crucial in the taking of fair, proportionate and responsive decisions in relation to health care. There is, of course, a clear need for the comprehensive education of voluntary board members and for standards in relation to board development and education to be applied. Public accountability is entirely consistent with the concept of voluntary board governance.[87] The public voluntary hospital board of the future is likely to be the product of a conscious design in contrast to the inherited philanthropic system of the past. In this way such future boards may well be 'hybrids' embracing features of the available 'models' to fit particular organisations or stages in the development of the organisation. All Boards will be more effective if they are subject to regular review and evaluation.

In relation to these consciously designed systems of governance two features will be especially important

(i)   The governance structures will embrace the Board but will encompass not only effective linkages with the CEO and the executive management but also key alliances and partnerships with other actors in the environment of the organisation

(ii) The voluntary board will have to adopt positive strategies to deal with their resource dependence upon the statutory health authorities. Such strategies might include

(a) adapting to the constraints imposed because they are for the common good; effective voluntary boards will accept that they have a primary responsibility to develop and maintain healthy relationships among major constituencies and to recognise the

---

[87] 'The Standards for Governing Bodies' used in Canadian healthcare provide a set of governance standards which might be applicable to both voluntary and statutory boards, see Appendix 'Accreditation Standards for the Governing Bodies of Hospitals' issued by the Canadian Council on Health Facilities Accreditation, pp 307-321 below

legitimate roles and responsibilities of other stakeholders and to avoid win—lose polarizations as far as possible.

(b) proposals actively pursued to persuade the public authorities to alter these constraints or to develop resourcing in a more favourable format. Voluntary boards to be effective must focus upon envisioning a direction and a shape to the strategic future of their organizations and contribute actively to the policies and approaches of the statutory authorities.

(c) building upon the interdependencies of health care organisations through mergers, alliances, consortia, joint ventures which facilitate the achievement of the goals of the public voluntary hospital to provide optimum health care for those they serve.

(d) seeking to change the legal framework or legitimacy of the environment by political action when required if not conducive to the values of voluntary governance.

Voluntary hospital boards will focus particularly on the organisation's mission, values and traditions to guide their decisions and they must act so as to exemplify and reinforce the organisation's core values and commitments. Voluntary hospital boards will be required to attain quality performance through the application of the highest standards of board governance.

The key element of a 'usable theory' for the future of voluntary hospital boards is clarity about how such boards add value to their hospitals and to health care generally. Voluntary boards add value by providing an independent citizen voice in determining the most effective use of public resources. Such boards can add enormously to the process of identifying and examining the most significant issues facing the organization from the patients (or potential users of the services) perspective. They can provide the necessary support for the CEO and management to encourage experimentation, trying out new approaches and alternative ways of dealing with issues; by helping to 'get outside the box' of old assumptions and patterns and constantly questioning the uniformity of approach which has to be a characteristic of statutory bodies. Voluntary board members precisely because they are *voluntary* model the behaviour of selfless commitment and care in the leadership of hospital staff who are devoted to such qualities of care. This provides the opportunity to evoke similar responses from both staff and voluntary supporters. This disinterested voluntary character provides the moral authority of the Board to recognise and reward in the hospital high quality contributions to care.

158

A board's influence is 'dictated by the circumstances of power in and around the organization': a board can play various roles 'some related to control and others to service of one kind or another'.[88] Mintzberg and others have shown that the 'real power' of a board often amounts to very little.[89] As Mintzberg argues 'if the board as a device to control the organization turns out to be weaker than is generally imagined, as a device to serve the organization, it turns out to be more useful'.

Table 7, over page, provides a summary of the 'usable theory' presented here for voluntary governance based on the four key elements discussed; power, environment/resource dependence, participatory democracy and board design, by way of asking the central questions which have arisen from the review of the prescriptive literature. The questions require to be answered in practical ways by *both* voluntary and statutory agencies.

In conclusion Mintzberg might be quoted in seeking to 'untangle' the roles of the board:

> In principle we have been able to distinguish the four service roles of the board from each other and from the three control roles [selecting the CEO, exercising direct control during periods of crisis, reviewing managerial decisions and performance]. Efforts to exercise power can flow into the organization from directors intent on controlling it, out of the organization to the directors it tries to co-opt, or in neither direction as directors are simply engaged to serve the organization by developing contacts or raising funds for it, helping to enhance its reputation, or providing it with advice. But in practice, how is one to know which role is really operative? Indeed, how can one distinguish, say control from co-optation, or advice from contacts, when two or more roles can very well operate concurrently? In other words, at the margins the real purposes of the directors can be very subtly intertwined, discernible if at all only through intensive study of the actual behaviour of board members.[90]

The case study which follows in the next chapter will focus upon the 'actual behaviour' of one set of board members as they addressed issues of governance and management in a public voluntary hospital in Ireland in the 1990s.

---

[88] Mintzberg, op. cit., p. 70

[89] Mintzberg concludes: 'when a board does indeed have control, its real power amounts to the capacity to dismiss and appoint the chief executive officer–and to the CEO's knowledge of that fact. That is all', op. cit., p. 78

[90] Mintzberg, op. cit., p. 86

Table 7   'Usable Theory' For Governance and Management of Voluntary Organisations— Key Questions on Four Elements

I.   POWER

    i.   Do 'active citizens' serving in an independent voluntary capacity form the 'dominant coalition' on the board and/or in the organisation which sets the goals and strategy of the organisation?

    ii. Does the board maintain internal and external focus on the voluntary mission, values and character of the organisation?

II.   ENVIRONMENT/RESOURCE DEPENDENCY

    i.   Does public policy embrace clarity about the legitimacy of voluntary organisations in service provision?

    ii. Do the 'active citizens' involved in governance serve the welfare of others through effective 'stewardship' and 'servant leadership'?

    iii. Has the voluntary board positive strategies in place to relate effectively with statutory authorities and with other organisations in their environment?

    iv. Are the statutory authorities prepared to develop 'active partnership' with citizen based voluntaristic boards?

III.   PARTICIPATORY DEMOCRACY

    i.   Is the concept of the 'active citizen' fulfilling social obligations in a pluralist democracy fully accepted as a means of governing organisations delivering public services?

    ii. Is the voluntary board aware that it 'adds value' by providing 'lay wisdom'—an independent 'citizen voice'—in determining the most effective use of public resources in the interests of those receiving the services?

IV.   BOARD DESIGN

    i.   Is the voluntary board structure the result of conscious design and subject to regular review and evaluation in order to attain the highest standards of board governance?

    ii. Do the governance structures involve effective linkages between the board and the CEO (and through CEO with senior management)?

CHAPTER 5

A Case Study: The Adelaide and Meath Hospital, Dublin, Incorporating The National Children's Hospital 1996-1999

'Boards of directors are hard to study. Often they conduct their business in secret; their members are busy people; the processes themselves are sometimes most effectively described by novelists. Nevertheless, study is possible, and pieces of evidence can be brought to bear. The difficulty of study is more than compensated for by the theoretical and practical importance of the problem.'

MAYER N. ZALD 'The Power and Functions of Boards of Directors: A Theoretical Synthesis', *American Journal of Sociology*, Vol. 75, No. 1, July 1969, p. 110

1. INTRODUCTION

The focus of this case study is the Board of the Adelaide and Meath Hospital Dublin, Incorporating the National Children's Hospital from 1 August 1996 to 31 July 1999.[1] This period covers the term of office of the first Board of the newly merged Hospital which was composed of three base hospitals: The Meath Hospital, founded in 1753, The National Children's Hospital, founded in 1821 and The Adelaide Hospital, founded in 1839.

This Board necessarily had to address governance and management structures in a public voluntary hospital and to oversee the remove of the three old city centre hospitals to a new single campus at Tallaght, Co. Dublin. This remove occurred on 21 June 1998. The Hospital was the single largest healthcare project undertaken by the State since independence and also the first new public voluntary hospital, resulting from a merger, built by State funds governed by a Charter rather than under a statutory instrument based upon the Health (Corporate Bodies) Act 1961. The Charter was formative and fundamental in the story of the first Board which provides what Stake has termed an 'instrumental case study': this particular case provides insight into the voluntary and statutory issues examined in this research study and will assist in the refinement of the theories concerning governance and management of voluntary organisations.[2]

A case study is an empirical inquiry that investigates a contemporary phenomenon within its 'real life context' when the boundaries between the phenomenon and the context are not very clearly evident and where multiple sources of evidence are used.[3] The contemporary phenomenon investigated in this case study is the first Board of The Adelaide and Meath Hospital, Dublin, Incorporating The National Children's Hospital from 1996 to 1999. This Board provides a 'real-life context' in which to seek answers to the questions underlying this study: is there a convincing philosophical justification for voluntary

[1] The Charter of The Adelaide and Meath Hospital, Dublin, Incorporating The National Children's Hospital took effect on 1 August 1996; it stated that 'All the powers of the Hospital shall be vested in and exercisable by the Board' (Clause (25)(1)) and that 'The general function of the Board shall be to manage the activities of the Hospital and the services provided by it' (Clause (12)(2)). The Board serves a three year term of office.

[2] see Robert E. Stake 'Case Studies' in *Handbook of Qualitative Research*, eds, N.K. Denzin and G.S. Lincoln (Sage, London, 1994), p. 237

[3] Robert K Yin *Case Study Research Design and Methods* (Revised edition, Sage Publications, London, 1989), p. 23

service provision and, if so, does this justification have implications for the governance and management of voluntary organisations? The case study may provide such 'answers' through examination of the effects or the implications, if any, of the conclusions which have emerged from the analysis of the historical background, the current policy context in respect of voluntary and statutory relationships in health care and from the exploration of the literature concerning board governance and organisation theory.

The case study traces the development of the Charter of the Hospital before 1996 to show how a voluntary organisation was conceived as the means of the expression of a particular set of values in health care and how the normative framework for the voluntary management of the new Hospital was approved by the Oireachtas. This is followed by an outline of how the new voluntary Board addressed governance and management under the Charter with reference to the models discussed in the previous chapter. The case study then traces in considerable detail how the resource dependency of the Board led to divergences from the Charter framework of governance and management through an experience of a very public financial crisis in which the Board effectively lost full control of its own work and future development. The approach of the Report of the consultants (appointed to address the financial issues) to the governance and management of the Hospital is assessed and the case study concludes with a discussion in respect of the experiences of the Board in the light of the previous conclusions drawn from the context and the literature.

2. THE DEVELOPMENT OF THE CHARTER

The Charter of the The Adelaide and Meath Hospital Dublin, Incorporating The National Children's Hospital, which took legal effect on 1 August 1996 was the result of extensive amendments to the Royal Charter of The Adelaide Hospital, Dublin. The Oireachtas approved these amendments in the Health Act, 1970 (Section 76) (Adelaide and Meath Hospital, Dublin, Incorporating The National Children's Hospital) Order 1996. This Order was facilitated by the Health (Amendment) (No. 2) Act, 1996. These statutory measures received all party support in both Seanad Éireann and Dáil Éireann in June and July 1996.

There was a long, and often controversial, prelude to this agreement on the Charter for the new Hospital in Tallaght. From the late 1980s discussions began concerning the future governance and management of the new Hospital at Tallaght which was to incorporate the Adelaide, Meath and National Children's Hospitals. The text of the amendments to the Adelaide Charter resulted from detailed discussions which took place in a Working Party established by the Minister for Health in 1990. The Working Party was chaired by Mr. David Kingston, Chief Executive, Irish Life and Professor David Kennedy, a management consultant and former Chief Executive of Aer Lingus. The Working Party was composed of representatives of the three Hospitals and it produced 'Heads of Agreement' which were approved by the Boards of the Hospitals in May 1993. Following Government acceptance of the 'Heads of Agreement' the Working Party produced a draft text of the Charter, based upon the 'Heads of Agreement' which was approved by the Boards of the three Hospitals in August 1995. The final text of the Charter, as expressed in the Order as laid before the Oireachtas, was based upon this draft text as advised by the Attorney-General and approved by Government.

The Charter of the Hospital was therefore the product of long and detailed consideration by the principal stakeholders in the new Hospital who each gave their approval to it. It received democratic approval in the Oireachtas in 1996. The Charter, therefore, provides the agreed legal framework for governing and managing this public voluntary hospital and embraces the values and ethos which were approved following detailed discussions and negotiations. These will be described below in some detail as necessary background to the case study. The Charter provides the benchmark against which the experiences of the first Board from 1 August 1996 to 31 July 1999 will be evaluated.

This background is important as it describes how a voluntary hospital, The Adelaide Hospital, with a deep commitment to a particular set of values, struggled to achieve a voluntary board management structure for the new Hospital in order to sustain the characteristics associated with voluntary action and a particular expression of values into the future. It provides the context for, and an insight into, the resonance of the Charter for the new Hospital.

The essence of the prehistory of the Charter as approved in 1996 concerned the future of the Adelaide Hospital particularly from the late 1980s. The then Chairman of the Meath Hospital, Cllr. Gerry Brady, has obsrved that the Meath Hospital did not see themselves as 'a voluntary hospital' in the same way as did the Adelaide Hospital: 'It wasn't a concept in the same way as I hear it now in the Board of the new Hospital. It was a Hospital that provided a service dependent on the Department of Health for money . . .'[4] With the rapid sequence of closures of voluntary hospitals associated with the Protestant community in the 1980s (such as Sir Patrick Dun's, Dr. Steeven's, Mercer's, Royal City of Dublin, Monkstown and Barrington's Hospital (Limerick), the Adelaide by 1989 remained the last voluntary teaching Hospital in the State under Protestant management. The Adelaide Hospital was governed by a Royal Charter of 1921 which stated that the Hospital was 'a religious and essentially Protestant institution'. Since 1961, under an Act establishing the Federated Dublin Voluntary Hospitals, it had an increasingly close association, through a Central Council of the Federation, with the Meath Hospital and the National Children's Hospital which were physically close to the Adelaide Hospital's location at Peter Street.

The Meath Hospital and County Dublin Infirmary represented a hybrid of different traditions in Irish hospital care.[5] Founded in 1753 it had long been governed, under an 1815 Private Act of Parliament, by a Board of Governors or Joint Committee as it was called. The 'golden age' of the Hospital had occurred in the nineteenth century when a succession of famous doctors made it a great centre of teaching and research during the period of Dublin's international medical fame. The Hospital had been constituted as the County Dublin Infirmary under an Act of the Irish Parliament in 1774 and this Act conferred on the medical staff the privilege of appointing their successors. There was a long connection with local government in the Meath through grants received as the County Infirmary. In 1949 there was a concerted effort organised by the Knights of Columbanus, a Catholic lay organisation, to oust the old predominantly Protestant Joint Committee. This led to legal and political controversy which ultimately resulted in the Meath Hospital Act, 1951. This Act removed the power of the medical staff of appointing their successors and set out a very substantial proportion of public representation in the composition of the new Joint Committee (or Board) of 23 as follows: Dublin County Council 6; General Council of County Councils 2; Dublin Corporation 6; Medical Board 4; Hospital Corporation (Meath Society of Governors and Governesses) 4 and 2 co-options. Since this period the Hospital, while interdenominational in

---

[4] Interview with Mr. Gerry Brady, 9 June 1999

[5] this brief account is based upon Peter Gatenby's recent history *Dublin's Meath Hospital 1753–1996* (Town House, Dublin, 1996) especially Ch. 13 'The Advance of the Knights, 1949–50'

character, assumed a more Catholic tone than it had in its previous long history as a Protestant led voluntary hospital; this widened the gap to be bridged in any merger with the Protestant ethos of the Adelaide Hospital in the 1990s.

The National Children's Hospital was founded in 1821 as the first teaching children's hospital in Ireland or Britain and it was governed by a lay voluntary Board; it took the legal form of a charitable company under the Companies Acts. The National Children's Hospital's background was similar to that of the Adelaide and it was perceived as a focus for Protestant participation in paediatric services as the only other children's hospitals in Dublin were under Catholic auspices.

The purpose of the 1961 Act establishing the Federated Dublin Voluntary Hospitals was to provide a framework for the eventual amalgamation of the seven relatively small teaching hospitals associated with the Medical School at Trinity College, Dublin into one major modern voluntary university teaching hospital. Four of the seven hospitals (Baggot Street, Sir Patrick Dun's, Mercer's and Dr. Steeven's) eventually closed and their services were combined to form St. James's Hospital which was governed by a Board appointed by the Minister for Health under the Health (Corporate Bodies) Act 1961. This left the Adelaide, Meath and National Children's Hospitals to form the new Hospital first proposed for Tallaght in 1977. These three hospitals were in the Federation and shared some common aspects such as common consultant appointments but they were not institutionally amalgamated until 1 August 1996.

In 1980 the task of planning the new Hospital at Tallaght was now given to the Central Council of the Federation but to a new Tallaght Hospital Planning Board established by a Statutory Order under the Health (Corporate Bodies) Act, 1961. As one key actor in the Adelaide Hospital, Professor David McConnell later noted this 'was a clear signal that powerful interests intended that the new hospital would not be managed as a 'voluntary hospital''.[6] Further evidence of the official intention to govern the new Hospital in a similar way to St. James' Hospital and Beaumont Hospital (opened in 1987), that is, by a Board

---

[6] see D. McConnell 'Regions and Minorities–The Adelaide Hospital–the last Protestant general teaching hospital in the Republic of Ireland' in *Culture in Ireland–Regions: Identity and Power* Proceedings of the Cultures of Ireland Group Conference, 27–29 November 1992, ed. P. O'Drisceoil (The Institute of Irish Studies, The Queen's University of Belfast 1993) p. 132

appointed by the Minister for Health under the 1961 Act, is provided by the long serving civil servant Brendan Hensey in his book on the Irish Health Services where this is stated.[7]

The new Planning Board, which remained in existence through the period of the first Board of the Hospital, 1996–1999, (it remains in existence as of March 2000) is an important element in the story of the first Board as it retained responsibility for commissioning, building and equipping the new Hospital at Tallaght.

The building of the new Hospital was delayed for many years. Following a major architectural competition in 1985 architects were appointed.[8] In 1988 discussions commenced on the future management structure for the new Hospital. The Adelaide Hospital proposed that it should be a 'public voluntary hospital' governed by an independent board with a continuing role in management for the Adelaide Hospital Society which managed the Adelaide Hospital under its Charter.[9]

In November and December 1988 the Department of Health proposed to amalgamate the management structures of the Meath, Adelaide and National Children's Hospitals in such a way that the hospitals would have lost their voluntary status and would have been dissociated from Trinity College, Dublin. The Department persisted in pressing their proposal and withheld notification of the 1989 financial allocation to the Adelaide for six months. This led to a public controversy and the direct involvement in the Adelaide Hospital's future of the Church leaders from the main Protestant churches. At this period the Adelaide contemplated a minority role on the proposed new voluntary Hospital Board as sufficient to ensure a continuation of its tradition and ethos. This stance changed in the controversies which ensued from 1989 to 1993. According to Professor David McConnell 'it learned in the next two years that there was substantial opposition to the Adelaide tradition—minority representation for the minority on

---

[7] B. Hensey *The Health Services of Ireland* 4th Edition, (Institute of Public Administration, Dublin, 1988) p. 121

[8] see *Tallaght Hospital Architectural Competition* ed. Neil Steedman (Tallaght Hospital Board, n.d. [1986]

[9] in November 1977 when the Board of the Adelaide Hospital agreed to move to the proposed new Hospital with the Meath Hospital it was 'on terms which would be acceptable to the Board with the constraint imposed on it by the Royal Charter of the Hospital'; see D. Mitchell A *'Peculiar' Place The Adelaide Hospital, Dublin, 1839–1989* (Blackwater Press [1989]) pp 227–8

the board of the new Hospital came to look more like a prescription for slow extinction'.[10]

From late 1988, then, the Adelaide Hospital faced severe financial and political pressure in order to amalgamate with the Meath and National Children's Hospital on the terms proposed by the Department of Health. There was an accumulated deficit of about IR£1 million by the end of 1988. The Minister for Health, Dr. Rory O'Hanlon, T.D., made it clear that unless the hospitals amalgamated there would be no approved allocation for 1989. He also sought to alter the structure of the Central Council of the Federation and to remove the right of Trinity College to nominate members to the Council and to replace the Chairman, Dr. Watts, then Provost of Trinity College.

During 1989 these pressures were resisted in a vigorous public debate and in private negotiations. A formal allocation was agreed in the middle of 1989. The proposal to change Central Council was dropped and there was further discussion of the formal amalgamation of the three hospitals.[11] A meeting between the Protestant Church leaders and An Taoiseach, Mr. Haughey, in September 1989 led to a positive response from Mr. Haughey who stated that he would wish to see the ethos represented by the Adelaide Hospital maintained 'as an integral part of the hospital system' and he asked the Church leaders to invite the Board of the Adelaide Hospital 'to present to the Department of Health a detailed plan of what they would regard as the most advantageous future for the Adelaide Hospital'.[12]

The Board of the Adelaide Hospital proposed that it play a significant and determining role in running a major teaching hospital and that it would welcome an invitation to run the new Hospital at Tallaght and believed it could provide for appropriate participation by the

---

[10] McConnell, 'Regions and Minorities' op. cit. p. 133

[11] during 1989 there was considerable media coverage of the Adelaide Hospital issue and the issue was raised at the Church of Ireland Synod, the Presbyterian General Assembly and Methodist Conference in May and June of that year; the editorial in *The Irish Times* 1 June 1989 and the article in *The Belfast Telegraph* 7 July 1989 entitled 'The Republic's 'Mater'' give the flavour of the public debate.

[12] McConnell 'Regions and Minorities', op. cit., p. 136; the financial situation was unrelieved and the Archbishop of Dublin, Most Rev. Dr. D. Caird, D.D. and the Chairman of the Hospital met with the Taoiseach, Mr. Haughey, in January 1990 to discuss the financial situation and the crisis was partly relieved; a further crisis developed in 1991 and 1992 and the Board of the Adelaide experienced the financial pressure as an attempt by the Department of Health to close the Hospital as had been experienced in the case of other hospital closures such as Dr. Steevens, Barrington's Hospital and Monkstown Hospital.

Meath and National Children's Hospitals in the new institution: there should, it felt, be one major voluntary hospital in the State managed with significant Protestant participation. There was no formal reply to the proposal.

The public debate continued in 1990.[13] The Minister for Health, Dr. O'Hanlon, established a Working Group, chaired by Mr. David Kingston, Chief Executive of Irish Life, to 'consider possible future management arrangements for the new public voluntary hospital with nursing school at Tallaght'. The Terms of Reference set out by the Minister for Health asked the Working Party to consider four management options:

- A management board established under the Health (Corporate Bodies) Act 1961

- A management board established under primary legislation providing for the establishment of a new public voluntary hospital

- A management board operating under an adapted Adelaide charter

- A management board established under the Companies Act

The proposals were to be based upon 'the premise that the traditions and emphases of the three hospitals are valuable and must be given expression in the management arrangements for Tallaght . . . In particular, the position of the Adelaide as a focus for Protestant participation in the health services and its particular denominational ethos must be continued in Tallaght'.[14]

The Working Group had members from each of the three hospitals. The Working Group chaired first by Mr. David Kingston and then jointly by Professor David Kennedy and Mr. Kingston continued its work until 1995 when it eventually produced an agreed draft amended Adelaide Charter. However, there were many delays along the way especially in May 1991 when the Meath Hospital Board rejected what had been agreed in the Working Group: a new board composed of 5 from the Adelaide, 4 from the Meath, 3 from the National Children's and 1 from Trinity College. Goodwill was undermined and the Adelaide resolved that the minority would require much stronger safeguards given the opposition to the May 1991 proposals.

---

[13] see for examples *The Irish Times* 19 May 1990; Seanad Éireann, debate, 1 May 1990

[14] Terms of Reference for The Kingston Working Group from The Minister for Health, Dr. O'Hanlon, July 1990; the Group was asked to submit its Report by 31 October 1990

Meanwhile the Government in 1992 asked Professor David Kennedy and a Committee to review the Tallaght Hospital Project. This resulted in a scaling down of the original planning brief of the Hospital from over 700 to 513 beds and this was to leave a critical and vexed agenda for the new Hospital Board in respect of bed numbers, car-parking, and inadequate accommodation. The downgrading was in response to the inability or unwillingness of the Government to fund the original plans. It was perceived by some as an attempt to jettison the concept of a teaching hospital at Tallaght. In 1992 the Minister for Health, Dr. John O'Connell, invited the Adelaide Hospital to withdraw from the Tallaght project; however the Adelaide Hospital's position both in respect of the Kennedy Review Committee and of the Government's invitation to withdraw was to give strong support for the full Tallaght Hospital project as a second major teaching hospital of the Faculty of Health Sciences at Trinity College, Dublin, and especially to support the large paediatric unit to be provided by the National Children's Hospital. This was and remained under specific threat and surfaced as a critical item on the agenda of the new Board in late 1998 and 1999 due to further attempts to reorganise paediatric services in Dublin.

It is important to identify the values which were expressed during the struggle about the future of the new Hospital as these values remained central to the contested territory of the new Board from 1996 even though they were enshrined in the Charter of the Hospital. The struggle was to develop and agree a voluntary management structure for the new Hospital so as to facilitate and safeguard the expression of these values in healthcare. The Charter was the formal means of agreeing the character and objects of the Hospital and the Board of Management was to be constructed to insure that the agreed goals and values of the Hospital would remain consistent with the formal statements in the Charter. Charles Perrow has made an important distinction between 'official' goals and 'operative' goals—the latter are the actual goals pursued by the organisation as revealed in operating policies and routine or critical decisions rather than what is officially set forth in authoritative public pronouncements such as the Charter.[15] Statements of the formal values and the agreement of the management structure had only resulted in the 'Heads of Agreement' of 1993 after a further financial crisis experienced by the Adelaide Hospital during

[15] see the pioneering case study of a Hospital in Charles Perrow 'Goals and Power Structures: A Historical Case Study' in *The Hospital in Modern Society* ed. Eliot Freidson (The Free Press of Glencoe, New York, 1963) p. 114

1992. Events to be outlined will demonstrate that the voluntary concept was less than wholeheartedly accepted by key actors in the ensuing drama surrounding the new Board's work.

On 11 May 1992 the Board of the Adelaide Hospital brought its case before the public at a Press Conference stating that 'large forces seem to be massed against the Adelaide' preventing a solution in relation to the new Hospital planned for Tallaght. The Adelaide Hospital Board were also prompted to make its case very public by what it described as 'systematic and sustained underfunding of the Hospital'. The use of financial resourcing of the Hospital as an instrument of policy by the Department in relation to future management structures had occurred in 1988 and 1989 in a very overt fashion and now in May 1992 the Adelaide Hospital described in detail the 'underfunding' in 1990, 1991 and for 1992.[16] At this time the seeds were sown for jaundiced perceptions of the funding provided for the new Board by the Department of Health. It was an anticipation of what was to occur in late 1998 '. . . the fact was that the hospital lost confidence in the Government in late 1991, leading to the Press conference of May'.[17] The Press Statement released by the Adelaide in May 1992 noted that in 1988 it had opened discussion 'on the important general principle that newly established state services might be run by voluntary agencies'.[18] The publicity which surrounded this unprecedented Press Conference (it was the first in the history of the Adelaide Hospital) brought immediate pressure on the Minister for Health and the Government. At the Church of Ireland Synod which shortly followed the Press Conference there occurred what was described as 'an emotion charged debate' on the future of the Adelaide Hospital.[19] The Primate, The Most Rev. Dr. Robin Eames observed that his 'blood boiled' when he saw what was being done to 'this great institution'; he contrasted the treatment of the minority community in the Republic 'with the way in which the minority community in Northern Ireland was being treated over the Mater Hospital'. In the debate Archdeacon

[16] The Adelaide Hospital was allocated £9.139 million for 1992 which was actually less than the Hospital had spent in 1991 and considerable staff lay offs were threatened, see detailed Press Statement by the Chairman, Professor David McConnell to Press Conference, 11 May 1992, in '1992 file' in Adelaide Hospital Society.

[17] D. McConnell, 'Regions and Minorities', op. cit., p. 153

[18] see detailed Press Statement by the Chairman, Professor David McConnell to Press Conference, 11 May 1992 in '1992 file' in Adelaide Hospital Society

[19] *The Church of Ireland Gazette*, 29 May 1992

Gordon Linney, a member of the Board of the Adelaide Hospital, said that the Adelaide 'was being edged out' of the health services as he had warned might happen at a previous Synod in 1989 when he referred to the 1988-89 attempt 'to break the Hospital' by the Department of Health. He went on to state the value of 'inclusiveness' in the provision of services in these terms:

> It is about the attitude of the State to a responsible minority willing to play its part in the national life. It is an opportunity here in the Republic to demonstrate how different strands and traditions can be listened to and accommodated. If we fail it will not just be the end of a great institution but a major blow to the credibility of Irish Nationalism as a comprehensive and tolerant movement. Many are watching and waiting.[20]

The Adelaide Hospital obtained an understanding from the Government that it would continue 'as a voluntary public teaching hospital with a nursing school' and that it would 'continue to act as a focus for Protestant participation in the health service, in such a way that its particular denominational ethos will be continued'.[21] It was stressed at a subsequent meeting with the Minister for Health on 21 July 1992 that 'the bottom line' was whether or not the Protestant community could be accommodated in a meaningful way in health care in Ireland. This could only be achieved through a genuinely voluntary basis for the governance and management of the new Hospital.

At the heart of any such accommodation through voluntary structures lay medical ethics: Professor Ian Graham, then Secretary of the Medical Board of the Adelaide Hospital, interviewed on 'Today at Five', the main evening radio news programme on RTE Radio 1 on 11 May 1992 stated that 'we would hope that the ethos of the Board of the new Tallaght Hospital will be inclusive and liberal'.[22] Professor David McConnell stated in an interview:

> We do not have much outward symbolism of religion in the hospital because we see religious belief as a private matter. Our ethics are based on very widely accepted Judeo-Christian principles combined with a respect for the differences in the belief of our patients and our staff. We care for each person as an individual and we try to let our patients know that.[23]

[20] ibid

[21] see, for example, agenda for meeting with Dr. John O'Connell, Minister for Health, 19 May 1992 in '1992 file' in Adelaide Hospital Society.

[22] see transcript of radio interview on subject of the Adelaide Hospital, 11 May 1992 in '1992 file' in the Adelaide Hospital Society

[23] see 'This Thing Called Ethos: What exactly does the Adelaide Hospital mean when it talks about 'ethos" in *The Consultant*, February 1993, p. 22

The medical ethics propounded by the Adelaide centred upon the privacy of the doctor/patient relationship which was based upon the importance of the individual's personal responsibility and upon freedom of conscience. In contrast to hospitals run by the Catholic Church or religious orders, where any procedures forbidden by the written ethical code of the Catholic Church could not be performed, the Adelaide wished to provide all medically required services which are legal in the State.[24]

As a result of sustained pressure and popular support at local meetings in various parts of Ireland political commitments were obtained in the General Election of November 1992 particularly from the Labour Party to support the Adelaide Hospital's future. In the Fianna Fáil-Labour Government's *Programme* agreed after the Election there was an explicit commitment to the future of the Adelaide's ethos in the new Hospital. Labour T.D. Mr. Brendan Howlin became Minister for Health. He was, of all the Ministers of Health which had dealt with the issue to date, at once the most sympathetic and the most effective in securing both an agreed management structure and the actual building of the new Hospital.

By May 1993 the Working Party, established in 1990, produced the 'Heads of Agreement', previously referred to, which were approved by the Boards of the three Hospitals. This Agreement was publicly welcomed and endorsed by the new Government which had come into office in late 1992. The 'Heads of Agreement' provided for governing the new Hospital under an amended Adelaide Charter. The new Hospital was to be called 'the Adelaide and Meath Hospital'. There was to be a President of the Hospital, the Church of Ireland Archbishop of Dublin, who would protect the ethos of the Hospital and nominate 6 members of the new Board of 23 people. A further 6 would be

---

[24] the particular stance favoured by the Adelaide Hospital Society came into very sharp focus from March 1998 when the Society made a detailed Submission to the Interdepartmental Working Group on Abortion which included a recommendation to confirm in legislation the availability of termination of pregnancy where medically indicated and in accordance with the consequences of the Supreme and High Court judgements in the X and C cases. The Submission received extensive publicity in May 1998 and the Hospital was subjected to a prolonged campaign by opponents of abortion see, *Submission To The Interdepartmental Working Party on Abortion* (The Adelaide Hospital Society, March 1998); Carol Coulter 'Hospital Urges Action on Crisis Pregnancies and number of abortions' *The Irish Times*, 12 May 1998; 'Hospital Calls for Abortion Availability in Tallaght', *The Irish Times*, 12 May 1998; editorial 'Abortion in Ireland' *The Irish Times*, 18 May 1998; Mary Henry 'Should Tallaght Offer Abortions?' *The Irish Independent*, 25 May 1998

appointed by the Adelaide Hospital Society, 6 by the Meath Hospital Foundation and 3 by the National Children's Hospital Foundation. There was one place provided for the local health authority and one place for a representative from Trinity College, Dublin. The voluntary bodies associated with the three base hospitals would continue as 'foundations' to support the work of the new public voluntary teaching hospital and to appoint the substantive part of the Board. The focus for Protestant participation in the health services was to be maintained in the Hospital and the Hospital was to have 'a multi-denominational and pluralist character'.[25]

In October 1993 the Minister for Health, Mr. Brendan Howlin, T.D. finally got the new Hospital building underway under the Tallaght Hospital Planning Board. The fact that the building, equipping and commissioning of the new Hospital remained with a separate Board was to cause the new Hospital Board which took office formally on 1 August 1996 major difficulties on the critical path towards opening the new Hospital which took place on 21 June 1998.

The amended Charter was drafted in the Working Party and it incorporated the 'Heads of Agreement'; the draft text was approved by the Boards of the three Hospitals in August 1995. The final text was based on the draft text as advised by the Attorney General and approved by Government. It received all party support in both Seanad Éireann (26 June 1996) and Dáil Éireann (3 July 1996).[26] The Minister for Health, Mr. Michael Noonan, T.D., when introducing the legislation to facilitate the Charter's approval in Dáil Éireann took the opportunity to place on record his appreciation 'of the invaluable contribution, made on a voluntary basis, by members of the boards of the three hospitals which are moving to Tallaght'. He went on to say that he had 'come to appreciate that an essential feature of our health services is the voluntary nature of many of our services and the contributions being made'.[27]

In the period from 1993 to 1996 there had, however, continued to be moments of great unease in the Adelaide Hospital and an apparent reluctance in the Meath Hospital to ratify the draft Charter based on the Heads of Agreement.

[25] see 'Heads of Agreement' 15 May 1993

[26] see *Charter of The Adelaide and Meath Hospital, Dublin, Incorporating The National Children's Hospital* printed by authority of the Board

[27] Mr. Michael Noonan, T.D., Minister for Health, *Dáil Éireann Parliamentary Debates*, Vol. 468, No. 1, Col. 18, 3 July 1996

In December 1994 The Adelaide Hospital made a submission to the Forum for Peace and Reconciliation (established in the wake of the Downing Street Declaration of 15 December 1993) entitled *The Adelaide Hospital: Symbol and Expression of a Plural Society.* It stated that the Adelaide Hospital 'has become a litmus test of the commitment to a pluralist society in the Republic'. It went on to outline that

> The Adelaide 'ethos' is a reflection of the Christian Gospel applied as a living reality every day in the Hospital setting. Love and care for the patient is paramount with total respect for the dignity and sacredness of human life. The Adelaide Hospital reflects ethical positions in relation to medical matters generally shared by the Protestant Churches. In brief this Christian perspective on medical ethics sees the patient as a morally responsible person before God in respect of treatment as advised in a confidential relationship with their medical advisers. The patient is supported in obtaining whatever spiritual advice they might wish to receive through a Hospital Chaplaincy service representing each major denomination. For all persons, staff or patients, freedom of conscience is completely honoured.

The Submission argued that

> Different traditions in a pluralist society can only make their full contribution through voluntary organisations and initiative. The State if it wishes to foster pluralism must support such voluntary effort as a matter of priority and in a positive way as against a creeping, centralising, homogenising form of government. It will be through such voluntary effort that diverse traditions will be able to make their special and distinctive contribution to the whole of society. In the case of the new Hospital at Tallaght the official instinct seemed to be to administer it as a State institution despite the fact that it was to incorporate three hugely respected voluntary Hospitals and the fact that voluntary public hospitals have an outstanding record in the provision of quality hospital services.

The Adelaide Hospital, alone of Irish hospitals, made a Submission to the Forum and met with the Forum in an oral hearing in October 1995. This was not without effect as a major paper on 'Obstacles to Reconciliation in the South' commissioned by the Forum noted

> It does seem rather strange that at a time when the issue of 'parity of esteem' is held to be an indispensable part of any settlement in Northern Ireland, there should have been any question mark at all over continuing to accord parity of esteem to the distinctive 'ethos' of the Adelaide in the reorganisation of hospital services in the Republic.

The paper went on to observe that 'real pluralist' questions include 'would it be possible for an independent Protestant institution to survive in an overwhelmingly Catholic State? Would it be possible to imagine and to sustain medical ethics which do not depend on Catholic teaching?'[28]

The answers to questions such as these and as to whether the new Hospital would flourish as a voluntary hospital, depended upon the specifications for governance and management in the Charter which are now briefly summarised and on how such specifications would be translated into practice.

The Charter specifies that the Hospital will be a 'public voluntary teaching hospital' governed by a Board in which all the powers of the Hospital are vested and are to be exercisable by the Board whose general function 'shall be to manage the activities of the Hospital and the services provided by it' {Clauses 5(a); (12)(2); (25)(1)}. The Board shall consist of 23 members appointed as follows:

> 6 members appointed by The Adelaide Hospital Society
>
> 6 members appointed by the Meath Hospital Foundation
>
> 3 members appointed by the National Children's Hospital Foundation
>
> 6 members nominated by the President of the Hospital, who is the Church of Ireland Archbishop of Dublin ad appointed by the Minister for Health and Children
>
> 2 members appointed by the Minister for Health and Children, one nominated by the Eastern Health Board (or any successor to its functions) and one nominated by the Board of Trinity College, Dublin.

The medical consultants in the Hospital may make proposals to these three voluntary bodies who must include at least one hospital consultant amongst their appointments. The Board is appointed for a three year term of office. The Charter specified that the first chairman of the Board would be appointed from the Adelaide Hospital Society appointees, the second from those of the Meath Hospital Foundation and subsequently the Chairman would be appointed generally from the Board membership. The Meath appointees included three local public representatives and the membership of the first Board included four serving local public representatives, Cllr. Gerry Brady, a member of

---

[28] see A. Aughey 'Obstacles to Reconciliation in the South' in *Building Trust in Ireland*, Studies Commissioned by the Forum for Peace and Reconciliation (The Blackstaff Press, Belfast, 1996) p. 32.

Kildare County Council, (Fianna Fáil); Cllr. Charles O'Connor, a member of South County Dublin Council (Fianna Fáil); Cllr. Kevin Ryan, a member of Wicklow County Council (Labour); another member Cllr. T. Keegan became ill and subsequently died and was replaced by Mr. Gerry Maguire. The first Board, was therefore a hybrid of two traditions the philanthropic voluntary tradition and the political public representative local government tradition. It would, therefore, present a great challenge to its Officers and members to achieve solidarity and unity of purpose given the different backgrounds of the members.

The President of the Hospital has the duty under the Charter of protecting the ethos of the Hospital as set out in the Charter. The ethos embraces the statement in the Charter that this public voluntary hospital is to be maintained 'as a focus for Protestant participation in the health service and thereby preserving its particular denominational ethos'. The Charter goes on to state the values and character of the Hospital in these terms:

> While maintaining this focus and preserving the denominational ethos, freedom of conscience and the free profession and practice of religion by all within the establishments operated by the Hospital are equally affirmed and guaranteed. The Hospital will therefore have a multidenominational and pluralist character. It is recognised in particular that religious welfare is part of the total welfare of the patient and the support of such religious welfare by chaplains of each major denomination is essential to the attainment of the object.[29]

A further object is 'to develop the tradition of voluntary support groups for the activities of the Hospital' in particular through the three voluntary bodies, The Adelaide Hospital Society, the Meath Hospital Foundation and the National Children's Hospital Foundation.[30]

3. HOW THE BOARD ADDRESSED GOVERNANCE AND MANAGEMENT UNDER THE CHARTER

The Adelaide and Meath Hospital, Dublin, Incorporating The National Children's Hospital was incorporated under its Charter on 1 August 1996. The new Board had been appointed in late 1995 and met informally from January 1996 until it assumed formal responsibility for the Hospital on 1 August 1996. The Board from January 1996 met every

---

[29] Charter, op. cit., Clauses (13)(1); (5)(j)
[30] ibid, Clause (5)(l)

fortnight for the first eighteen months in order to prepare for the senior staff recruitment process, to develop common policies and to address critical issues in relation either to the services already being provided or the requirements of these services in the new buildings at Tallaght. In addition there were a number of specially facilitated meetings to assist in Board development and in the sharing of views and values.

The main focus of the Board in the period prior to August 1996 was the search process and appointment procedure in relation to a new Chief Executive Officer (CEO). Dr. David McCutcheon, after a lengthy process, was appointed CEO in September 1996.[31] Previously Dr. McCutcheon was the senior health administrator in Hamilton Civic Hospitals, Ontario, Canada. The Board sought, and believed it had found, a CEO who had the experience necessary in order to design new policies and approaches and to lead the Hospital successfully through the merger and transition to Tallaght.

The merger provided an opportunity to design a new management structure and a new set of policies and approaches to be applied in place of the traditional and diverse policies or approaches in the previously separate base institutions.[32] In addition the Hospital was felt by many to be atypical amongst large Irish hospitals in that it was governed by a Charter which had received specific Oireachtas approval in 1996.

(i)   *The Board Committee Structure*
The Charter specified not only the composition of the Board but also established a number of other key bodies such as the Medical Board, the Paediatric Committee and the Paediatric Medical Advisory Committee. The Charter also embraced a commitment to all of the staff of the base hospitals under an Industrial Relations Protocol negotiated through the Department of Health with the trade unions. A

---

[31] this appointment required unique arrangements in order to ensure a remuneration package which though considerably less than in Canada, would allow Dr. McCutcheon to move to Ireland; the Hospital, Trinity College, Dublin, and the three Foundations in the Hospital each contributed by way of separate contractual agreements to the package and received from Dr. McCutcheon teaching or consultancy services.

[32] in this context note should be taken of the warning in M.Dixon, A. Baker *A Management Development Strategy for the Health and Personal Social Services in Ireland* (commissioned and published by Department of Health, December 1996) that 'widespread acceptance of traditional custom and practice and an unwillingness to challenge how things are done are significant impediments to change' (p. ii)

Charter commitment to the appointment of staff on merit in fair and equitable procedures was honoured in all interview and selection systems under a template approved by the Board. An extensive consultation process took place to agree the Mission Statement of the Hospital stemming from the Charter and this process was led by a sub-committee of the informal Board in early 1996.

The appointment of Dr. McCutcheon and the general context of the merger under the Charter indicated a significant shift towards a new paradigm in governance and management led by the new CEO. In November 1996 a Governance Committee of the Board was appointed and commissioned 'to make recommendations on the design of the Board and processes that will ensure effective governance of the Hospital within the framework of the Charter'.[33] Dr. McCutcheon provided each member of the Committee with material to study including an example of one merged hospital's structure as detailed in its By-Laws, the Canadian Accreditation Standards for Governance of Health Facilities, chapters from John Carver's book *Boards That Make a Difference* and the Taylor, Chait and Holland article from *Harvard Business Review* 'The New Work of the Nonprofit Board'.[34] The Governance Committee met every Wednesday from early December seeking to complete its work on the proposals by the end of February 1997.

The Committee took note of the legal framework of the Board's responsibilities including not only the Charter but the various health acts including the recent Health (Amendment) No. 3 Act 1996 known as 'the accountability legislation' which was requested by the Committee from the Department of Health. The subsequent implications of this Act was not then apparent as it specifically addressed only health boards directly. It was not then clear that it would be applied to voluntary agencies as well.

By early January 1997 an outline of the Board Committee structure had emerged and detailed terms of reference were drafted for each proposed Committee including the main responsibilities of the Board of Management. The Governance Committee also drafted a 'committee

---

[33] the account here is based upon the Governance Committee file in the Hospital; the author of this study was a member of this Committee; the membership was Mrs. Melissa Webb, Ms Betty O'Dwyer, Dr. John Barragry, Mr. Randall Plunkett, Dr. David McCutcheon, Dr. Fergus O'Ferrall and Professor Davis Coakley who was appointed later to the Committee and was then appointed by the Committee to chair the Committee.

[34] this literature is discussed in the previous chapter

template' which set out how frequently the Committees would meet, the structure of their membership, the setting of annual goals and how each Committee would be subject to both self-evaluation according to an approved protocol and to regular external review by an Ad hoc Committee of the Board. The membership of each Board Committee was suggested to be a maximum of 12 with the majority being staff of the Hospital as follows:

- 4 Board members (one who will Chair)
- Chair of the Board (ex officio)
- CEO (ex officio)
- Management team members(s) especially the member of Management Team who would provide staff support for Committee
- Medical Board member(s)—two were agreed
- Staff member(s) as necessary to ensure relevant expertise
- Members drawn from any of the three Foundations
- A 'community' member appointed by the Board.

The template to populate the Committees, therefore, facilitated the Medical Board, staff and management in the development of Hospital Board policies and to 'own' the outcomes. This was based upon a view that important issues cannot be neatly subdivided into policy/governance as distinct from management/administration.

The Governance Committee consulted as to the proposed Terms of Reference of the suggested committees. For example the three Matrons of the base hospitals were consulted as to the role of the proposed Nursing Committee. Considerable consultation was necessary to produce agreement as to the relationship between the Medical Board and the Board. The Medical Board was established by the Charter composed of the consultant medical staff of the Hospital. The Chairman and Secretary of the Medical Board are entitled to attend and participate in all meetings of the Hospital Board; they do not have votes at the Board but 'shall report to the Hospital Board in relation to the activities of the Medical Board in such manner and at such intervals as the Hospital Board may determine'. (Clause 16 (5))

The Charter also provided for a Paediatric Committee, known as the National Children's Hospital Committee, to be 'responsible for all paediatric services, and services relating thereto, provided by the

Hospital' subject 'to the superintendence of the Hospital Board' (Clause 16 (6)). The membership of this Committee is appointed by the National Children's Hospital Foundation. The Charter also provided for a Paediatric Medical Advisory Committee composed of those members of the Medical Board who provide paediatric services to assist the Paediatric Committee in carrying out its duties.

The Governance Committee also drafted Standing Orders for the Board covering attendance, appointment of Officers, the duties of Officers, the conduct of Board meetings and the work of Board Committees. By March 1997 the Board had completed its approval of the proposals of the Governance Committee and in April it approved the Standing Orders. The Board then proceeded to appoint Chairs of the Committees and Board members to each Committee; it also requested the composition of each Committee according to the approved 'Committee Template'. Board members were requested in writing to indicate preferences for the Committees and the Chairman and the Executive Committee under the new Standing Orders brought to the Board the proposed final composition. The Executive Committee of the Board was composed of the Chair of each of the Committees and the Officers of the Board. The Executive Committee was to be seen as a 'service' committee to the Board as there were fears expressed by some that it had the potential to erode the full Board's role.

The distribution of the Chairs of the Committees amongst nine of the Board members and the even-handed distribution of the members amongst the 'internal coalitions' (The Adelaide Hospital Society, the Meath Hospital Foundation and The National Children's Hospital Foundation and those nominated to the Board by the Archbishop as President) brought the new Board into a consensus mode of operation which worked extremely well on many critical issues. This consensus sundered badly only in December 1998 on how the issue of the under-funding of the Hospital was handled in the wake of the Deloitte and Touche Report which will be described below.

(ii)   *The new Management Team Structure*
As the work of the Governance Committee was commencing the CEO, Dr. McCutcheon, made a very important presentation to the Board in December 1996 on 'Organisation Structure'. He set out what he termed a 'Preliminary Draft Vision Statement' for the new Hospital and then outlined a proposed new Management Team structure under

which each new Director would have an agreed 'portfolio' of responsibilities.

The crucial elements highlighted in the 'Draft Vision' were, in the words of the overhead visual aid used for presentation purposes at the Board:

- A patient focussed approach
- Caring for the caregivers
- The academic mission of the Hospital
- The need for flexibility, quality management, to be a learning organisation
- The need to be a best cost hospital
- Integration with other health care providers
- An emphasis on leadership, integration and multidisciplinary team participation by all professions
- A productive relationship with the Department of Health and funding agencies
- A new role for Human Resources
- A new role for financial management
- Effective Board governance.

The objective outlined by the CEO was to implement the proposed new Management Team structure as the transition to the new Hospital took place. The Board approved the Management Team structure of nine Directors which together with the CEO composed the senior management of the Hospital. A full formal review of this structure was to occur after July 1998 when the new Hospital had opened and the merger and move had been completed. It took many months in 1997 before the full Team was appointed; indeed the Director of Finance was only appointed in October 1997 due to the inability to secure a suitable internal candidate and the relatively low remuneration possible in the health services for this senior appointment.

As the Management Team took shape in 1997 there were now three key formal groups in place in relation to governance and management in the new Hospital: first, the Board of the Hospital beginning to learn how to operate its own new Committee structures; second the Medical Board learning how to involve a very large consultant body at a time of great change and thirdly a newly appointed Management Team, led by a new CEO. This was a classic '3 legged stool' model and the leadership and successful management of the new Hospital now crucially depended upon the successful interaction of these three bodies at a time when they were literally 'finding their feet'.[35]

The governance structures for the new Hospital were produced by what may be termed a voluntary 'dominant coalition' in the formation of the Hospital led by the Adelaide Hospital Society nominated Chairman, Mrs. Rosemary French. The shape given to them was heavily influenced by the CEO, Dr. David McCutcheon. Both of these key leaders were heavily committed to the norms of the Charter and to the advantages of voluntary boards and to the need for board members together with management staff to work together on policy issues.[36] This concept of actively committed and involved board members may be closely related to the 'new work' of the non profit board as outlined by Taylor, Chait and Holland in the previous chapter where the voluntary board seeks mechanisms to have real power and influence in the organisation by being engaged in work that matters. This voluntary 'new work' model of governance and management was soon put under severe pressure and effectively stopped in its tracks in late 1998.

4.   PERFORMING UNDER PRESSURE: THE BOARD 1996–1999

By any measure the responsibilities and work programme of the new Hospital Board were great and the Board had constantly to perform under pressure. The 'general orientation' outlined by Zald is most valuable is assessing the Board's performance:

> . . . in the relationships among boards (as collectivities), individual board members, and executives, each party brings to bear 'resources'. These resources may be based in legal rights, in monetary control, in knowledge, or even in force of personality and traditions. Resources may be crudely

[35] the detailed arrangements are outlined in *Guide To Governance and Management of the Hospital* Volume 1: September 1998 (Produced by the Strategic Planning and Communications Committee of the Board for the information of staff)

[36] see Interview with Dr. David McCutcheon, 31 March 1999, where, inter alia, he states 'It's very important, I think, that the Board provides leadership in terms of the values of the organisation and I think that gets reflected very quickly all the way through'; and Interview with Mrs. Rosemary French, 29 June 1999, where, inter alia, she states '. . . what distinguishes it from other hospitals by having a voluntary board whose interests should just be that of the patient with no other interests at all, and putting the patient first on all decisions. That in a way gives it an independence and a freedom to do things in the patients' interests . . .'

classified as 'detachable' resources, personal characteristics, and strategic contingency situations. It is the balance of resources for specific situations and decisions that determines the attribution of relative power in the encounter between boards and executives.[37]

Although not stated by Zald this 'orientation' is also particularly valuable in understanding the board-environment linkages such as that between a hospital and its funding agency, the Department of Health.[38] The capacity, as Zald notes, of the different actors to bring to bear 'resources' fluctuates from situation to situation: examination 'of the functioning of a board over long periods of time would reveal an ebb and flow of board functions, importance, and power during different phases of organizational development and activity'.[39] Zald's concept of 'strategic contingencies'—events of organizational life cycles, such as mergers, major programme and goal changes, and the selection of chief executives—is most useful in this case study. 'Strategic contingencies situations' arose for the new Board frequently such as the appointment of the first CEO in 1996 or deciding and implementing the decision to open the Hospital on 21 June 1998. Zald formulates a general proposition about such situations:

> It is during the handling of major phase problems, or strategic decision points, that board power is most likely to be asserted. It is at such times, too, that basic conflicts and divisions both within the board and between the managers and the board are likely to be pronounced'.[40]

The most critical 'strategic contingency situation' confronting the Board was to be the financial crisis which led to the appointment in late September 1998 of the Deloitte and Touche Consultants to review independently the Hospital's management processes in view of the Hospital's then projected major financial deficits. The new Hospital Board might well have believed that it had achieved its major tasks in completing the transition to the new facility after a successful merger of three hospitals into an effective single hospital on a new site. *The Deloitte and Touche Consultants Report* in December 1998 stated 'The merger

[37] Mayer N. Zald 'The Power and Functions of Boards of Directors: A Theoretical Synthesis' *American Journal of Sociology*, Vol, 75, No. 1, July 1969, p. 98

[38] see J. Pfeffer, G.R. Salancik *The External Control of Organisations A Resource Dependence Perspective* (Harper & Row, New York, 1978) especially pp 170–4

[39] Zald, op. cit., p. 107

[40] ibid, p. 107; for another exploration of the cycle of board behaviour see Miriam W. Wood 'Is Governing Board Behaviour Cyclical?' *Nonprofit Management & Leadership*, Vol. 3, No. 2, Winter 1992, pp 139–162

strategies adopted appear to have been successful in merging the cultures of the base hospitals. Indeed there is a strong sense of commitment to the new organisation among the Board, management and staff.'[41] The Report stated that 'it would appear that the Board is highly motivated and has gelled well together as a group'.[42] This 'crisis', however, revealed, in Zald's phrase, the 'basic conflicts and divisions' within the Board in contrast to any previous problem it had dealt with and indicated the effect of power relationships and resource dependent relationships on governance and management in a very stark fashion. For these reasons this 'crisis' is now analysed in some detail.

The origin of the financial crisis encountered by the Board of the Hospital was the Letter of Determination of Health Expenditure for 1998 issued to the Hospital on 4 December 1997.[43] This provided IR£53.659m (this was slightly revised to IR£53.762m in January 1998) for non-capital expenditure for the coming year. The key feature of the Letter was the fact that the Health (Amendment)(No 3) Act, 1996 became fully operational on 1 January 1998. The Letter stated:

This legislation does not apply to your agency. It is the intention, however, to apply in an administrative way any terms of the legislation that are relevant in the Department's dealings with agencies. Your co-operation in this regard is anticipated.

Under the Act the Hospital was required to adopt a Service Plan specifying the services to be provided within the financial allocation of IR£53.659m not later than 42 days after receipt of this Letter.

1998 was, therefore, a year of very significant change in respect of funding arrangements for the whole healthcare system. For the Hospital, however, it was also the year when it was to move all services to a new campus. This made it extremely difficult to estimate a full year's expenditure given that the historical track record of activity levels

---

[41] *Management Reporting and Control, Service Planning, and the Financial Position of the Adelaide and Meath Hospital, Dublin, Incorporating The National Children's Hospital, December 1998* Deloitte and Touche Consultants Report To The Minister for Health and Children, hereafter cited as 'Deloitte and Touche Report' p. 5; the Report pointed out that the merger process was incomplete in a number of respects such as integration and organisation of certain administrative and support services, the organisation structure at senior management level and certain operational policies

[42] ibid, p. 57

[43] The Letter of Determination is attached as Appendix 1 to the *Deloitte and Touche Report*

provides the core building block of a Service Plan in an Irish health agency. 1998 was also the first year for which consolidated budgets were prepared for the Hospital from the three base hospitals. These difficulties were compounded by the separate responsibilities of the Tallaght Hospital Board for the planning, building, equipping and furnishing of the Hospital. During 1997 there had been developing concern at the perceived failure of the Planning Board to have the Hospital built, equipped and furnished for the scheduled opening date in August 1997 or indeed for a revised opening date in January 1998. On 17 September 1997 the Minister for Health, Mr. Brian Cowen, T.D. met with the Hospital Board to emphasise the importance of opening as quickly as possible the new Hospital.

The Board of the new Hospital experienced very strong pressure from the Minister and the Department to open the Hospital while the Board continued to express 'concern and dismay' at the failure of the Planning Board to equip the Hospital; the Hospital Board sought a single authority in place of the two separate Boards.[44]

The Secretary-General, Mr. J. O'Dwyer, had not been present when the full Board of the Hospital met the Minister on 17 September 1997. He wrote on 24 September 1997 to the Chairman requesting a meeting with the Officers of the Board and requesting

(i) 'a report outlining the progress made since May last against your plan for the opening of the hospital in January 1998' and

(ii) 'an assessment of the factors (structures, personnel, systems) which have contributed to the present disappointing position'.

He wished to discuss these reports and 'to decide what action' needed to be taken 'to open the hospital as soon as possible'[45] Mrs. R. French replied on 25 September 1997 that the Board was responding to the issues 'discussed in detail with the Minister' and while she could not accept 'the proposed terms of your meeting' the Board had authorised the Officers and the Chief Executive Officer 'to meet with you to pursue the issues discussed with the Minister'.[46] The significant point

[44] see letter by Mrs. Rosemary French, Chairman to Mr. Brian Cowen, T.D., Minister for Health and Children, 24 September 1997, stating 'the need for a single authority and tight control by our Board and its staff is the single most important step in achieving the earliest and most effective date to open the Hospital'.

[45] Mr. J. O'Dwyer to Mrs. R. French, 24 September 1997, marked 'Confidential'

[46] Mrs. R. French to Mr. J. O'Dwyer, 25 September 1997

she felt was the inclusion of the Chief Executive Officer who, although he was just a year in post, was in danger of being made to shoulder responsibility for any delay in opening the Hospital.

The Minister wrote on 14 October 1997 to Mrs. French expressing his 'appreciation of the enormous commitment and dedication that you and the members of your Board have shown during the past eighteen months'. He stated that the Department had a 'major concern' about 'the enormity of the responsibilities faced by your new board in its first year of operation:'

> These responsibilities include the sensitive and complex task of merging the three transferring hospitals as well as continuing to manage these at their existing locations, the recruitment of a Chief Executive Officer and Management Team and the putting in place of the necessary measures, including the development of private facilities, to ensure a successful transfer to Tallaght.

The Minister stated that he regarded 'the task of laying proper governance foundations as of equal importance to the completion of the physical facilities of the new hospital'. He stated that the functions and responsibilities of the Tallaght Hospital Planning Board would be transferred no later than 30 April 1998 and that the Chairman of the Planning Board had agreed to ensure that the equipping programme 'will be rescheduled so that the bulk of the equipping will be completed by the end of January 1998'. He asked that the Hospital Board consider 'a phased opening with the majority of services being transferred and operational by the beginning of May 1998'.[47] On 23 October 1997 at a meeting between representatives of the Hospital and the Department to review progress when a tabled document indicated an opening date of 1 August 1998 a 'representative of the Department of Health & Children indicated that if the tabled document became known more widely in the Department of Health & Children, the revenue earmarked for 1998 would disappear in 24 hours'.[48] There was strong pressure to open the Hospital as soon as possible. Because

---

[47] Mr. Brian Cowen, Minister for Health and Children to Mr. R. French, 14 October 1997; Mrs. R. French in her reply 23 October 1997 referred to how the Board since the meeting on 17 September had become 'increasingly concerned and dismayed as a result of reports from the Tallaght Hospital Board as it has transpired that the equipping problems are even more profound than originally perceived.'

[48] see *Deloitte & Touche Report* p. 85 and 'Response To Deloitte & Touche Report' presented by CEO to Board December 1998.

opening was deferred until 21 June 1998 the incremental budget allocation available was reduced by almost 50%, i.e. by IR£5m.

On 27 November 1997 the Board was able to confirm to the Minister the opening date of 21 June 1998 and the Department and the Hospital had agreed to work together on 'significant milestones' to achieve this target date.[49] This followed indepth analysis of all the 'critical path' issues related to the opening of the Hospital. The prevailing mindset on the Board was that the crucial task was to open the Hospital and to open it safely from a patient care point of view. It believed that the Department's efforts were totally committed to this also and that this reflected the political direction of the Minister. A mode of tripartite operating commenced between the Hospital Board, the Department and the Planning Board, called a Joint Equipping Committee, to address the issues and resolve then so that the opening date would be achieved.[50]

It was in this context that the Hospital submitted draft 1998 budget proposals in three options: the option which attempted to identify the expenditure levels for the base hospitals remaining as they were for the first half of 1998 and that of a similar institution on a single site for the second half of 1998 showed a net expenditure of IR£66.954m.[51] It was obvious to the Management Team on receipt of the Letter of Determination that negotiations would be necessary for additional funding to meet the requirements for clinical care on the Tallaght site. As the Deloitte & Touche Report recognised, the fundamental problem with the Letter of Determination was that it was based on an incremental budgeting model and was not an appropriate instrument to determine funding for a new hospital on a greenfield site.[52]

Some extent of the difficulties in framing a budget and a Service Plan for 1998 may be gauged by the fact that there was as yet no agreed manpower plan for the Hospital in December 1997 or January 1998. Any such plan would require to be agreed with the Department of Health and Children. This was another critical issue amongst a whole

[49] Mrs. R. French to Mr. Brian Cowen, Minister for Health and Children, 27 November 1997

[50] see, for example, Dr. Ruth Barrington, Assistant Secretary to Mrs. R. French, 26 November 1997 for the agreed approaches and reporting arrangements for the 'Hospital Opening Strategy'

[51] see *Deloitte & Touche Report* p. 86

[52] ibid p. 25–6

range of matters which were subject to ongoing discussion with the Department.[53]

On 26 January 1998 the CEO wrote a very detailed letter to the Secretary-General, Mr. J. O'Dwyer and he stated

> Obviously under normal circumstances it would be the policy of the hospital management to ensure that all known liabilities and normal levels of expenditures/cost would be included in our hospital's Service Plan. Under the exceptional environment in which we are presently operating within, i.e. the operating of three indigenous hospitals, combined with the opening of one of the largest acute hospitals in the State, representing the largest investment by the State in healthcare, it may not be possible to foresee and quantify all possible eventualities . . . In the exceptional circumstances prevailing, i.e. the opening of a new acute hospital servicing a new catchment area, our recent or historic experience may not be an adequate measure of future occurrences.

The CEO requested a formal process of review of exceptional expenditure between the Hospital and the Department on a quarterly basis. This letter outlined the services and budgets for the year.

At a meeting with Department officials on 13 February 1998 the Hospital was requested to analyse projected activity for both halves of the year with costings for development and commissioning expenses. These were forwarded on 4 March 1998 indicating a total budget adjustment of £20.6m. The Hospital's management and indeed the Board were finding it impossible to reconcile the provision of the existing levels of services (which was accepted as a commitment under the Charter and upon which the base allocation in the Letter of Determination was predicated), the move of the hospital (and associated costs) and the amount allocated in the Letter of Determination. In addition during February there was a critical situation in respect of capital funding in the work of The Tallaght Hospital Planning Board which threatened to jeopardise the opening of the Hospital.[54]

---

[53] regular 'Critical Path Issues' covering ten or more major issues were reported on a fortnightly basis to the Department and to the Board of the Hospital most of which were extremely complex. Examples included a new laboratory service, a new sterile supply service for the new facility and a new radiology system known as PACS, private car-park development because of the inadequacy of what was planned, the extension of the outpatients department, additional bed block to rectify the loss of bed numbers compared with the base hospitals due to the Kennedy Review of 1992 and others of an equally complex and critical nature

[54] see Mrs. R. French to Mr. J. O'Dwyer, Secretary-General, 19 February and 27 February 1998

Following meetings on 4 March with the Secretary-General and meetings with officials on 6 March a detailed letter was sent by the CEO to the Department on 13 March 1998 showing that while funding in the Letter of Determination was adequate to fund the provision of existing services it did not adequately fund costs associated with the commissioning of the new Hospital, revenue costs for the new pathology department, costs specific to the new facility, costs relating to additional approved posts, costs of the new technology and other costs to a net amount estimated at IR£4.893m. At a meeting in the Department on the same day it was acknowledged by the Department that it was difficult to gauge service pressures in the new location in Tallaght and it was recognised that there would be ongoing discussions regarding additional funding, and that a strategy for dealing with agreed deficiencies over the next few years could be agreed:

> The DoH&C also indicated at the meeting that it was not going to walk away from Tallaght in terms of its needs, but its wants are a different matter. The DoH&C notes of the meeting record that they 'thought that we had put enough funds aside, while it does not look like that now, the amount is set'.[55]

The Board of the Hospital on 25 March 1998 was briefed on the detailed discussions with the Department and they noted the solemn agreement to ensure the same level of service in the new hospital as in the base hospitals which required an additional allocation of IR£5m approximately. At a further Board meeting on 27 March to consider various strategies to bridge the funding deficit for 1998 it was agreed to maintain the current level of activity in a deficit situation and that the CEO was to proceed with the conclusion of the Service Plan on this basis. This was the first meeting in which the Board noted in detail the Letter of Determination and the responses made by the management of the Hospital. Up to this point the CEO and management with advice from the Resources Committee of the Board believed that they were negotiating about the funds required and had not reached conclusions to present to Board.[56]

On 27 March the CEO wrote to the Department pointing out that the financial situation had not changed significantly: there was a

---

[55] *Deloitte and Touche Report* p. 95

[56] those involved stated that the reference on page 2 of the Letter of Determination to it being an 'initial Letter of Determination' meant that further discussion and negotiation was required before the final allocation should be presented for approval with service activity to the Board see *Deloitte and Touche Report* p. 103

shortfall of IR£5m and he stated that the Hospital 'has been operating within the constraints of the IR Protocol and with the solemn agreement to continue our existing level of service'. The IR Protocol, agreed with the unions and the Department, guaranteed all permanent staff in the base hospitals a position in the new facility so there was no significant room to adjust staffing costs in the short term.

On 1 April there was a further special Board meeting regarding the Service Plan. While the Department was adamant that the provision of services must be carried out within the allocated budget the only room for discussion appeared to be whether items in the sum of IR£4.4m in revenue could meet capital expenditure criteria in the light of the costs attached to the new facility. The problem was that such capital funding was not available at present and the Resources Committee on 7 April decided to recommend that the Board adopt the Service Plan which included an excess of IR£5.9m over the amount in the Letter of Determination.

On 8 April with great reluctance the Board at a special meeting approved the Service Plan on the recommendation of the Resources Committee. In March Lesley Buckley & Associates, management consultants, had been appointed by the Department to assist the Management Team with the difficulties in funding and the Board noted that the Service Plan had the confidence of these consultants. The only options available to the Board were

1) to defer the opening of the Hospital set for 21 June 1998

2) to reduce service activity radically, i.e. the closure of 80 beds approximately for the balance of the year

3) to approve the Service Plan budget IR£5.883m over the Letter of Determination with an understanding that ongoing negotiations would be successful with the Department.

The Management Team at the Hospital and the Board understood that the Department were extremely supportive in all meetings (formal and informal) so as to achieve a satisfactory outcome to the funding situation and so that the opening date of the Hospital would not be jeopardised. Members of the Board stated to the Deloitte and Touche consultants

> That the decision to adopt a Service Plan in excess of Determination was not taken lightly, and was only done on the basis that the CEO, and certain of the members themselves, had the clear impression from discussions with

representatives of the DoH&C that further funding could be obtained, and that a mechanism to achieve this was to assess the extent that expenditure, contained in the Service Plan under revenue, could be reclassified as capital expenditure . . . they believed that [the Department] had sought IR£11m additional funding for [the Hospital] for 1998 and that this had effectively been halved because the opening was delayed from January 1998 to June 1998. They believed that the discussions on reclassification of items as capital were a recognition on the part of [the Department] that there were funding difficulties associated with the reduction in incremental funding from the IR£11m initially sought to the IR£5.9m ultimately obtained in the Determination. . .[57]

The fact that the Hospital's Service Plan was never formally rejected by the Department of Health lends weight to this understanding: the funding issue was 'parked' in order to open the Hospital. There was a clear indication that the Department would consider 'one off' costs as capital items and capital monies it was believed would be more readily available to the Department later in the year. Had a formal rejection of the Service Plan been forthcoming then the Hospital would have been left with no option but to defer the transfer and to reduce service activity for the rest of the year in order to remain within the Letter of Determination. The Board and Management Team understood that every effort was being made by the Department to source the necessary additional funding (probably through capital funding of items related to the opening of the new facility) and to support the decision to move on 21 June 1998 which was a very major logistical operation.

The shortfall in the funding of the new Hospital became a matter of public controversy from April. The Fine Gael Spokesperson on Health and Children, Mr. Alan Shatter issued a detailed press statement on 29 April 1998 which asked why Tallaght Hospital 'has the lowest current budget allocation of any of the major Dublin hospitals'.[58] The Minister for Health and Children was asked a Question in the Dáil on 31 April 1998 by Mr. Shatter whether he would sanction additional funding for Tallaght Hospital. He replied that

It has been agreed with the hospital management for some time that the first task in commissioning the new hospital is to transfer existing services, including the psychiatric services from St. Loman's Hospital, to Tallaght and to immediately bring onstream at the new hospital those enhanced

[57] *Deloitte and Touche Report* p. 103

[58] 'Shatter Calls for More Funding for Tallaght Hospital' Press Statement, 29 April 1998, issued by Fine Gael National Press Office, Leinster House.

facilities which are necessary for the functioning of a major acute hospital. These new facilities include on-site laboratory services, more sophisticated theatres, state of the art sterile services, a 'best of breed' information system-information technology system and an ultra modern filmless radiology system known as PACS—Picture Archiving Communication System.

The Minister paid tribute to the work of both the Tallaght Hospital Board whose work was 'now in its final stages' and to the Hospital Board for its 'tremendous achievements' since 'its inception less than two year ago'. He admitted that he had not visited the new Hospital. He stated that 'increased allocations to the hospital will be made on the basis of ensuring that health and safety regulations are met'. He went on to state that 'as in line with the original plans, the existing services in the four hospitals will be transferred. It will include enhanced services and those existing services in the four hospitals being merged and transferred to Tallaght and there will be further increased services which will come on stream in 1999 as planned'.[59]

This did not sound like a rejection of the Service Plan but clearly reinforced the view that the Hospital Board had the Minister's commitment to open and to be progressively funded in order to bring all the existing services in 1998 to Tallaght and to develop the planned enhanced services for 1999. A serious problem arose in late April because of the shortage of available beds in the new facility as compared with the existing base hospitals due to the fact that the 77 beds for private use had not been constructed. On 29 April the Board decided to defer the transfer of the acute psychiatric services from St. Loman's Hospital which was an Eastern Health Board Hospital until 1 August 1999. This decision greatly angered the Department who felt it was clear ministerial policy to transfer St. Loman's as soon as possible.[60]

---

[59] Dáil Éireann *Parliamentary Debates* 31 April 1998; in fact the transfer of the responsibilities of the Tallaght Hospital Board to the Hospital Board about which the Minister had given a commitment to secure by the end of April did not occur as the Hospital Board required indemnification against any liabilities which the Planning Board might have and later it was planned to ensure that the legal transfer was secured through an amended Ministerial Order.

[60] The Department effectively demanded a detailed report from the CEO as to the basis for the decision, see Mr. T. Morris to Dr. D. McCutcheon, 1 May 1998 and the detailed statement supplied by CEO 'Defer The Opening of St. Loman's On Site–The basis for the CEO recommendation to the Board' written on 4 May and included with Dr. D. McCutcheon to Mr. T. Morris 4 May 1998; in actual fact because of industrial relations issues for the staff of St. Loman's Hospital services did not transfer to Tallaght until August 1999

Intensive discussions followed with the Secretary-General Mr. J. O'Dwyer and officials which were highly significant as far as the Hospital was concerned in respect of the resources which were to be made available to the Hospital in 1998.

On 6 May 1998 the Board was able to reverse its decision to defer the St. Loman's transfer because of a detailed agreement reached between the Hospital, the Department and the Eastern Health Board. Under this agreement the Health Board agreed to provide a 35 bed facility (by leasing part of the Meath Hospital) to the Hospital to prevent beds being 'blocked' in the new Hospital by long stay patients who did not have acute illnesses and the Department agreed in principle to enhance patient management systems in the new Hospital. The Secretary-General, Mr. O'Dwyer referred on 13 May to the 6 May agreement as 'probably the most important decision made in recent months and is critical for the future of the hospital, its status, its reputation and its relationships with the wider health service environment in which it operates'.[61]

The significance of this 'St. Loman's Agreement' in May is that the Hospital now believed that the annualised cost of approximately IR£5m of the agreed enhanced patient management systems greatly resolved the funding issues for 1998. The intensive discussions had given ample opportunity to revert to the 8 April Service Plan but in making the 6 May agreement and related correspondence there is no anticipated difficulty in this regard.[62]

After the very successful opening of the new Hospital on 21 June 1998 discussions between the Hospital and the Department continued in relation to what portion of future expenditure might be considered capital and about the role of the Tallaght Hospital Planning Board in relation to this expenditure. As documented in the Deloitte and Touche Report the Tallaght Hospital Planning Board had failed to fully discharge their responsibilities to build, equip and furnish the new

[61] see Mr. J. O'Dwyer to Mrs. R. French, 13 May 1998 and Mr. J. O'Dwyer to Mrs. R. French, 6 May 1998 and Mrs R. French to Mr. J. O'Dwyer, 7 May 1998

[62] on 28 May 1998 there was a meeting between the Hospital and the Department to discuss the results to 30 April 1998 and there was concern that activity was up in all base hospitals which was increasing costs. The Department minute of the meeting notes that 'the Service Plan was rejected by the DoH&C' and that the Secretary-General had confirmed that no further funding would be available; see *Deloitte and Touche Report* p 99.; on 7 July 1998 the Resources Committee of the Board noted that the Service Plan had not been accepted by the Department, ibid, p. 100.

Hospital before the opening date and the Hospital Board had to take many decisions to spend money on basic equipment and furnishings in order to achieve the safe opening of the new facilities. The Department were fully informed at a meeting on 27 July 1998 of the projected out-turn of revenue and capital expenditure; it was agreed to meet on a monthly basis to review the expenditure profile as it unfolded. According to the Response to the Deloitte and Touche Report provided by the CEO to the Board in December 1998.

> The DoH&C recognised the cash deficit that this expenditure was causing the Hospital and discussions followed on the basis of funding this deficit. The discussions revolved around the issue of obtaining capital funding or short-term banking facilities. The DoH&C proposed that additional overdraft facilities be granted to the Hospital for a short-term period of £3m until the funding issues were resolved. The proposed meetings were tentatively agreed for September, October and November 1998.

> On August 24 1998 the CEO . . . met with the Secretary-General . . . regarding the developing financial problems. During that meeting discussions took place on a process to agree the resolution of the funding issue. The CEO proposed that a team comprising members of the DoH&C and the Hospital's Management Team together with an independent consultant would review the financial situation and make recommendations to resolve the problems to the CEO and the Secretary-General. The CEO reported this to the Board and indicated that there was indeed a collective willingness to resolve the situation.[63]

On 1 September the bank balances of the Hospital were IR£1.9m overdrawn and the Hospital was holding cheques to the value of IR£2.7m approximately including a PAYE cheque of IR£1.1m.[64] It is clear that it was very difficult to obtain a full picture of the expenditure and costs because there were different organisations incurring liabilities: the Tallaght Hospital Planning Board, the Hospital Board, and the Federated Dublin Voluntary Hospitals.[65] The Project Director reporting to the Tallaght Hospital Planning Board also served as Director of Environmental Services reporting to the CEO of the Hospital Board

---

[63] *Response to Deloitte & Touche Report*, December 1998, p. 13; this is recorded in Dr. D. McCutcheon to Mr. J. O'Dwyer, 1 September 1998

[64] Dr. D. McCutcheon to Mr. J. O'Dwyer, 1 September 1998; this situation left the Hospital in breach of its statutory obligations to creditors under the Prompt Payments Act.

[65] Dr. D. McCutcheon to Mr. J. O'Dwyer, 9 September 1998; see also Mrs. R. French to Mr. J. O'Dwyer 24 September 1998 and Financial Report 24 September 1998 of the Hospital

and the Deloitte & Touche Consultants found that this conflict of interest had not been well handled.[66] These dual responsibilities arose because it had been believed that the Tallaght Hospital Planning Board's work would have been very quickly folded into the Hospital Board's responsibilities under the Charter. This was not achieved during the life of the first Board of the Hospital because the Hospital Board wished to have clarification of the nature and extent of the liabilities being assumed as well as explicit legal powers in relation to the responsibilities to be transferred. The cash shortfall in the Hospital arose from the fact that the Department's cash provision was based upon the allocation in the Letter of Determination while the Hospital's expenditure was based upon the budget in the Service Plan.

The requirements of the newly merged Hospital for a greatly increased annual financial allocation is demonstrated by the following figures (based upon the Letters of Determination issued by the Department of Health and Children for the years 1997 to 2000 which include the final approved additional amounts for each year): In 1997 £43.59m was allocated and a revised figure of £49.973m was approved by year end. In 1998 £53.659m was allocated and a revised figure of £60.640m was approved by year end. In 1999 £68.6m was allocated and a revised figure of £77.678m was approved by year end.

In 2000 the Letter of Determination in respect of the Hospital provided for £83.889m and, as usual, further amounts will be approved by year end. These figures undermine the statement in the Deloitte & Touche Report (p. 210), for which no evidence was adduced, that an annual operating cost profile of £87m for the Hospital would be significantly out of line with other acute hospitals. This was a remarkably inaccurate conclusion given that the funding allocations to the other four large acute hospitals in Dublin in 1999 were averaging about that amount per hospital per annum.

At the end of September 1998 Deloitte and Touche Consultants were appointed by agreement between the Department and the Board of the Hospital to conduct an independent review in the context of the merger and move to the new Hospital in view of the projected deficit and current financial difficulties and to work in co-operation with Mr. Tom McCarthy of Leslie Buckley and Associates who was nominated by

---

[66] *The Deloitte & Touche Report*, op. cit., p. 61, found that the Director of Environment Services handled the 'conflict of interest' in an 'unsatisfactory manner'

the Board to facilitate the review. Later Dr. David McCutcheon stated about the circumstances of the appointment of the consultants:

> We were informed the Deloitte & Touche were being sent in to validate a case for a submission to the Department of Finance for extra funding. We opened our doors and hearts on that basis.[67]

Significantly the review did not include the Tallaght Hospital Planning Board where most of the capital expenditure responsibilities lay. The Report from Deloitte & Touche was to be made 'within a period of three weeks' to the Minister who would make the Report available to the Board of the Hospital.[68] In fact the Report was not presented formally until 3 December 1998 to the Minister and by him to the Hospital until 9 December 1998.

The period from the end of September 1998 to the end of the Board's term of office in July 1999 was a sort of 'Babylonian Captivity' for the Board with its scope for independent work and action gravely compromised as it first awaited the Report from the consultants, then dealt with the aftermath, saw any prospect for planned developments long-fingered until financial stability was restored, coped with external control under a 'troika' appointed by the Minister in the wake of the Deloitte and Touche Report and was faced with the resignation of the CEO in January 1999. The Board had then to oversee the recruitment and appointment of a new CEO and to deal with the allocation for 1999 and Service Plan. This last year in the life of the first Board of the new Hospital graphically illustrates the effects of resource dependency upon governance and management.

---

[67] Dr. D. McCutcheon in interview with Fergal Bowers 'Minister must accept some responsibility for Tallaght Hospital crisis' *Irish Medical News* 22 March 1999; in another major interview Dr. McCutcheon stated of the period from early 1998 in respect of discussions with the Department '..the information that we were getting was that we will find a way to deal with this problem. And go ahead and get the hospital opened', Dr. David McCutcheon 'Today with Pat Kenny' RTE Radio, 15 March 1999

[68] see 'Brief for Independent Review by Deloitte & Touche on behalf of the Minister for Health & Children' 29.9.1998; the Chairman, Mrs. French sought for the brief to include 'review of the adequacy of the funding allocation in the hospital's determination for 1998' but the Department would not accept this 'because the terms of the Letter of Determination are unambiguous with regard to the process required and the absolute necessity for the Hospital to remain within budget and to plan its activities accordingly' Mr. T. Morris to Mrs. R. French 16 October 1998 marked 'Private and Confidential'; the Fine Gael spokesperson, Mr. Alan Shatter T.D. stated 'it was a scandal that the terms of reference of the management consultants forbade them from looking at the adequacy of the official Department of Health funding level', see *The Sunday Tribune* 11 October 1998

5. DIVERGENCE FROM THE CHARTER FRAMEWORK OF GOVERNANCE AND MANAGEMENT

In August 1998 the CEO laid before the Board of the Hospital a set of 14 Goals and Objectives for 1998 and 1999.[69] This document clearly demonstrates that the work of the Board and the Management Team was to be reviewed prior to the appointment of the Deloitte and Touche consultants in late September. There was to be a major review through a Management Audit and a restructuring, if appropriate, of the Management Team. There was a clear wish for a smaller and tighter Management Team than had been necessary for the merger and move of the Hospital. A major goal was to develop 'an enhanced working relationship with the Department of Health and Children so as to

- secure the necessary funding for our strategic intention
- provide timely reports on financial performance
- improve communications on all developments
- present a cohesive and unified approach to the Department
- provide a timely response to all enquiries'

Another goal was to complete the merger and move process which was clearly incomplete at this stage so shortly after the opening on 21 June 1998. Thus the final year of the first Board of the Hospital was intended to be devoted to the refinement of the structures for governance and management in the light of experience and the successful merger and opening on the new campus. There was also much unfinished business—The Planning Board's work had to be transferred to the Hospital Board as specified in the Charter; the responsibilities of the Central Council of the Dublin Federation Voluntary Hospitals were also to be assumed by the Hospital Board under a similar Charter provision; St. Loman's Hospital psychiatric services were due to be transferred to the new Hospital campus by an agreement with the Eastern Health Board; the new Ward Extension Block had to be built and incorporated into the work of the Hospital; the extension to the outpatients department had to be furnished, equipped and staffed and there were many critical teething problems to be considered and resolved.

---

[69] 'CEO Goals and Objectives 98/99' dated 26/08/1998

During October there was intense media interest and public pressure on the Board and the Hospital as reports that the Hospital had overspent by up to IR£15m or IR£21m were carried in the press.[70] It appeared that the Department and the Minister were taking measures to 'shape' the story as it unfolded and to allocate any 'fallout' or blame for 'overspending' on to Dr. McCutcheon and the Hospital. The press were briefed by the Department that 'this is the first time an independent consultancy was asked to go into a hospital in this manner';[71] it was stated by 'a source close to the Minister' that 'the budget had overrun by £15m'.[72] Another report noted that 'a political source close to Cowen said : 'The Minister is not impressed by the extent of the budget overrun, which is several million pounds at least. He is not of a mind to be lenient with the Hospital management, he is going to be very tough with them'. Sources were also speculating that the CEO's job 'may be on the line after the review is completed' and the high level of his salary was generally linked to such speculation in a negative way. One story noted

> A medical source said:
> Cowen will have a free hand to do a hatchet job on the board, if that is what the consultants say should be done. On the other hand, Deloitte & Touche could be quite scathing about the Department as well and accuse it of forcing the hospital to open before it was ready.'

Phrases which had been used in confidential discussions with the Department began to appear in media reports and it was an open question whether Dr. McCutcheon was to be made 'a scapegoat'[73] Fears for the character of the Hospital were also expressed.

> Hospital figures and opposition parties in the Dáil believe that there may be more to be dispute than just a row over money. They believe that ultimately it may form part of a plan by the Department of Health to axe Tallaght's status as an independent voluntary hospital and to place it under the control of the Eastern Health Board. There are also conspiracy

[70] see, for example, '£15m crisis at top Irish hospital' *The Sunday Times* 4 October 1998 and 'Tallaght Hospital facing cash crisis' *The Irish Independent* 5 October 1998

[71] see Carol Coulter 'Tallaght Hospital confident of funding increase' *The Irish Times* 6 October 1998

[72] see Geraldine Collins 'Tallaght Hospital facing cash crisis' *Irish Independent* 5 October 1998

[73] see John Burns '£15m crisis at top Irish hospital' *The Sunday Times* 4 October 1998; one report stated the CEO's salary to be £110,000 although the press had been told the accurate amount of £80,000 see M. Wall 'Haemorrhaging losses' *The Sunday Tribune* 11 October 1998 where it is stated that the CEO was paid 'far more than that paid to Cowen or to the Secretary-General of the Department of Health, Jerry O'Dwyer'.

theories that the Department of Health was to use the current cash crisis to get its hands on more money from the forthcoming sales of the city centre premises owned by the private boards which ran the Meath, Adelaide and Harcourt Street hospitals.[74]

The fears and conspiracy theories would have not been so pervasive had there been a clear policy framework and commitment to the development of voluntary organisations in the health service. As it was, many felt that the Charter structure approved by the Oireachtas in 1996 for the new Hospital was not receiving the necessary enthusiastic support at the highest political or official levels at a crucial formative period.[75] A brief Senate Adjournment debate on the funding of the Hospital took place on 21 October 1998 during which Senator David Norris attempted to set the Hospital's finances in context and sought a more sympathetic response from the Minister for Health; he enquired what happened to a previous report commissioned from Leslie Buckley and Associates and whether the report from these consultants was 'favourable to the hospital budgetary position'.[76]

The Deloitte & Touche Report was expected from the end of October but in fact the consultants spent much longer getting to grips with a very complex situation; they were briefed in great detail by Hospital management and by members of the Board. Other 'normal' developments had to be suspended because the exercise of preparing their Report took on very extensive proportions as aspects of expenditure were researched and records examined. The proposed major Management Audit and Review of the Management Team was suspended and management generally was distracted from operational matters. A key Management Team review 'weekend' was cancelled putting the Management Audit on ice. External control of what was happening on a day to day basis had clearly begun. Staff concerns had to be allayed especially about the media reports.[77] The Board was also

[74] see M.Wall 'Haemorrhaging Losses' *The Sunday Tribune* 11 October 1998

[75] the unwillingness to send in the consultants to the Tallaght Hospital Planning Board was noted as the capital expenditures which were accrued by this Board were glibly and erroneously attributed to the alleged 'overspending' by the Hospital Board; it appeared all the responsibility was being attributed to the Board which had the voluntary character as set out in the Charter, see, for example, profile of Dr. D. McCutcheon by Charles Hogan 'Medical boss who needs a cure for his hospital's cash crisis' *The Sunday Business Post* 11 October 1998

[76] Seanad Éireann, Adjournment Debate, Wednesday, 21 October 1998

[77] see, for example, 'Letter to All Staff' from the Chairman, Mrs. Rosemary French, *Pulses* 21 October 1998

finding it difficult to maintain a positive posture under the pressure.[78] There were clear 'leaks' of Board papers also which undermined the confidence of other members of the Board. The *Irish Medical Times* in early November was able to circulate copies of draft Board minutes from the October meeting.[79] Such breaches of confidence by someone in possession of Board papers had occurred from time to time since 1996 and it was learned later that at least one member of the Board had been in telephone contact at a very significant point during a Board meeting with a key official in the Department of Health and with a member of the Management Team.[80] In the increasingly fraught atmosphere the standard of behaviour normally expected of Board members in honouring the duties of loyalty and confidentiality was not universally adhered to and this added to a sense of things being outside the control of the Board which began to prevail as crucial events for the Board now followed in rapid succession.

The publicity given in November 1998 to the internal problems in the Department of Health & Children was a further factor in diminishing confidence in the relationships between the Department and the Hospital with headlines such as 'Job Case Sparks 'bloody' civil war in Department'. During a High Court action an Assistant Secretary at the Department in an affidavit claimed that the Secretary-General had engaged in 'a litany of untruths and deceptions' and that 'Mr. O'Dwyer's general attitude was that the problems would go away if he dismissed or ignored them'.[81] These internal difficulties remained at this period in the Department and worried many that these problems would colour how they would handle the Hospital's very public crisis.[82]

[78] see 'Hospital Surprised by Department's Concern about budget overrun' *The Irish Times* 13 October 1998 where Dr. David McConnell sought to explain that the Board believed it 'had a degree of comfort from the Department in relation to the additional funding' and that the Board 'have welcomed the appointment of consultants Deloitte and Touche to examine the budget and arrangements for service planning'.

[79] See 'Crisis at Tallaght Hospital Intensifies' *Irish Medical Times* 5 November 1998 and copy of press statement issued by *Irish Medical Times* confirming their documentary evidence for the story

[80] see Board Minutes, 27 January 1999

[81] see 'O'Dwyer accused of dismissing problems of hepatitis C crisis' *The Irish Times* 19 November 1998 referring to a High Court action by an officer of the Department of Health; see also 'Civil servant denies going out of her way to find controversy' *The Irish Times* 20 November 1998 'Job Case Sparks 'bloody' Civil War in Department' *The Sunday Independent* 29 November 1998

[82] see also M. Wall 'Civil Service row 'affecting health service'' *The Sunday Tribune* 21 February 1999 and 'Cowen adviser resigns over internal dispute' *The Sunday Tribune* 28 February 1999; see also 'Another job row action for Health Department' *The Irish Times* 6 March 1999 and 'Health staff morale hits all-time low' *The Sunday Tribune* 7 March 1999

The Deloitte & Touche Report was submitted formally to the Minister for Health and Children on 3 December 1998.[83] The Report ran to 211 pages with additional pages of appendices. There were two key findings:

1) the Hospital Board should not have approved the 1998 Service Plan in excess of the Letter of Determination as a matter of proper governance.

2) the Department of Health and Children's method of funding in arriving at the 1998 Determination of IR£53.6m was 'inappropriate' and a 'blunt instrument' in the context of the merger and move in 1998.

The Minister in presenting the Report to representatives of the Board on Wednesday, 9 December 1998 stated that while the Report indicated a revenue deficit of £13.2m the statutory adjustments permitted under the Letter of Determination would bring the deficit to £8.5m which he insisted was the full responsibility of the Board. Capital expenditure would be reviewed separately. The £8.5m revenue expenditure included capital expenditure incurred by the Hospital Board in order to open the Hospital safely to the amount of £4m approximately.[84] In 1998 the Hospital had recurring net expenditure on a monthly basis of c £6.1m while the Letter of Determination funding available to it was c £4.5m per month on average so that the deficit was increasing at the rate of c £1.6m per month in effect.[85] The Minister outlined his proposal for a 'troika' a structure of three people one appointed by the Minister, one appointed by the Hospital President, the Archbishop of Dublin and an independent Chairman which would work to oversee the recommendations in the Report in respect of governance and management.

---

[83] there have been subsequent questions asked about the drafting or re-drafting of the Report in discussions with the Department of Health and Children, see Mr. A. Shatter, Dáil Éireann *Parliamentary Debates*, 16 February 1999, Col. 797 where he states: 'The Minister and his Department have been loathe to release documentation concerning the contacts between Departmental officials and the Deloitte & Touche during the course of carrying out their consultancy. We now know there were three different draft versions of this Report before it was finally published. [He challenged the Minister to release all the documentation] so that we will know finally whether this was truly an independent Report or whether to some degree it was influenced by secret discussions that took place with Departmental officials'.

[84] see 'Response To Deloitte and Touche Report', December 1998, p. 4

[85] *Deloitte & Touche Report* p 2

It was agreed at the meeting with the Minister on 9 December that there should be no preliminary public debate until there was agreement on the way forward in resolving the problems. The Hospital agreed to be bound by this and it was agreed that a joint press statement should be issued next day after the Hospital Board meeting that evening. However, while the Board was meeting that evening and considering how to keep the Report confidential as agreed it became known that the Minister had issued a press statement stating that the Report contained 'serious governance and general management problems';[86] the Board felt this was in gross breach of the agreement made that morning. The need to 'shape' the public perception was evidently stronger than the need to honour an agreed approach. The report next morning in *The Irish Times* was headed 'Cowen to install his own team at Tallaght hospital' which contained briefings from 'Department of Health sources' to the effect that the Report was 'seriously critical' of the Hospital.[87] On 'Morning Ireland' RTE Radio 1 Thursday, 10 December, Rory Hafford of *Medicine Weekly* commented that the Minister was engaged in a 'sort of sabre rattling and it's Brian Cowen playing politics as well'.[88]

In the Dáil on Thursday, 10 December, the Opposition called for the Minister to resign as he was 'addressing issues relating to the hospital with the sensitivity of a stampeding herd of rhinos'; at this stage the Minister was not prepared to publish the Report. Mr. Shatter, the Opposition Spokesperson accused the Minister of 'an unprecedented breach of faith towards the hospital's board and management . . . The Minister's strategy was to point the finger at the Board as being solely responsible for any difficulties and target them for the blame'.[89]

[86] Press statement from Press Office, Department of Health and Children, 9 December 1998

[87] 'Cowen To Install his own Team at Tallaght hospital Report Reveals serious management problems' *The Irish Times* 10 December 1998

[88] Transcript of 'Tallaght Hospital Report' 'Morning Ireland' RTE Radio 1, 10 December 1998

[89] 'Cowen is criticised over hospital finances' *The Irish Times*, 11 December 1998; Mr. Shatter in an article written for the *Irish Independent* called for the Minister to 'adopt the correct approach to the proper funding of this hospital. It is essential that he not only provide the funding required to maintain existing services but also the additional funding necessary to bring on stream the enhanced services for which the hospital was originally built and for which he previously stated he would provide funding in 1999.' In conclusion Mr. Shatter stated 'It would be a tragedy if Tallaght Hospital was to become the latest casualty of an inept Minister presiding over a deeply divided Department in which senior officials are engaged in trench warfare as evidenced by a recent much publicised High Court case'

The Minister of Health, Mr. Cowen, at the 10 December Dáil 'Adjournment Debate' on the content of the Deloitte & Touche Report stated that the financial problem only arose in late August and September as the results for the first six months of the year were in line with the hospital's budget. The Hospital Board in fact had been advising the Department of Health of the additional requirements of the new facility from the beginning of the year; the Board had approved the Service Plan £5.8m over the Letter of Determination allocation in April and its budget based on the Plan was reported monthly to the Department. There had been considerable publicity also about the funding needs of the Hospital as early as March and April 1998 and in June 1998. At the meeting on 9 December the Minister stated that he would not fund the deficit of £8.5m and the Hospital Board felt that this issue was a matter for discussion at the very least at that point as to who was responsible for it and that they had been given time by the Minister for such discussion, before the matter would be foreclosed in public by the Minister. The Board was aware that the Minister, under the 1996 Act, had the power to vary the Determination originally made for 1998 and felt that their unique circumstances justified a variation. It was felt that the Minister had pre-empted such a discussion having placed his position on the Dáil record.[90]

The political heat was being felt at Ministerial level and the Board felt betrayed: it was not a good context to resolve the financial crisis. *The Sunday Times* on 13 December 1998 ran a front page story entitled 'Irish hospital chief under pressure to quit £100,000 job' written by Ursula Halligan who had obviously been briefed with the as yet unpublished Report with the objective of blaming the CEO for the crisis which it was claimed was 'the latest in a litany of disasters to beset the hospital'. As a result of the actions of the Department since 9 December the Chairman of the Board, Mrs. Rosemary French, issued a lengthy and unprecedentedly strong statement on 13 December that she was

---

[90] Statement by Mr. Brian Cowen, T.D., Minister for Health and Children, to Adjournment Debate on Thursday, 10 December 1998 in Dáil Éireann; subsequently it emerged that the Department of Finance was not informed of any 'special problem' in relation to the new Hospital in Tallaght up to August and September so that news of the deficit came as 'an unpleasant surprise' to the Department of Finance see 'Cost Overruns at Tallaght Hospital' Paper from Department of Finance sent in March 1999 to Committee of Public Accounts, Dáil Éireann

deeply concerned at the failure of the Department of Health & Children to live up to its undertakings, in particular those made by the Secretary-General of the Department of Health & Children to the new Hospital at Tallaght. The Chairman is reluctantly forced to conclude that the Minister for Health & Children and the Department of Health & Children are failing the new Hospital and the people of Tallaght. It is anticipated that the Board will have to consider seriously how it will be possible at the most senior level of Government, to re-establish a positive working relationship with the Department of Health and Children.

The Chairman went on to say that she

had been appalled by the breach of trust by the Department of Health & Children which had undertaken not to comment in public on the Deloitte & Touche Report until the Board had had an opportunity to consider it. The Department of Health & Children released a critical and biased press statement to the press on Wednesday evening while the Board was meeting. This deception has been compounded by the leaking of a confidential Department of Health & Children memorandum in the Sunday papers, and the premature, hasty and misleading statement by the Minister for Health & Children to the Dáil last Thursday which did not reflect the balance of the Deloitte & Touche Report. The Chairman has been forced to conclude that the Department of Health & Children has set out to campaign against and pillory the Hospital.

The Chairman's statement posed five questions for the 'Minister and his officials to answer' and concluded by affirming the Board's total confidence in the CEO, Dr. McCutcheon 'who has masterminded the hugely successful transfer of patients and medical services to the new site and taken on many extra responsibilities which have been unnecessarily imposed by the inadequate procedures of the Department of Health & Children'. The Chairman stated that 'she now feels totally betrayed by the outrageous statements made by the Department of Health & Children in the last week'.[91]

The five questions posed by the Chairman were

1) Since the Deloittte & Touche Report has been received, why has the Department of Health & Children, while fully involved in the planning of the new Hospital, and fully informed during the entire process of building, equipping, furnishing and commissioning it and in particular fully informed by the Chief Executive of the Hospital of the costs involved in the move to Tallaght, found it necessary to attempt to undermine the Hospital just at the time when its success seemed assured?

[91] 'Minister Failing New Hospital and People of Tallaght', Press Statement, Sunday, 13 December 1998

2) Why did the Department of Health & Children find it possible to write off the capital overrun incurred by the Tallaght Hospital Planning Board, chaired by Prof.. Richard Conroy, which was responsible for funding, equipping and furnishing the new Hospital (many of whose responsibilities were unfulfilled by 21 June 1998) but impossible to meet the revenue overrun currently being experienced by the Board of the Hospital?

3) How was it ever possible to believe let alone persist in the belief that a new hospital could be commissioned, opened and run for many millions less than it costs merely to run established hospitals serving similar catchment populations?

4) Why did the Minister for Health & Children and his officials find it necessary to put intense pressure on the hospital to open in 1998, to signal clearly in many consultation with the Chairman, the Chief Executive and other officers that financial problems would be dealt with, and then to refuse to accept responsibility for the over-run?

5) The Deloitte & Touche Report clearly indicates that a Letter of Determination was an inappropriate method ('blunt instrument') for deciding on a correct level of funding in the opening period of a new Hospital. Why did the Department of Health & Children persist in using this mechanism when the Hospital informed it repeatedly of the obvious financial difficulties and uncertainties? Why does the Department of Health & Children now propose to use the same defective mechanism for 1999 while the Hospital is still not fully established?

On 'Morning Ireland' RTE Radio 1, on Monday 14 December the Hon. Treasurer, Professor D. McConnell gave a detailed and trenchant interview based on the Chairman's Statement. He was very critical of the Minister and of the Department of Health and Children implying clearly that the problems would have to be resolved by the Government as a whole. Professor McConnell called for the Minister to publish the Report and the Minister responded with a Statement that day announcing publication for the next day: he stated 'I and my Department now stand accused by the Board of Management of selectively leaking the Report. I wish to refute that categorically'.[92]

---

[92] Statement by Brian Cowen, T.D., Minister for Health and Children re Tallaght Hospital 14 December 1998

The Report was published on Tuesday 15 December as *The Irish Times* put it 'against a background of bitter recrimination'. The Minister rejected the accusation that he had misled the Dáil. He also denied that 'he or his Department had selectively leaked the Report'. The implication of Professor McConnell's remarks on the Radio, that the matter should be taken out of the Minister's hands and be handled henceforth at the 'highest level of Government', in fact probably reinforced the Minister's hand in Government which either had to back him or sack him; naturally they backed him: 'Mr. Cowen responded sharply that he was the Minister and, with his Department, would deal with the matter'.[93]

The Hospital was receiving public support: John Considine, an economist specialising in health and social spending, wrote an article in *The Irish Independent* on Tuesday 15 December 1998 broadly critical of the Minister's approach: 'he has made a rod for his back and his opponents are not sparing it'. The Opposition Spokesperson on Health wrote an article stating that the Hospital 'has been treated disgracefully' by the Minister:

> There would have been no crisis had the Minister had the political courage to publish the Report a day after furnishing it to the Tallaght Board and to then admit that he, his Department and the Hospital Board and Management had issues to face.[94]

The Medical Board of the Hospital met on Monday evening, 14 December, and 'voted unanimously to declare their full support for the Chief Executive Officer, Dr. David McCutcheon and the Board of Management of the new Hospital'.[95]

The Hospital Board was a different matter: the political storm which had arisen now put almost intolerable pressures on the various coalitions reflected in the composition of the Board which hitherto had maintained a unified approach in the face of a series of successive 'critical contingency situations'.

The Board met on Wednesday 16 December to consider in detail the response to the Minister and to the Report. Those appointed to the

[93] 'Cowen Denies he misled Dáil on Tallaght Hospital Report' *The Irish Times* 15 December 1998

[94] see J. Considine 'Funding Row Reopens old wounds' and A. Shatter 'Minister's own headache' in *The Irish Independent*, 15 December 1998

[95] see Medical Board Press Release, Tuesday 15 December 1998

Board by the Meath Hospital Foundation and other members, expressed deep concern about the Chairman's Press Statement and Professor McConnell's radio interview. There was no prospect of a united Board position to confront the Minister and the Department. A united stance by the Board was essential to have any prospect of obtaining concessions of more funding from the Government and even then perhaps the Minister would have continued to hold to his line. The price of keeping a semblance of Board unity was to concede to the Minister's proposals to address the crisis. At his Press Conference on Tuesday 15 December when asked about his confidence in the ability of the Hospital Board and management to solve the crisis, the Minister stated 'There's a lot of work to be done before the Board and management can stand alone'.[96] The internal dynamics of the Board had now changed fundamentally as the Chairman's public position was effectively undermined. What emerged from this crisis in the last year of the Board was a new 'dominant coalition' oriented to the statutory authorities and made up of the 'troika' appointed by the Minister and those members of the Hospital Board who saw that their only option was to agree to the Minister's prescriptions.

Thus the response of the Board to the Minister's proposals was not to accept formal responsibility for the IR£8.5m deficit but in practice to find ways of funding it from income sources such as the private car park. The Board accepted the need to address governance and management issues raised in the Report as it had clearly been aware of the need for review and refinement after the move in any event well before the Consultants had been appointed. The Board acquiesced in the appointment of a 'troika' which would have expertise and knowledge in the health field and its systems. A priority was to obtain the Letter of Determination for 1999 which the Department would not issue until it got satisfaction on these issues.

The Officers of the Board met with the Minister and officials on Thursday 17 December and reported back to a resumed meeting that evening. It had been agreed that a further meeting would take place on Friday 18 December with the Minister and his officials following this resumed Board meeting. Many Board members were intensely discomforted at seeking to respond to the Minister's proposals which they believed was 'justifying injustice; others felt more pragmatically that the

---

[96] See Carol Coulter 'Cowen may have his eye on the assets of Tallaght foundations' *The Irish Times* 19 December 1998

power lay with the Minister and his Department and that the Board must accept that position.'[97]

On Friday 18 December at the meeting with the Minister 'agreement in principle' was reached 'on the mechanism to oversee implementation of the Deloitte & Touche Report'. The Hospital agreed to meet the 1998 projected deficit by way of a long-term bank loan and it was agreed the Letter of Determination for 1999 would be issued to the Hospital in the following week.[98]

The press coverage on Saturday 19 December 1998 continued to be favourable to the Hospital as it was not yet clearly appreciated that the Board had in effect succumbed to external control because of its resource dependency upon the Department of Health & Children which had exposed the fissures in the 'hybrid' construction of the Board. In a situation of a public power play a 'hybrid' voluntary board, with constituent elements either vulnerable to political pressure or reluctant to confront a powerful Minister and his Department in public, more power resided with the Minister and he prevailed. The attempt to have power exercised at a higher level than the Department had failed. Bruce Arnold wrote on the Saturday

> What should happen now is that the Board should stand firm, and demand from the Department the sorting out of the financial mess . . . Secondly, the Taoiseach should recognise that the issues here transcend health on its own. If people could recall more clearly the ethical debate which was so vital a part of the evolution of Tallaght Hospital, far greater sensitivity might have been the result.[99]

A success which might be claimed on the Hospital side was that the three voluntary Foundations in the Hospital avoided the clear threat to their voluntary funds as a source of rectifying the debt. In any event any such threat was quite inappropriate given the charitable trusts involved in the funds of these Foundations. This has ensured an ongoing source of voluntary commitment to 'new and enhanced services' at the Hospital by these voluntary bodies which will continue to appoint 15 Board members out of 23 members every three years.[100]

[97] Board Minutes, 16/17 December 1998

[98] Joint Press Statement, 18 December 1998, by Hospital Board and Department of Health and Children

[99] Bruce Arnold 'Tallaght Hospital saga—it's a question of 'Not so fast, Minister Cowen'' *The Irish Independent* 19 December 1998

[100] see Carol Coulter 'Cowen may have his eye on the assets of Tallaght foundations' *The Irish Times* 19 December 1998

Carol Coulter reported that 'the mood in the Tallaght Hospital board has been a mixture of anger and betrayal during the week. But it has not been one of surrender'; her report went on

> As the Northern peace agreement takes another creeping step forward, there must be some muttering to politicians about the signals which would be sent North if it appeared that the plug was pulled on the State's only multidenominational hospital, pledged to protect a Protestant ethos.[101]

The Board did not 'surrender' in the sense of resigning as it might well have done on the basis that it could not accept the degrading of the Hospital implied by the underfunding of the existing and planned services. This was described as the 'worst-case scenario' by a 'source close to the Board'.[102] However, the completion of the first Board's term of office between January and July 1999 was to be punctuated with a further series of major events which were the direct consequence of the financial crisis and which circumscribed the ability of the Board to govern and the Hospital management to develop and plan for the future work of the Hospital.

On 19 January 1999 the CEO Dr. David McCutcheon's resignation was presented to a special meeting of the Board which was accepted 'with the utmost regret'.[103] The Hospital President, Most Reverend Dr. W.N.F. Empey, wrote an open letter to the staff of the Hospital on that day and he visited the Hospital, expressing 'the sense of shock' which he shared with the staff and stating

> From the time of his appointment, Dr. McCutcheon has shown himself to be a man of principle, vision, courage and skill. It is a huge task to bring three hospitals together, each with its own proud tradition of care for patients. Dr. McCutcheon has played a key and essential role in bringing this vision to reality. His resignation is an enormous loss to the Hospital . . .

[101] ibid; Miss Mary Harney, T.D., in the Dáil Debate approving the Charter had welcomed 'the pluralism and multi-denominational aspects at play in this joint venture' and had hoped that 'the manner in which anxieties were dealt with will become a blueprint for tackling other issues in this society' see *Dáil Éireann Parliamentary Debates* Vol. 468, No. 1, 3 July 1996, Col. 27

[102] Carol Coulter, 19 December 1999, op. cit.

[103] Minutes of Board, 19 January 1999; the Board gave Dr. McCutcheon a standing ovation in tribute to his achievement in the Hospital since October 1996; subsequently Dr. David McCutcheon was appointed CEO of the Sunnybrook & Women's College Health Sciences Centre in Toronto, Canada which is an acute hospital of approx. 1,200 beds affiliated to University of Toronto with an annual revenue budget of IR£170m approx. see his 'Letter to all Staff' 3 March 1999 issued as he ceased his responsibilities as CEO of the Hospital at Tallaght.

The evidence of his efforts is to be seen visibly in the form of the new hospital.. . .The Board of the Hospital has also worked very hard and I want to pay tribute to it also for the way it has surmounted the many obstacles that have come its way. The dedication of its members is of the highest order as they grappled with the many problems that were not of their making. The Board has my full confidence'.[104]

Dr. McCutcheon later stated publicly why he resigned:

> . . ..I resigned because understandings that I had with a group of people that I trusted in the Department of Health, those understandings . . . were not carried out . . . we made what we thought was a deal, an agreement on May the sixth, with the Department of Health . . . That was a written undertaking . . . I am saying . . . that my understanding which was based on trust with Department officials, that that trust has been breached . . . I don't want to be the Chief Executive in a system that allows that to take place . . . The trust is broken.[105]

Dr. McCutcheon insisted that the Department of Health agreed that there would be a 'bubble of costs' associated with the new Hospital that would be funded for some years.[106] He stated that the Deloitte & Touche initiative undermined his role as CEO: 'It was the wrong time, just 15 weeks after opening, and it disrupted the management process. We had already identified the problems and had scheduled a strategic planning conference'. He added that many viewed the move as a 'kick in the teeth' and 'an attempt by the Department to gain control of a voluntary hospital'.[107] Following this resignation there was much talk of how the CEO had fallen victim to the 'convoluted Irish way of doing things'. The Chairman of the Medical Board in the Hospital, Dr. David FitzPatrick believed that Dr. McCutcheon's management style was 'too advanced for the Department of Health to fully appreciate'; stating

> He had much clearer ideas on a management structure for a hospital than we would normally see in an Irish hospital. Even though the Deloitte and Touche Report criticised the multiplicity of committees which he had set

[104] Letter to Staff of the Adelaide and Meath Hospital, Incorporating the National Children's Hospital from the Hospital President 19 January 1999

[105] 'Transcript of Interview between Dr. David McCutcheon and Pat Kenny' RTE Radio 1, 15 March 1999; he told the staff: 'I believe that we must always be guided by our principles, particularly during times of tumultuous change when our principles may be our only constant', Dr. D. McCutcheon 'Letter to All Staff' 3 March 1999

[106] Interview between Dr. McCutcheon and Fergal Bowers 'Minister must accept some responsibility for Tallaght Hospital Crisis' *Irish Medical News* 22 March 1999

[107] ibid; Dr. McCutcheon stated that 'the personalised attacks' on him were also hurtful and difficult for his family.

up, they failed to appreciate that they all had a purpose, primarily to get the hospital up and functioning. The idea was that they would be reduced later. This was devolved management, even though he was accused of not devolving enough. A prophet is without honour in his own country.[108]

The problems confronting the Board in Tallaght in January 1999 were further compounded by a public perception of a general crisis in the Irish health services with a surge in demand for services especially in Dublin and the Hospital at Tallaght was the focal point of concern. The waiting lists were continuing to grow during the early months of 1999.[109] While the Minister continued to insist on proper governance and management procedures and controls as being the core issue in Tallaght those involved noted the irony when the Comptroller and Auditor General accused the Department of Health itself of a 'fundamental abuse' of public financial procedures in 1997 and stated that 'a coach and four' was driven through normal public financial procedures by the Department in respect of a IR£20 million transaction due from the British Health Authorities. The Chairman of the Committee of Public Accounts, Mr. Jim Mitchell, T.D., said the Department of Health's behaviour was 'as big an exercise in cooking the books' as he had seen in a while.[110] In public the Minister was criticised for selectively treating the Deloitte and Touche Report 'as a blueprint for getting out of the difficulties into which he and his Department have driven the whole complex set of structures' but then not accepting within the Report 'the deep and fundamental criticism of himself and the Department over the way they set up and then monitored the creation of the hospital'. There was a danger that this would threaten the appointment of any new Chief Executive:

> It also threatens the independence of the Tallaght Board, which occupies a very special position within Irish medicine . . . The basic mistake over Tallaght remains the original under-funding . . . At the same time he claims an absolute control over budget—he said yesterday: 'We decide budget, not the Board'—yet holds up a Report which tells us that the Department was wrong and confused about the very budget it was meant to decide.[111]

[108] A. O'Connor 'Tallaght Hospital boss fall victim to convoluted Irish way of going things' *The Irish Times* 23 January 1999

[109] Transcript of Interview Between Minister Brian Cowen and Pat Kenny, RTE Radio 1, 22 January 1999

[110] 'Department accused of basic abuse of financial procedures' *The Irish Times* 29 January 1999

[111] Bruce Arnold 'The Undermining of Tallaght' *The Irish Independent* 23 January 1999

The wider implications of the 'disaster' which has 'struck Tallaght Hospital' to use Bruce Arnold's phraseology were noted by historian Ronan Fanning in seeking to answer a question raised by the Taoiseach Mr. Ahern:

Why is even a pluralist Ireland foreign to unionists? Tallaght is the answer . . . Our new pluralist Ireland is foreign to unionists because the Department of Health, as agents of the State, want to ride rough-shod over the ethos of the independent Protestant hospitals embodied in the Tallaght Hospital . . . Dr. McCutcheon's fate was to fall foul of the faceless mandarins of the old Ireland.

There are moments when health policy issues become too important to be left in the hands of officials in the Department of Health. The most histori- cally momentous of which was the Mother and Child controversy of 1951. The crisis over the Tallaght Hospital is another such moment . . . Tallaght Hospital has become the symbol of whether this has become a more pluralist State.[112]

However the punitive path set out for the Board of the Hospital by the Minister did not become any easier; on the contrary it was announced that the Hospital was 'to be stripped of children's cancer unit' in the very paper which carried Ronan Fanning's explicit article.[113] A letter was received that a Ministerial decision had been made that 'every child with cancer should be seen initially at Our Lady's Hospital, Crumlin' with no prior discussion with the Board of the Adelaide & Meath Hospital. This was clearly perceived as a breach of the Charter of the Hospital which was designed to protect the existing paediatric services of the National Children's Hospital because it provided the only children's hospital services in the country not under Catholic auspices. It was revealed later in February that the Department 'Briefing Note' for the Minister of Health referred to this Charter commitment but still recommended all cancers, including leukaemia, should be referred to Crumlin for initial diagnosis and treatment planning.[114]

[112] R. Fanning 'Bertie's New Ireland: just an empty formula?' *The Sunday Independent* 24 January 1999

[113] Fergal Bowers 'Tallaght to be stripped of children's cancer unit' *The Sunday Independent* 24 January 1999

[114] see Carol Coulter'Department fears led to switch from Tallaght' *The Irish Times*, 27 February 1999 and Carol Coulter 'Members of hospital board seek to fight changes' *The Irish Times* 2 March 1999 which quoted one member of the Board stating 'that the Board should consider what steps are necessary to clarify the status of the Charter, and whether it has any meaning or not'; the steps considered would include legal action, he said: 'What should have been a symbol of unity and reconciliation has been turned into a symbol of betrayal and mistrust, of how you can edge minorities out of health care'

Meanwhile the Board was struggling to come to terms with the loss of the CEO, the preparation of the 1999 Service Plan based up an allocation of IR£64.690m which was widely perceived to be insufficient to maintain existing staff numbers and service activity levels, and the arrival of the 'troika' to supervise the behaviour and response of the Board and management and to report on this to the Minister.

The Board appointed an Acting Deputy Chief Executive for a period of six months on 19 January 1999 as work intensified to produce a Service Plan and to take out a loan to cover the £8.5m deficit from 1998.

The Minister requested that the Board should postpone its final decision on the Service Plan for 1999 to allow for the participation of the Troika group.[115] These three experts were appointed to ensure that

i) The Hospital retains fully the confidence of the public, staff and suppliers;

ii) The recommendations of the Deloitte & Touche Report are implemented fully as speedily as possible

iii) Governance and high level management are secured to a level which will enable the planned phased development of services at the hospital to be resumed.[116]

The President of the Hospital, Archbishop Empey had declined the Minister's invitation to become involved in appointing the 'troika' but he was to be kept advised by the Minister of their assessment of progress and the 'troika' was to remain in place for a term to be decided by the Minister in consultation with the President.[117]

The Service Plan for 1999 was approved by the Board on 16 February 1999 in controversial circumstances on the very day a 'No

[115] Board minutes, 27 January 1999

[116] Terms of Reference of the 'Troika' January 1999; the three members were Professor John Murray, Professor of Business Studies, Trinity College, Dublin, nominated by Hospital Board, Mr. Donal O'Shea, Chairman of the Eastern Regional Health Authority Task Force and CEO, North Eastern Health Board and Mr. Kevin Bonner, of Business Insight who had been Secretary-General of the Department of Enterprise and Employment; they were to be assisted by Deloitte & Touche Consultants.

[117] it is of note that the Hospital solicitors advised the Board that the implementation of the proposed terms of reference of the 'troika' could be 'ultra vires' as they could involve the powers exercisable by the Board being exercised by the three person group who would report to the Minister and not to the Board; the recommendations of the solicitors were not accepted by the Board which felt it had no alternative but to accede to the Minister's proposals, see A & L Goodbody to Dr. D. McCutcheon, 21 December 1998

confidence' motion was debated in Dáil Éireann in respect of the Minister for Health and Children in which the Hospital's financial situation was seen as critical. The Minister on that day informed the Dáil that the Service Plan 'on the basis of the information now available to me, will comply with the requirements set out in the Letter of Determination'. The approved Plan included provision for IR£1m additional monies in 1999 provided by letter delivered to the Board on 16 February 'to develop top priority services' when the recommendations of the Deloitte & Touche Report were satisfactorily addressed.[119]

In the course of the 'No Confidence' debate Mr. Pat Rabbite T.D., a local representative, stated

> The Board has been browbeaten into reluctantly endorsing a Service Plan which a majority do not believe can work. The realpolitik of the situation dictates that they had no choice but to bend the knee to the Department . . . We have lost a Chief Executive of international standing and embroiled a new Hospital in unnecessary conflict . . . It is a pity, for whatever reason, the Minister has chosen to spoil the ship for a ha'p'orth of tar. It was unnecessary that this tremendous new hospital for which the people of Tallaght waited so long should have been born in conflict and controversy.[120]

There is no doubt that 'cold winds of change' were blowing as hospital cutbacks were awaited following the controversy which had now been so public for almost six months. One journalist's account:

> Along the corridors, union stewards carry bulky ballot boxes in preparation for industrial action as anxious workers make eager enquiries as to when they can cast their vote. In a quiet corner, a group of catering staff, terrified for their livelihoods, probe each other for information. One of them a girl in her twenties, is in tears claiming she can take no more.
> A junior doctor, clearly rushed off his feet, tries to assuage the anger of an elderly woman who is worn out with waiting. At the doorway a young mother tends to her toddler's bleeding face, complaining to herself about the long delay they have been subjected to. Just seven months since the

---

[118] Mr. Brian Cowen, T.D., *Dáil Éireann Parliamentary Debates*, Vol. 500, No. 4, 16 February 1999, Col. 789

[119] The Board, in approving the 1999 Service Plan, noted how difficult it would be to achieve what was laid out in the Plan despite the best effort and determination of all involved; serious reservations were expressed in writing to the Chairman of the 'Troika' that the targets may not be possible with the available resources. The Plan was approved with one vote against and one abstention with a total of nineteen Board members present, Board minutes, 16 February 1999

[120] Mr. Pat Rabbitte, T.D. *Dáil Éireann Parliamentary Debates*, Vol. 500, No. 5, 17 February 1999, Cols, 1132–3

opening of this state-of-the-art medical facility in one of Europe's fastest growing centres of population, staff morale has reached an all-time low and public dissatisfaction has never been higher.

The hospital that was supposed to be the beacon of light in the Irish health service is showing symptoms of terminal illness.[121]

This was perhaps the lowest point; at a number of Board meetings in March steps were taken to begin to build a better prospect for the new Board which would take office from the 1 August 1999. People were attempting to learn from the grim circumstances that had 'captured' the Board from the previous September.

In February the Board had commenced the process of recruiting a new CEO despite the unfavourable public circumstances for this critical appointment. By June 1999 a new appointment was approved when Mr.Michael Lyons, Chief Executive of Aut Even Hospital, Kilkenny, was appointed CEO from 1 September 1999. This provided new hope that with a new Board from 1 August 1999 and the actions taken in response to the Deloitte & Touche Report that a stable environment might be allowed to ensue for the Hospital's steady development.

On 10 March the Board appointed as Interim CEO, Mr. Nicholas Jermyn, the Chief Executive of St. Vincent's Hospital, on a part-time basis. This facilitated a most difficult transition and prepared the ground for the new permanent appointment. On 31 March the Board approved a three month moratorium on Board Committees, effectively ending the governance structures introduced in 1997, in order to allow the Management Team of the Hospital to focus exclusively on implementing the Service Plan: it was crucial to the Hospital to stay within the Letter of Determination for 1999 and the role of the Board became, for the remaining period of office, the more limited one of receiving reports from the management and the Officers who communicated with the 'troika'. A challenge for the new Board will be to resume full responsibility for the governance of the Hospital. The constituent groups on the Board were now looking forward to the new Board and the Board appointment process had commenced from the end of March in order to have the Charter procedures discharged and the new Board in place by 1 August 1999.

The Board received regular reports on the implementation of the recommendations of the Deloitte & Touche Report and on the advice of the 'troika'. None of the recommendations proved controversial for

[121] Gemma Doherty 'D-day for Tallaght–cold wind of change blows as hospital cutback details are awaited' *The Irish Independent* 16 February 1999

the Board underlining the Board's general understanding that they reflected management changes and improvements contemplated before the appointment of the Consultants in September 1998. New governance arrangements for the Board were clearly going to be a matter for the new Board and Officers in conjunction with the new CEO their having had the benefit of the advice of the 'troika' and having considered the Governance Initiative Discussion Document issued by the Department of Health and Children in June 1999.

6. GOVERNANCE AND MANAGEMENT IMPLICATIONS: THE CHARTER FRAMEWORK AND THE DELOITTE & TOUCHE REPORT—AN ANALYSIS

Given that the decisive issue for the governance and management of organisations relates to who sets the organisation's goals the experiences which have been described of the first Board of the Hospital, as a public voluntary hospital, are instructive.[122] It is apparent that a series of divergences from the governance and management arrangements made by the Board and inspired by the Charter's voluntary principles occurred in rapid succession from September 1998.

The divergences began with the effects of the appointment in September 1998 of the Deloitte & Touche Consultants: it is clear that both the Board and senior management were distracted from the Board's own goals and work programme set out in August 1998 which became effectively delayed and derailed. The financial crisis and the appointment of Deloitte and Touche Consultants just over a hundred days, after the major logistical task of transferring three functioning hospitals to one site without a break in service, 'aborted' the planned review and further development of the governance and management structures. The last Goal as presented by the CEO in August 1998 was to achieve the other Goals 'consistent with the values of the organisation'. With the arrival of the Consultants external control of the work of the Board and the Hospital became manifest. The resource dependency of the Hospital upon its paymasters, the Department of Health and Children, in effect coerced the Board towards a different model of governance and management than it had hitherto wished to pursue: it was no longer effectively in charge of its own character and shape as had been from 1996. A kind of 'Babylonian Captivity' of the Board had commenced due to the rigid application of 'service planning' at a

---

[122] see above Chapter 4 pp 152-155

crucial formative period of the new Hospital's development. The unsympathetic shape given to the 'public' story of the Hospital's position by the Department of Health and Children from September 1998 onwards illustrates the absence of a clear commitment and framework in respect of voluntary organisations. It revealed a degree of antipathy from the statutory side which is contrary to the stated public policy to respect the independence and autonomy of voluntary agencies.

The imposition of an 'external control' mechanism on the Board, through the appointment of the 'troika' from January 1999, despite the reservations of the Hospital Board's legal advisers about the Board's powers under the Charter being put at risk, and the ignoring of the Charter commitments in the blunt announcement of the changes to the paediatric services in the same month is further evidence of a pattern of behaviour by the statutory authorities which undermined confidence in the voluntary character enshrined in the Charter. By March 1999 the Board had ceased to use its committee structure at all, except for the Resources Committee, and effectively left detailed consideration of matters to its Officers in conjunction with the 'troika' and senior management. This is evidence of the erosion of the voluntary ethos which had characterised the Board's own preferred approach to governance and management.

The Board of the Hospital had provided a newly designed model for governance and management as described in section 3 above. The Deloitte & Touche Report provided a critique of this model and made recommendations which are important to consider as to the extent to which the Report's analysis provides for the voluntary character of the Hospital operating under the Charter. The Report recommended a better definition of the roles of the Board and its committees by reference to strategic and policy matters:

> In our view, the manner in which committees conduct their business is focussed to a large extent on operational matters, some of which should be handled by the senior management team. This approach has its origins in the base hospitals, where governance and management were inextricably linked at Board level. This is a common feature of the way in which well intentional and committed people in many voluntary agencies operate. However, in a Hospital as large and complex as Tallaght it is essential that the Board and its committees are structured to focus on strategic and policy matters.[123]

---

[123] *Deloitte & Touche Report*, op. cit., pp 31–2

218

The Report argued that there was a need to avoid confusion as to responsibilities as it saw 'a consensual approach to decision making' as a problem in the management team.[124] It stated that 'there is an absolute requirement for the Board to devolve all management responsibility to a properly structured and effective hospital management team'.[125] The Report did note that the Charter states that the function of the Board 'shall be to manage the activities of the Hospital and the services provided by it' and it went on

> It is important to note the use of the word 'manage', rather than governance, which might be considered a more normal remit for a Board. This remit and the general enthusiasm of what is a voluntary board are reflected in an operational approach of the Board to the running of the Hospital.

The Report outlined the eight committees of the Board established in 1997 and the standard framework for their composition and noted 'It would appear that the Board is highly motivated and has gelled well together as a group'. However on the core issue of 'governance versus mangement' the Report stated:

> The Boards of the base hospitals had a participative approach to the running of the hospitals, and were clearly involved in management and operational functions. There is evidence that this approach has continued into the new Hospital. The focus should be on governance and not management. It is our view that the Board devotes a disproportionate amount of time to operational activity instead of strategy and policy development.[127]

In relation to the 'core issue' of the committee structure it stated

> The committee structure reflects certain elements of the Charter and is supported enormously by the voluntary board members. However, the focus of the committee structure has been too operational. The development of the committee structure was appropriate given the size of the Board. It is clear however that the number of committees and their operational focus places a strain on the resources of the management team. The committees also provide an ambiguity for the Management Team in terms of where accountability lies e.g. is the committee accountable or is the relevant portfolio director accountable. This is a particular problem given the inexperience of some of the portfolio directors.[128]

[124] ibid, p. 32
[125] ibid, p. 37
[126] ibid, pp 56–57
[127] ibid, pp 57–8
[128] ibid, p. 57

The Report recognised that the CEO had been recruited 'because of his open participative management style' which was important for the merger process and that there was 'an acceptance amongst staff that this openness is refreshing'.[129] However it went on:

> One downside of this approach is that the CEO is seen more as a facilitator than 'commander-in-chief'. His approach is consistent with helping to build openness and participation which we would regard as being in keeping with the Charter and with a smooth merger of the cultures of the base hospitals. However, a less consensual, more decisive approach to decision making is required for the future, a matter that will be facilitated by having a smaller senior management team.[130]

In reflecting upon the critique by the Deloitte & Touche Report of the Hospital's governance and management structures it is important to note that the model designed in 1997 was new and was in place for just over a year. The Board had planned a review of its governance using internationally accepted accreditation standards as the basis for the review before the appointment of the Consultants in September 1998. The Governance Committee's written set of Board responsibilities which the Board had approved included 'establishing, implementing and evaluating a quality management system for the regular assessment and review of patient care and Hospital Governance' and in August 1998 the first goal cited by the CEO was to support the Board and to review the Committee structure. The Board had already recognised that the structures designed to effect the commissioning, the merger, the move and the immediate aftermath would require a major audit and this had been planned before the Deloitte & Touche consultancy commenced. Structures for a single entity on one campus in a more stable environment would be less elaborate and more streamlined than those required up to mid-1998.

The Report by Deloitte & Touche prescribes, without setting out the required evidence, a particular view on governance and management; that is, the view that the Board's focus should be on 'governance' (policy and strategic issues) rather than 'management' which should be delegated to a small team under an authoritative CEO who acts as 'commander-in-chief'. The Report states a requirement for less 'consensus' decision making in the future even though it adverts to the

---

[129] ibid, p. 57, p. 61

[130] ibid, p. 61; the Report had noted that with ten members of the senior management team the 'span of control' was 'far too wide' and that best practice would suggest a maximum management team size of six, ibid, p. 59

advantages which have resulted from 'consensus' decision making in the merger and move of the base hospitals. As has been demonstrated from the prescriptive literature reviewed on governance and management in Chapter 4 there *is* no agreed basis for the assumptions the Report makes. The proponents of the 'new work' of the non-profit board, for example, would not agree in the sharp division between 'governance' and 'management'.

The 'simple' corporate approach that the Report suggests is indeed very questionable in terms of hospital governance. Hospitals are made up of complex interacting and interdependent (and independent) groups which very often have clinical and professional independence or separate lines of regulation and authority. Of course voluntary boards of such entities may well use effective strategies borrowed from the business or public sectors. In a hospital, however, based upon a complex merger and a move to a new campus the approach indicated by the Report is even more questionable than in a hospital in a stable environment. Dr. McCutcheon stated in a major radio interview in regard to his consensual style

> . . . I believe in the new way of management, which is that the people who know best about how things are done, are those who are working directly in the process. So to translate that into the health system, that means the people who know best about nursing care and medical care are doctors, not administrators. And the role of the administrator is to facilitate good clinical care. You can't do that in a situation where you are acting as the dictator. You have to function as the coach or the facilitator. And that is an absolute belief of mine. I put it before the Committee when I was being recruited, it has been my style all along, and it is going to be my style, it is actually the style for the new hospital.[131]

It has been noted in Chapter 4 that the characteristics associated with voluntary boards do require a much richer involvement by board members such as that described by Taylor, Chait and Holland as 'new work'.

The 'command and control' model drawn upon by the Deloitte & Touche Report is unsuitable for heterogeneous and complex hospital organisation which requires many diverse groups to co-operate and support each other in pursuit of common objectives: this co-operation and mutual support requires consensual structures built upon frequent personal interaction at group or committee level, openness and trust as

---

[131] Major interview with Dr. David McCutcheon 'Today with Pat Kenny' RTE Radio 1, 15 March 1999

well as mutual respect amongst a very wide range of disciplines and occupations.[132] It is indeed arguable, on the evidence from 1996, that the 'open' consensual structures designed by the first Board delivered on the move and merger in a very short time (less than two years) and that a more 'closed' commander-in-chief model would almost certainly have failed in that timespan given the potential of a wide range of groups or power blocs to slow or halt progress should they have felt either left out or not sufficiently involved in the critical decisions.

The Deloitte & Touche Report does advert to the Charter and to the aspects of the Board's governance and management which were consistent with it; however it then recommends contrary approaches providing no evidential base for the recommendations it presents, except an assumed 'managerialist' ideological view that a 'chief' with 'indians' would be more decisive and effective.[133] As has been argued in Chapter 4 a voluntary board has the capacity through 'active citizenship' (and the Report does acknowledge the enthusiastic involvement of Board members) and through structures such as Board committees to engage with management and staff to facilitate the lived expression of the values espoused by the organisation.

The board of a public voluntary hospital, then, has an opportunity to have board and management work together to address policy issues in the light of the vision, mission and values which have been agreed through open processes in which all stakeholders have been involved. This approach does not necessarily confuse governance and management or 'steering' and 'rowing' as the Report suggests happened in the Hospital.[134] The fear of such confusion and of the absence of clear lines of accountability may be addressed through a number of ways. First the terms of reference of Board committees should make it clear that their focus is on the policy issues delegated to it by the Board. Second the

---

[132] Dr. McCutcheon noted in an interview 'You cannot beat a new culture into people especially where a different ethos exists. That approach might be okay in car manufacturing, but we were supporting a hospital system which is caring for people who are ill', see interview with Fergal Bowers 'Minister must accept some responsibility for Tallaght Hospital crisis' *Irish Medical News*, 22 March 1999

[133] there is a further critique of 'managerialism' as it affects both the public and voluntary sectors in Chapter 6 below.

[134] this is the fundamental distinction made in *Governance & Hospital Boards Discussion Document* (Department of Health and Children, June 1999): 'The purpose of a Board is to steer while those directly involved in the organisation's work do the rowing. Those who row may of course also participate in steering, but must do so in the full knowledge that this is a separate role with separate duties and accountabilities', p. 2

management team members who are designated to service the Board committees need to be clear on the role they have in ensuring that policy issues remain the focus of the work of the committees. This is no different than the skills required by professional staff who service voluntary boards generally. Thirdly the CEO and the managers need to be clear on the separation of the process of policy discussion and formulation for Board approval from that of holding staff accountable for the execution of approved policy and staff responsibilities generally. This is not particularly difficult to achieve and its achievement allows for staff and board members to share in policy development to address the serious issues they both face and are concerned about.[135]

7. CONCLUSION

The experiences of the first Board of the Adelaide and Meath Hospital underline the conclusion reached in Part One that there is a lack of clarity in Irish health policy as to the definition and constitution of voluntary organisations. It took a number of years and a major struggle to establish the voluntary concept for the governance and management of the new Hospital as eventually expressed in the Charter in 1996. Despite the fact that the Charter received national democratic approval in the Oireachtas the absence of a generally accepted public philosophy legitimising such a voluntary organisation to provide health services meant that the new Board very quickly was confronted with an unsympathetic policy environment (exemplified in the 'fiscal control' approach applied in the Service Plan) and with attempts to reorient the governance and management of the Hospital towards a mould shaped by the Department of Health and Children.

The first Board of the Hospital attempted not unsuccessfully (given the effective merger and move) to demonstrate the principles of a voluntary organisation in the model adopted in 1997 for governance and management of the Hospital. However, the approach was either not appreciated by the Hospital's key resource provider (The Department of Health and Children) or was judged inappropriate by

---

[135] on this see especially R.D. Herman, R.D. Heimovics *Executive Leadership in Nonprofit Organizations New Strategies for Shaping Executive Board Dynamics* (Jossey-Bass publishers, San Francisco, 1991); the Board's performance 'can only be understood and improved in relation' to the rest of the organization' p. xiii and Herman and Heimovics demonstrate the executive capacity through the CEO in the resource dependent open system context of nonprofit organisations to develop more powerful boards

the statutory authorities and their advisers (i.e. the Consultant's Report): there was little or no acknowledgement that a voluntary organisation ought to be governed and managed differently in order to capitalise upon the advantages of such agencies. It seems clear from this case study that the operant policy was to ensure compliance with the 'dependent partnership' model of voluntary—statutory relationships through the mechanism of the 'troika' and through the use of resourcing to ensure compliance.

CHAPTER 6

Perceptions and Prescriptions

'What matters in history is the great outline and the significant detail'

LEWIS NAMIER quoted in John Brooke 'Sir Lewis Bernstein Namier 1888–1960' in *Brief Lives Twentieth—Century Pen Portraits From The Dictionary of National Biography* Selected by Colin Matthew (Oxford University Press, Oxford, 1997) p. 411

1. INTRODUCTION

The concerns explored in this study arose from the quest for answers to the questions whether there is a convincing philosophical justification for voluntary action in society in general (and thus in healthcare in particular) and if so, what might the implications be for the governance and management of voluntary organisations and in particular for voluntary healthcare organisations such as public voluntary hospitals. The first question concerning the legitimacy of voluntary action might be seen as 'the great outline' while the implications for how voluntary organisations are governed and managed might be seen as 'the significant detail' in terms of the quotation from Lewis Namier at the head of this chapter: as Namier understood both are important. This study has attempted to attend to both the 'great outline' of a theory of active citizenship in a pluralist society which legitimates voluntary action and to the 'significant detail' of how such voluntary citizenship in practice finds scope for development in governing and managing voluntary organisations in a key domain such as health.

The purpose of this chapter is to reflect upon the analysis of the context, the theoretical perspectives and the experiences surrounding one voluntary board in providing some concluding responses to the questions which prompted the study. This reflection will be richer than just a personal reflection because it incorporates the views of key statutory and voluntary practitioners in the Irish healthcare system based upon six in-depth interviews including one group interview of Department of Health and Children officials, conducted from March to June 1999.[1] These 'semi-structured' interviews sought to 'get behind' the stances of both statutory and voluntary practitioners in order to obtain better understanding of their perceptions and prescriptions and

---

[1] Interviews were conducted with Dr. David McCutcheon, CEO of The Adelaide and Meath Hospital, Dublin, Incorporating The National Children's Hospital, 1996–1999; Mr. Gerry Brady, former Chairman of The Meath Hospital, member of the Eastern Health Board, public representative, Vice Chairman 1996–1999, The Adelaide and Meath Hospital, Dublin, Incorporating the National Children's Hospital; Mr. Jerry O'Dwyer, Secretary General, Department of Health and Children; Mr. Nicholas Jermyn, CEO St. Vincent's University Hospital, Dublin, member of the Task Force for the new Eastern Regional Health Authority and Acting CEO of The Adelaide and Meath Hospital, Dublin, Incorporating The National Children's Hospital; Mrs. Rosemary French, Chairman of The Adelaide and Meath Hospital, Dublin, Incorporating The National Children's Hospital and a group interview with Ms Angela Fitzgerald, Mr. Tony Morris, Mr. Vincent Barton and Mr. Denis O'Sullivan, senior officials in The Department of Health and Children; further insight was available from the transcript of the major radio interview given by Dr. David McCutcheon on RTE Radio, 15 March 1999

to some extent to tease out possibilities for addressing concerns and issues. The interviewees from the Department of Health and Children were key officials concerned with secondary care policy and through the use of a group interview these officials were able to react to the comments made by their colleagues and to provide insights into the policy formulation process in respect of voluntary and statutory relationships. The interviews produced high quality and rich reflections from statutory and voluntary practitioners whose day to day concerns relate to voluntary and statutory relationships and to the governance and management of health care agencies and in particular to Irish hospitals.

As the interviews were conducted some lines from T.S. Eliot seemed appropriate

> We had the experience but missed the meaning
> And approach to the meaning restores the experience
> In a different form . . .[2]

The pace of change has been such in Irish society in general and in the healthcare system in particular that there are great dangers from unreflecting responses and actions in both statutory and voluntary agencies based upon stereotypes, or even prejudice. It is hoped that the 'conversation' based on the interviews will assist 'the approach to meaning' and so 'restore the experience' of voluntary and statutory relationships 'in a different form': the test of such relationships must be whether they facilitate optimum conditions for citizens and their healthcare.

The reflections from the interviews in the section which follows focus upon four key themes (which overlap from time to time) in this study: legitimacy (the philosophical justifications for voluntary action and what constitutes or defines voluntary organisations); voluntary—statutory relationships (and how they should be optimised); governance and management (views, prescriptions, and issues) and 'partnership' and service planning (models and approaches to resourcing providers). Following these reflections there is an analysis of the two alternative 'prescriptions' for governance, that prescribed from statutory perspectives and that implied by the 'usable theory' for governance as presented in this study, as these alternatives apply to what are termed 'public voluntary hospitals' in the Irish context.

[2] T.S. Eliot, 'The Dry Salvages' in T.S. Eliot, *The Complete Poems and Plays* (Faber and Faber, London, 1969) p. 186

2. PERCEPTIONS: LEGITIMACY

A core concern of this study has been to explore the philosophical justification for voluntary action as a basis for the legitimacy of such action in public policy. The Secretary General of The Department of Health and Children, Mr. J. O'Dwyer, pointing out that all health organisations 'are going to have to put the patient at the centre' noted that there are 'vestiges of paternalism' attaching to voluntary providers

> I think that in some respects the problems we have in creating a patient centred service are actually a throw back to charity medicine where people were made to feel that they ought to be grateful. That does not cut any ice anymore. I think that in terms of looking at where they are going they have to look at services from the point of view of the patient.
>
> I think the second thing they have to look at is how much realistically can people, giving up their time on a voluntary basis, how much can they realistically contribute? And what is the most effective way in which they can contribute? What is the added value that they can bring to the organisation? I think that the added value that they can bring to the organisation now is very different to the added value that they might have brought even in 1950. So I think the second thing in going forward and looking way down the line is how they transmit their values. This is a particular problem for the religious orders but it is also a problem for other organisations. If you think your values are worth transmitting and some of them may not (we cannot take it for granted that they are) if you say these are our values we think that they are important, we think they have continuing importance, how do you transmit them? Now a lot of work has already been done in this area by religious orders in the States particularly those who have faced up to their own demise. There is a lesson there to be learned in relation to the things they have picked out as the key factors. The effective control of the membership of the Board; their retention of absolutely minimal but critical things to the Board and, in particular, the appointment of the Chief Executive Officer. They have also accepted that to a large extent the values will be transmitted by the executives that they appoint not by themselves. Concentration on a very small number of critical issues and I think much more thought given to governance . . . I think that one of the issues that we would be trying to focus on in the discussions that we are having about governance is what is critical in terms of being a voluntary governor of an organisation?[3]

Mrs. Rosemary French, drawing upon her experiences as Chairman of a voluntary hospital, believes that voluntary action gives 'a richness to society' by allowing citizens 'to make a difference' in other ways than earning a living; through voluntary action without monetary reward citizens care for each other

[3] Interview with Mr. J. O'Dwyer, Secretary-General, Department of Health and Children, 25 May 1999

Within health care a lot of different needs would be overlooked if people didn't have the opportunity. When I look at the care of the mentally handicapped people or people with disabilities, they just would be overlooked if those who know about those areas didn't identify them and do something about them and do them in a voluntary way always initially and then maybe it would be taken over by the State.

Mrs. French believes that voluntary action in healthcare is about providing a quality of service: 'It's not about just providing a service; it's how we provide that service'. The State, she believes, can only do so much in a uniform way so services may be enhanced by voluntary effort: 'how your care is delivered to you . . . in different hospitals it's different'. Without voluntary providers there would be a danger of 'a mono-culture' in healthcare when there would not be any 'choice and variety': 'allowing the opportunity to participate is what I think people should have' and there is a need 'to activate a feeling of caring for others'.[4]

Mr. N. Jermyn, CEO of the major voluntary hospital, St. Vincent's University Hospital, believes voluntary action to be

> people willingly offering their services free gratis for the cause and they genuinely want to give something back to society. They're there because they want to be there and not because they're being paid and they have to be there.

He agrees that a voluntary hospital can provide 'a quality service' for the sick and less well off who can be catered for by the State 'to a certain extent': voluntary hospitals will merit public funding, he believes because of their services 'because we provide good services and quality services and we're giving people what they need and want'.[5]

Dr. David McCutcheon compares the legitimacy of a voluntary board in the health service to that of citizens fulfilling their civic duties and responsibilities in jury service

> . . . if you're going to judge on the guilt or innocence of an individual I don't see any reason why that mechanism can't be used to judge the wisdom of health policy or the application of Government health principles into the system. To me, when you have a voluntary Board there is much less potential for conflict of interest in the Board.

[4] Mrs. Rosemary French in Interview, 29 June 1999

[5] Interview with Mr. N. Jermyn, 14 June 1999

With politically appointed boards the conflict of interest, in Dr. McCutcheon's view, emerges in this form 'are you keeping the Minister clean or are you doing what is best for the community?'[6]

It is important to note in the context of legitimacy the particularities associated with the voluntary sector in the Irish health services. Mr. Tony Morris, a senior official in the Department of Health and Children, comments about public voluntary hospitals in the Irish context

> . . . 'voluntary' has a different meaning than it has in the context, of let's say a Third World agency or in the context, of say St. Vincent de Paul. It isn't the same because the service it's providing or the service it's overseeing the provision of, which it is responsible for overseeing and providing is so expensive that it's not feasible for it to be utterly self-financing and as such it is dependent on public funds. Now that doesn't mean that it can't have its own identity, its independence, its focus on the particular . . . but it is done in a particular way and in a sense for that voluntary hospital to claim the same level of, . . . independence as we'll say, St. Vincent de Paul or Trocaire or Concern or whatever, it doesn't really have that right, for the want of a better word, to claim that level of independence and it doesn't have a mandate as such . . . not simply because of it's dependency on the State for money but because of its dependency on a whole range of aspects within the system . . . it shouldn't function in isolation to the rest of the health service.[7]

The Secretary-General of the Department, Mr. O'Dwyer, described the characteristics of the voluntary sector in the Irish health services

> It is quite a special type of voluntary sector. Voluntary Hospitals as organisations have been there a very long time. Firstly, they have built up their own particular ethos. The second thing is they are very heavily dependent on the State for their funding. The third thing is their staff enjoy (or whatever word is appropriate) all the terms and conditions of the statutory side because they exist as members of the same unions. So if you want to look at a unifying force as between statutory and voluntary one of the forces is the unions that represent staff. Many of the things that would normally be in the control of a voluntary organisation are effectively not in their control. Their numbers of staff are regulated, their conditions are regulated and the staff certainly, insofar as they may think about it, may see themselves as part of a wider system part of which is voluntary, part of which is statutory . . .

The Secretary-General noted that while the strengths of the voluntary sector 'are very obvious'

---

[6] Interview with Dr. D. McCutcheon, 31 March 1999

[7] Mr. Tony Morris, in Group Interview, 18 June 1999

It has a weakness from the point of view of providing an integrated health service. It tends to draw out and encourage disportionate concern with the organisation among the people in it. One of the challenges to the voluntary sector, in the climate that we are now in, is to get a better balance between blind loyalty to the organisation and a recognition that they are players within a wider system.[8]

Those interviewed from the Department of Health and Children were clearly aware of the legitimacy of the voluntary 'ethos' and the sense of 'ownership' which voluntary hospitals have of their mission and service. As Ms Angela Fitzgerald of the Department explained

> . . . there is a complex relationship between the voluntary providers and ourselves and the voluntary providers and the statutory providers. Some of the complexity lies in the fact that the voluntary, in many senses, is about the private ownership of those hospitals, which has implications for governance of those bodies, but yet, there is a dependence on the State for funding. So I think ownership, that concept, is very relevant and the other thing that is very interesting is the issue of ethos and while obviously there is evidence of a particular ethos, (different types of ethos in hospitals), it doesn't permeate the operation of the hospitals by and large, I think, in the context of the relationship we have with them; but yet they would be the two things that they would talk about.

In terms, then, of a working or operational definition of the voluntary sector and, of public voluntary hospitals in particular, the key officials in the Department of Health and Children would identify (a) a particular ethos or set of values, (b) a sense of ownership or independence at board or governance level, (c) a dependence of public funds bringing with it a prerequisite to integrate and be part of a wider system. As Angela Fitzgerald added

> I think in the context of governance particularly the issue of ownership is key because they hold on very carefully to the notion that they have independence; that they have the right to identify needs, to define the branches in which they work and yet they are entirely funded by the State.[9]

There is a clear sense amongst the officials of the Department who were interviewed that these voluntary concepts are in need of updating. Vincent Barton explains

[8] Interview with Mr. J. O'Dwyer, Secretary-General, Department of Health and Children, 25 May 1999

[9] Ms Angela Fitzgerald, Group Interview, 18 June 1999; the voluntary hospitals are largely funded by the State but it is not accurate to say they are 'entirely' funded as they earn income from private patients, have access to voluntary funds and use assets often owned by voluntary bodies

To some degree or other I feel that now the voluntary sector seeks to identify too closely with things that are much less relevant than they were formerly at the expense of things which they could bring to the sector and in some ways that they're clinging on to the least important aspects of their role now . . . if you talk to the voluntary hospitals about their role they often mention being the advocate for particular sorts of service or particular sorts of needs. That derives from a time when there was no one else whose job it was to look at that need and indeed there was no one else providing the service even if the need had been identified. I think that that can easily flip over into the services being 'Whatever we think we want to provide'. In other words a self-fulfilling role and I sometimes feel that the voluntary hospitals, in particular, aren't aware of the extent of which they have become enthralled by what are essentially their own vested interests.[10]

The expression of values is stated to be an important aspect of voluntary action and voluntary provision. Mr. Gerry Brady, for example, noted that having voluntary boards in hospitals gives 'a certain comfort' to minorities if they have 'a direct involvement that they wouldn't be enveloped in the larger system'.[11] Dr. David McCutcheon gave the example of women's health

. . . it is more likely to come as a health issue through women's groups and women's groups influencing hospitals and health facilities and so I think the health of minorities rather than majorities is a significant issue and I think that type of influence is something that will be secured through voluntary involvement.[12]

However, this raises the question about values in the health care system as a whole and about whether it is public policy to support a diverse range of health service providers with a spectrum of value orientations or positions. As Mr. Tony Morris of the Department of Health and Children asks

Now, who sets the values? Is it the citizens and the patients as citizens rather than the patients as customers or is it a small group of people at the centre who set down the values without a particular mandate to do so.[13]

In a democracy the citizens ought to set the values of that society and obviously that is now emerging as a key issue in health policy more so than it was in the past. Vincent Barton explains

[10] Mr. Vincent Barton, Group Interview, 18 June 1999

[11] Mr. Gerry Brady, Interview, 9 June 1999

[12] Dr. David McCutcheon, Interview, 31 March 1999

[13] Mr. Tony Morris, Group Interview, 18 June 1999

Our system, the political system here and the people in the Department could be accused . . . of somehow reneging on the stewardship role which would be expected of them. But the thinking amongst the citizens of that role has evolved so far that in some sense from a situation where as recently as 50 or 60 years ago the State, to a large degree, did not discharge that function for hospital care to a point where the State is seen as very immediately and directly responsible for individual acts of patient care . . . Our general social structures have evolved so fast that I don't think that perhaps the participants such as the voluntary and non-voluntary hospitals have kept their legitimacy, if you wish, up to date.[14]

Mr. Tony Morris of the Department of Health and Children puts the added value of voluntary bodies in the health service as follows

I think the big value that voluntary bodies have is that they can be free of the political system, per se, and they can be a voice of independence on behalf of, we'll say, the individual and I'm thinking, for example, in the area of the mentally handicapped where 15–20 years ago that voluntary sector became the advocate of that particular sector. But, in the acute hospital system, the public voluntary hospital system . . . I think there is need for clarification; if you turn around the other way, 'values expressive', what values from a patient perspective are there to be in a voluntary hospital? Now, the values there I see as long-term in the sense that that voluntary hospital will identify issues, needs and probably speak on behalf of the patient a lot clearer than a health board has historically.[15]

The logic of funding voluntary providers with diverse sets of values as well as statutory providers in a single public health system is that the system is a pluralist system with a choice for the patients as to which provider they wish to attend for any particular service.[16]

It would be fair to say that these key participants on both the statutory and voluntary side of the health service believe that the fundamental legitimacy of voluntary organisations is that they are vehicles through which citizens jointly and voluntarily undertake to provide public services that are not adequately or appropriately provided by business or government. As voluntary organisations providing public services they are justified to the extent that they add value to the health services, by being directed by citizen volunteers, who accept responsibilities for services as part of a democratically governed national health system; this circumscribes their indepen-

[14] Mr. Vincent Barton, Group Interview, 18 June 1999

[15] Mr. Tony Morris, Group Interview, 18 June 1999

[16] 'Dr. O'Ferrall: I mean you'll end up with a pluralist type of system in a sense. Vincent Barton: I think we have it', Group Interview, 18 June 1999

dence in the interests of the integration and the needs of the wider system of which they are a part. It is possible to have such voluntary provision and it is a positive aspect to be encouraged in a publicly administered health system.

3. PERCEPTIONS: VOLUNTARY-STATUTORY RELATIONSHIPS

The lack of a clear and agreed framework for voluntary and statutory relationships emerged from both statutory and voluntary informants. The relationship between the state and public voluntary hospitals has developed on an ad hoc basis as Mr. Tony Morris, of the Department of Health and Children, observed

> . . . I think that what has happened traditionally is that because the voluntary hospitals, if you like, initially provided the nucleus of a quite good acute hospital service and because of their connections with the teaching institutions, they've evolved I would say as a major force in the acute hospital sector. I don't recollect finding any historical major policy decision as such by a Government or any Department of Health that we would develop these. So the development has been to some extent ad hoc.[17]

Mrs. Rosemary French believes that the statutory side of the relationship do not understand what the voluntary organisations in health care are about and that they are seen as awkward parts of the system

> . . . I think it's a continual battle in getting them to try to understand because it would be much cleaner and simpler for them as deliverers of health care on behalf of the State if everything was done the same. If you have different hospitals that want to do things differently and different boards that want to run things slightly differently it's a real headache to them. But we really have to convince them and I think we've an awful long way to go.[18]

Mrs. French believes a great deal stems from the centralisation of the Irish State

> I've become aware of how much in this State everything, not just in health care, everything is centralised and I've really become quite frightened by that. It was pointed out to me that this is the most centralised country in Western Europe and I believe that now having experienced what I've experienced and its quite frightening.

[17] Mr. Tony Morris, Group Interview, 18 June 1999
[18] Mrs. Rosemary French, Interview, 29 June 1999

She believes that public policy can be made 'by just a couple of people and you're very very vulnerable then as citizens in a country that you'll be influenced by just a couple of people'.[19]

The officials in the Department of Health and Children, as we have seen, express the virtues and legitimacy of the voluntary sector in terms quite similar to the key voluntary practitioners interviewed; however, they are concerned to develop a comprehensive and integrated health care system based upon the policy established in the 1990s. Vincent Barton, of the Department, observed

> If I was marketing in some sense an independent voluntary board, what I would be worried about now would be that what was defining me wasn't actually different enough and that I don't have the right sort of justification for what I'm doing. As Tony said [Mr. Tony Morris] part of the independence policy of voluntarism meant in reality that the kind of prohibition or the reflex of instincts against the co-operation, be it with other voluntary agencies or with the statutory sector, demonstrably worked against the patient. Once you're inside our walls you're great, but what got you there and what looks after you outside and that's perhaps a good example of how in some sense what you might characterise as the statutory responsibilities are an effort to set the right context for the virtues of voluntarism.[20]

Mrs. French enthusiastically agreed with the need for co-ordination

> If it can be done right and fairly, I think that the new health board (ERHA) is a super thing because I think there has been no co-ordination for the patients within the different areas. In the Dublin area especially where you have the voluntary hospitals, you're left as a patient hanging-out to dry when you move to the health board for your care.[21]

She believes, however, that the statutory authorities, the State, sees 'the voluntary hospitals as a huge threat' particularly 'our one which cherishes its independence'. She states her concern for the future

> I suppose when I look into the next while I'm probably most concerned about our relationship and the inter-understanding ours of the Department and the Department of Health with us and we can substitute the new Eastern Regional Health Authority with the Department of Health. I'm very concerned about that because I think that has been the underlying problem in all that we've suffered over the last while because I do think that there was a deliberate intention to destroy us. I think maybe

---

[19] Mrs. Rosemary French, Interview, 29 June 1999

[20] Mr. Vincent Barton, Group Interview, 18 June 1999

[21] Mrs. Rosemary French, Interview, 29 June 1999

they were motivated to do that because they didn't understand what we were about and I think that unless we do something to create a better understanding, that feeling against us will continue and we won't flourish. That's my biggest worry'.

The expressed policy and view of the Department of Health and Children is to support and respect the voluntary sector as a 'partner'. Mr. O'Dwyer observes

> . . . I think that if we are going to encourage the continuance of a voluntary sector which is relevant to the day we have to do a number of things. We have first of all in so far as is possible to respect its operational autonomy. At the same time we have to facilitate and encourage it to modernise its own thinking and its own actions. It has a right to expect that in so far as that can be helped that we will do it. Now, I think that it would be very sad if we weren't able to find a modern way of maintaining a strong voluntary sector. I think that the big onus on the voluntary sector is, in return for the continuing autonomy, to be very clear as to its accountability.[22]

Mrs. French notes that the Charter of the Hospital, approved by the Oireachtas in 1996 was a 'small example' of a written compact between the voluntary and the statutory sides of the relationship

> You put so much work into getting agreement and getting it all down on paper and the North of Ireland Agreement, the Good Friday Agreement, is another one [example]. But there's another thing actually making it work and I think in our Hospital we're just in the foothills in actually getting it to work. It looked as if we could deliver on it but I don't think we have. I think it's been shoved into the background - the Charter—or our understanding of the Charter has, what was intended to be. And it actually hasn't made that much difference to us.[23]

The officials in the Department of Health state that they see the requirements placed by the statutory authorities upon voluntary providers as no more demanding than that required by 'good governance':

> . . . I certainly don't ask for information or accountability or anything that good governance within the hospital shouldn't ask for anyway. We call it a Service Plan. We put down what we think we need in that Service Plan. I would actually see that as a very basic document that any good governance would require.[24]

[22] Mr. J. O'Dwyer, Secretary General, The Department of Health and Children, Interview, 25 May 1999

[23] Mrs. Rosemary French, Interview, 29 June 1999

[24] Mr. Tony Morris, Group Interview, 18 June 1999

Kramer's metaphors or paradigms for voluntary and statutory relationships as 'partnership', 'market', 'control or power game' were discussed in the group interview with officials of the Department, and Mr. Morris commented in respect of the data required

> We're looking for it for monetary accountability there will be an element of control but it's not purely for control. We need to control certain issues within the service. We need to ensure that we can control the situation where we're getting the service that we're paying for. We need to control, for example, numbers throughout the service because that discipline is imposed by our own needs and external needs. So I think that you can actually, if you want to block it, if you like partnership, market, control or power game. I think that there's another box and that's if you like, the question of what's right anyway: I mean if you are trying to run a service what should you be doing? You should be planning properly, strategically planning, operationally planning, you should be budgeting properly, overall budgeting, and departmental budgeting, service budgeting.[25]

The actions of the statutory authorities are, however, experienced by the voluntary agencies as extremely negative; Dr. David McCutcheon is clear that the issue is about control

> The Department of Health in its great hunger for control, gets less confused if information is provided in a universal and uniform kind of way and I think they're looking for that. They're also shell-shocked after the Blood Tribunal, etc. and some of them, I think, what some of them are doing is really quite defensive—I think they're 'cloaking' all this under better governance. What most amazed me was at the recent seminar or workshop on governance with John Murray, the focus was on political intrigue in the background rather than on good governance. So I think the body-language is simply saying that governance is not the issue, the issue here is control.[26]

Mrs. French, who experienced the crisis in 1998 over the Hospital's Service Plan says rather than encouraging voluntary board members the opposite is happening:

> I mean just probably in the last year I have become very aware that there's a movement the other way to try and bash people out of it, that they actually have no right to be there, that the most important thing is to have

[25] Mr. Tony Morris, Group Interview, 18 June 1999; see R.M. Kramer 'Voluntary Agencies and the Contract Culture: "Dream or Nightmare?"' *Social Service Review* Vol. 68, No. 1, March 1994, pp 33–60; this article was referred to in this context at the group interview.

[26] Dr. David McCutcheon, Interview, 31 March 1999: the seminar referred was part of the Governance Initiative and Professor John Murray of Trinity College made a key-note presentation

the figure right at the bottom of the page and this is very important but there's lots of other areas but if you [i.e. voluntary board members] have time to spare well you should be off doing something else with it and keep you nose out of this.[27]

4. PERCEPTIONS: GOVERNANCE AND MANAGEMENT

The independence of a voluntary board is an agreed characteristic in both public policy and in the perceptions of voluntary practitioners. Who appoints the board is therefore crucial. Mrs. French notes that State appointed boards 'can be unappointed' by the State: 'So, it's just like having the Department of Health running our Hospital'.[28] Dr. David McCutcheon observes of a voluntary board

> They have so much to give and the opportunity to be able to seek the counsel of those people is just superb. If they were all elected the perspective would be, well, what's politically correct and what's not politically correct. The health system is not a system to be politically correct, so you need to have bankers and lawyers and financiers and community workers and those kind of people.[29]

Mrs. French maintained that what distinguishes a voluntary board is that it is a board

> whose interests should just be that of the patient with no other interests at all and putting the patient first on all decisions. That in a way gives it an independence and a freedom to do things in the patients' interest and then, obviously, from a financial point of view, if it's a voluntary hospital it would have funds itself which would enhance what the State is prepared to pay for and maybe make that difference.[30]

She argues strongly for accountability but also for quality of service

> I think we all have to spend the money very carefully because it's the State's money and it's the people's money that we're spending. It's accountability, it's very very important. It's not just the money, it's how you spend it.[31]

In comparing statutory boards and voluntary boards the Secretary-General of The Department of Health and Children observes

---

[27] Mrs. Rosemary French, Interview, 29 June 1999

[28] Mrs. Rosemary French, Interview, 29 June 1999

[29] Dr. D. McCutcheon, Interview, 31 March 1999

[30] Mrs. Rosemary French, Interview, 29 June 1999

[31] Mrs. Rosemary French, Interview, 29 June 1999

I think they have more in common than they are different. I think there are certain essential things that if you are in a governance role you have to do whether you are statutory or voluntary; I think there are differences and those differences will to some extent depend on the particular circumstances of the organisation. The type of person that ends up in a governance role on a statutory body is often representative. Therefore, they feel that they are fulfilling a number of roles. They are representing constituents who may have indirectly voted for them, their performance on a particular body may be a factor whether they stay in public life. I think that they see themselves very much as the consumer representative. I think that they may be more conscious than their opposite numbers on the voluntary side in terms of the wider political atmosphere in which they operate. I think that what is required of them, as governors, is not different. The style they might adopt is different but there are certain things that they must do. They have to ensure that there is a sense of direction for the organisation. They have to be able to check whether they are getting it right. They have to be concerned with the quality and the performance of their management. They have to protect the assets of the organisation. This is a common range of responsibilities of governors.[32]

Mrs. French from her voluntary perspective is very alarmed at the political effects of Government appointments: she says political appointees 'are there for political reasons just by their very nature so that they do operate in a different way and that terrifies me':

It's the reasons that they do things, their motivation is different and the control on them is terrifying, the political control on them because of the political system maybe in this country . . . They're answerable to masters beyond the table that we're sitting at.[33]

Dr. David McCutcheon contrasts political appointees with voluntary members as follows

If you were to watch the behaviour in board meetings you would find a political representative, not because they're bad people, you'd find them quickly trying to scan the information that they should have studied the night before. They may not be listening to what is going on, they may be concerned about some other issue that's outside. So they are distracted whereas the volunteers are much more focussed. So, I think the contribution that can be made by volunteers has to be very focussed and is much better.[34]

[32] Mr. J. O'Dwyer, Interview, 25 May 1999

[33] Mrs. Rosemary French, Interview, 29 June 1999

[34] Dr. David McCutcheon, Interview, 31 March 1999

There is, however, broad agreement from both voluntary and statutory perspectives that the requirements of good governance, 'the common range of responsibilities' described by Mr. O'Dwyer must be fulfilled. There is also recognition that a set of principles governing the wider relationships are also required. As Angela Fitzgerald observes from her experience in the Department of Health and Children

> I think we need principles set down which say what is the governance, what do we expect, what is the relationship between themselves and ourselves in the first instance (and themselves and the statutory sector) and now the client group; those principles, you know there's a lack of clarity attached and that's one of the areas where the lack of clarity lies. I think the fact that there is a slightly different structure in voluntary hospitals does not necessarily mean that we compromise good governance.[35]

The key roles of the Chairman of the Board and of the CEO were stated very clearly by the officials in the Department. Mr. O'Dwyer, the Secretary-General, observed

> Well, if you look at the net position, if you have a very good Chairman and a very good CEO it's actually hard to go wrong. That's the one lesson we've learned. If you are missing either of those you're in trouble . . . the CEO attracts good staff. The Chairman runs the Board well.[36]

The needs of the Chairman for time and facilities has become an important consideration especially for, as Vincent Barton put it, 'the Minister for Foreign Affairs function', that is relating to the environment:

> The environment is so important and so all-defining that that should be the key competence. [of the Chairman] We've done some work, . . . we did most work with St. James's over the last two-an-a-half years on what a 21st century board should be like and, for example, we've incorporated things like a balance of skills, not constituency interest, a rolling renewal so the appointments are now staggered, a structured process for replacements search, start off with a strategic plan for the hospital which identifies the mission and all the rest and move from that to identify your constituencies which should have representation rather than the other way round which has been traditional.[37]

The function of the Board and its committees relies upon being facilitated by the CEO and the management team: there is a need to put in

[35] Mrs. Angela Fitzgerald, Group Interview, 18 June 1999

[36] Mr. J. O'Dwyer, Secretary-General, Department of Health and Children, 25 May 1999

[37] Mr. Vincent Barton, Department of Health and Children Group Interview, 18 June 1999

place systems so that the Board knows that 'the place is working right' as Mrs. French says

> ... I have a problem in sort of oiling and greasing the working of the board so that it has confidence in it [i.e. the Hospital], that the wheels are going round right, without getting involved in things that it can't get involved in ... How do you know that the people are being looked after particularly in our Hospital to be sure that the people are looked after in the way they want to be looked after? How can we actually sit as 23 confident Board members and think that our Hospital is running as the Charter says it should run? I am not confident in that at all.[38]

Mr. Jerry O'Dwyer offers this perspective on board committees

> ... I think that because a lot of voluntary bodies had to discharge many of the management functions they tended to appoint committees to do this or that. I think with the appointment of professional CEO's and management teams and with the need to have a clear cut division of responsibility, I think that the type of committee and the number of committees that will be under either statutory or voluntary boards is certainly changing. Maybe those committees will be much more concerned in the future with strategic issues. Where are we going? What are our values? Are we reflecting that? How do we check that we are giving the kind of service that we are expected to give? How are we interlinking with other parts of the system? What are the challenges ahead? How are we in relation to emerging issues?

The expertise on the Board should be focussed upon issues not management because 'if they don't look at the areas that we will broadly describe as values and direction then nobody is going to do it or else, they are going to be the puppet of a CEO'.[39]

5. PERCEPTIONS: 'PARTNERSHIP' AND SERVICE PLANNING

There are conceptual differences in the views expressed by the key informants in the interviews in relation to 'partnership' and service planning. The Secretary-General, Mr. Jerry O'Dwyer outlines the statutory approach in Ireland:

> I think that it is important that people appreciate we are quite unusual in Western Europe and unlike North America, Australia and New Zealand we have actually gone for co-operation/partnership. We haven't gone for dividing things up. I think control is, I suppose, the way people see it, but I think they will all be familiar in their own lives with accountability, they

[38] Mrs. R. French, Interview, 29 June 1999

[39] Interview with Mr. J. O'Dwyer, Secretary-General, Department of Health and Children, 25 May 1999

might not call it that but they know what it is. It is a question really of getting people to understand . . . you enter a compact, you say I want to be a player in this. I want to play, I can deliver this, I will deliver this, you give me X and Y and I will deliver and further more I will participate in shaping the future with you. The giver, on behalf of the taxpayer, is saying we are going to facilitate you to participate. Not only are we concerned with trying to manage the present, we have to plot the future together and the structures to support that.[40]

The voluntary practitioners would endorse that approach to 'partnership' because it implies an 'active partnership' in shaping the future together rather than the 'dependent partnership' which they have felt they have experienced so far with service planning. Mr. Nicholas Jermyn, as CEO of a large public voluntary hospital, sees service planning as a

tremendous opportunity rather than a control factor. I think in fact it's going to expose the public funders and everybody to a situation where the voluntary hospitals will be, if they get their act together, well equipped to demonstrate that they are good value.[41]

Mr. Jermyn foresees, over the coming three to five years, clear stipulation of what services are being resourced and the weaknesses in the system being exposed; therefore it will be easier to address them and that hospitals will develop services around evidenced-based needs and that they 'will not carry the baby for something that we were not resourced to provide. This will demand very effective managers'.[42]

On the other hand, Mrs. French, as Chairman of a voluntary hospital which encountered major problems in service planning, observes

We sailed very close to the wind over the last eighteen months or so in realising where the control comes from. I think it's been quite shattering but obviously you can perform as far as the funding goes and they can say if you don't do this this way we won't give you the funding and of course that's where the Service Planning comes in.

Mrs. French believes that there is 'a game played' and 'you only have to look at the other Dublin hospitals to see playing the game has definitely been rewarded'.[43] Mr. Gerard Brady, with both a statutory and

[40] Interview with Mr. J. O'Dwyer, Secretary-General, Department of Health and Children, 25 May 1999

[41] Interview with Mr. N. Jermyn, 14 June 1999

[42] ibid

[43] Mrs. R. French, Interview, 29 June 1999

voluntary board background, has observed 'the game' which he hopes will change: 'the system' he notes

> is very tight in Dublin and it seemed to be how well you got on with officials as to how well you were funded in difficulty. Now, that may be wrong but it was my perception. That's going to change now I think because the ERHA is going to remove the Department of Health from the scene and I think that will be good for everybody, not that the Department of Health haven't done a good job but I think it's such a small system and people met socially or whatever, it was very small and everybody knew what was going on and some people believed, rightly or wrongly, as to how friendly you were with your official system how well you did in terms of funding.[44]

The range of 'partnerships' involved is extensive in the view of key officials in the Department. As Mr. Tony Morris explains

> When you take the voluntary hospital sector, the primary partnership, I would say, if we're talking about it, is probably between the staff and governance of the hospital, that's probably the primary partnership. From our perspective, our partnership will be with the board of the hospital, it will be with the management of the hospital, it will be with the unions representing that hospital; it will be with other hospitals who might have an interest in that hospital. How does the governance and management of that hospital marry into that partnership? I think that's a very big challenge, to understand, first of all, what are the partnerships and where are the key partnerships?[45]

Mr. Vincent Barton, also from the Department, adds a further point to this complex set of relationships

> The nub of the problem lies in the fact that it is very difficult to reconcile partnership in the generic sense with accountability but it's almost impossible to have partnership without being clear where accountability lies.[46]

Ms Angela Fitzgerald, of the Department, comments on how problematic 'partnership' is in the absence of an agreed framework:

> I think there are a lot of very interesting issues around the whole concept of partnership and what is means; because, I think, in terms of thinking of governance at a strategic level and thinking about the interface between hospitals and the Department, you've got to really get underneath what's understood by the concept of partnership. Can you have partnership where there is an asymmetry of power in partnership in the context of the Department's control over funds, etc. Certainly you can see a situation

[44] Mr. Gerry Brady, Interview, 9 June 1999

[45] Mr. Tony Morris, Group Interview, 18 June 1999

[46] Mr. Vincent Barton, Group Interview, 18 June 1999

where you have partnership between statutory and voluntary providers. You can see perhaps opportunities for strategic co-operation at ownership level and the Department but whether you should have partnership and, if you have it, in what context? Certainly, I think without some common understanding of the principles, you will always have the kind of Tallaght situation.[47]

6. PRESCRIPTIONS: THE STATUTORY 'NEW MODEL' AND THE VOLUNTARY 'NEW MODEL'

The Department of Health and Children has worked with St. James's Hospital recently, as noted by Mr. Vincent Barton above, to provide a 'new model' of what 'a 21st century board should be like'.[48] It is therefore possible to describe this statutory 'new model' and to compare and contrast it with the 'usable theory' proposed for public voluntary hospitals in Chapter 4.[49] This theory would result in what might be termed the voluntary 'new model'.

A statutory model for good governance in hospitals has been developed for St. James's Hospital in 1998 and this will be the model for the development of the board structures and governance in other hospitals governed by Statutory Order under the Health (Corporate Bodies) Act 1961.[50] It is important, therefore, to describe this model briefly and to comment on how it compares and contrasts with a voluntary hospital board.

The new Board for St. James's Hospital has 15 members (reduced from 18) appointed as follows:

2 members appointed by the Minister, one of whom shall be appointed by the Minister to be Chairperson of the Board

4 members of Dublin Corporation shall be appointed by the Minister representative of the geographic area served by the Hospital

2 members appointed by the Minister, one of which shall be a Clinical Director (a consultant medical doctor appointed by the

---

[47] Ms Angela Fitzgerald, Group Interview, 18 June 1999

[48] Mr. Vincent Barton, Group Interview, 18 June 1999

[49] see Chapter 4, above, pp 150-160

[50] see St. James's Hospital Board (Establishment) Order, 1971 (Amendment) Order, 1998, Statutory Instrument S.I. No. 538 of 1998

Chief Executive Officer to manage a defined clinical unit of management at the Hospital) on the nomination of the Medical Board of the Hospital

2 members appointed by the Minister, one of whom shall be a member of the nursing staff on the nomination of the group of trade unions representing the non-medical staff of the Hospital

2 members appointed by the Minister on the nomination of the University of Dublin which shall consult with the Chairman and Chief Executive Officer before making nominations to the Minister

1 member appointed by the Minister on the nomination of the Board of Directors of the St. James's Hospital Foundation which shall consult with the Chairman and Chief Executive Officer before making a nomination to the Minister

2 members appointed by the Minister on the nomination of the Chairman in consultation with the Chief Executive Officer.

The terms of office of the Board members varies from the six years for the Chairperson and the other direct Ministerial appointment (or whatever period the Minister determines) to the period of office of the elected Dublin Corporation, to three years in the case of hospital staff reverting to six years after the first set of appointments in order to provide continuity and change in the Board. Members shall cease to be a member on being requested by the Minister to resign.

The St. James's Hospital Board has been designed, according to the official background documentation, to reflect the substantial development and reorientation of the governance function in hospitals in recent years and to align more accurately membership skills, professions and constituencies with the governance role. The Minister continues to play a key role because of 'the national status of the Hospital, the public service ethos, the need to maintain relationships between the Hospital , the Minister and the Department of Health and Children at the highest level and the need to maintain the Hospital's position in and contribution to health policy'.[51]

The role of the Chairman and the CEO in the composition of the Board has been remarkably strengthened in this new model: not only

---

[51] see 'Board/Governance Proposals for Changes in Establishment Order' Department of Health and Children, n.d.

may they nominate two members but they must be consulted about the nomination of three other members who represent the University and the St. James's Hospital Foundation which is the one remaining 'voluntary' strand on this Board.

The rationale underlying the composition of this Board includes the need for 'key Ministerial involvement in the Board', the importance of the relationship between the Minister, Department of Health and Children, and the Chairman; the need to facilitate and reflect hospital professional and representative needs; local catchment area representation designed to facilitate community input, the need to maintain voluntary sector linkages through a representative of the Hospital Foundation and the requirement for specific expertise on the Board (e.g.s law, finance, estate management, etc.) through nominees of the Chairman and Chief Executive Officer.[52] The background document on the Board states that the primary focus of the Board should be on

- Providing proactive leadership

- Approaching its task from a systems perspective (not solely hospital)

- Adopting a continuum of care perspective (including prevention/ promotion/post-acute)

- Developing a mission/strategy focus for review and control (not process/operations/representative)

- Assuring consistent and fast decision making

- Providing governance of delivery and financing of services and outcomes

- Adopting a public/societal contribution/gains focus

- Adopting a price/benchmarking focus (as against cost/existing practice).[53]

It is envisaged that the role of the Board 'should be clearly defined around the following key considerations': mission definition, development of mission consistent strategies: statutory/legal role; public/

[52] see 'Board/Governance Proposals for Changes in Establishment Order' Department of Health and Children, n.d.

[53] ibid; see also 'Governance Issues Position Paper' Department of Health and Children, July 1997

community and other constituency advocacy role; staff welfare/development role; external relationships role; finance roles and overall performance.[54]

It will be recollected that 'the essential governance question concerns the nature of power, its 'ownership', exercise and limits'.[55] It is clear in the statutory 'new model' that the power resides in the Minister for Health and Children in respect of the St James's Board with scope provided for other key interested actors to be represented. In contrast the 'theory' for a new design for voluntary governance would have as its first element that the Board would be composed of members of a voluntary organisation separate from, and to a greater or lesser extent, independent of statutory structures: these members would be active citizens committed to the values espoused by their organisation. The statutory 'new model' provides for citizens to perform a public service on behalf of the Minister and at the Minister's discretion; the voluntary 'new model' requires responsible community or voluntary ownership by committed, active citizens who are not dependent upon the State for their Board membership.

In noting this key difference it is worth recalling the internationally accepted definition of 'non profit' or 'voluntary' organisations as outlined in Chapter 1 above and indeed which Beveridge and other have stated to be the hallmark of voluntary agencies.[56] Beveridge, for example, stated that voluntary action should be action which was 'not under the directions of any authority wielding the power of the State' while being action 'for a public purpose—for social advance'; the defining characteristic of voluntary action, he believed was 'independence from public control'.[57] A defining characteristic of a voluntary organisation is that it be institutionally separate from government and the 'new model' for St. James's Hospital is clearly that of an instrument of government or statutory policy.

The strong emphasis in the statutory 'new model' upon the role of the Chief Executive Officer is also found in the prescriptive literature on voluntary governance and management:

[54] see 'Board/Governance Proposals for Changes in Establishment Order' Department of Health and Children, n.d.

[55] K. Starkey 'Opening Up Corporate Governance' *Human Relations* Vol. 48, 1995, p. 838, quoted in Chapter 4 above p. 152

[56] see Chapter 2 above, p. 55 and Chapter 1 above pp 20-21

[57] see Chapter 1 above pp 20-21

Boards can help or hinder organizational management. If the governance team and each management team forge strong and skilled partnerships for carrying out their duties, the organization can achieve its potential. A basic function of a board-management partnership is to maintain focus on the institution's mission. Central questions are 'What is our purpose?' and 'How should we carry it out in the years ahead?'[58]

Peter Drucker has identified that non-profit organisations have provided superior board governance in the United States to that provided by business.[59] To some extent it is ironical that private sector governance models are recommended so confidently for voluntary organisations as 'corporate governance' in business has been a matter of inquiry and growing concern as to its effectiveness or adequacy.[60] Nonprofit boards have not become 'rubber stamps' because they have members who are committed and active and they have learned that the CEO and the board work together for the same goals. Drucker writes 'the key to making a board effective . . . is not to talk about its function but to organize its work . . . To restore management's ability to manage we will have to make boards effective again—and that should be considered a responsibility of the CEO.'[61] The pivotal role of executive leadership in voluntary organisations emerges in empirical research which identifies that the Chief Executive Officer has the responsibility of engaging the board in defining the mission and in clarifying their respective and mutually shared roles and responsibilities.[62] This is in contrast to either a hierarchical model in which the CEO and management are subordinate to the Board or the manipulative model whereby the CEO and management structure activities so that the board merely ratifies their decisions.

Herman and Heimovics argue that 'the board problem is really a nonprofit organization problem—that stems from an inadequate understanding of the unique character of nonprofit organizations and

[58] T.P. Holland, R.A. Ritvo, A.R. Kovner *Improving Board Effectiveness Practical Lessons for Nonprofit Health Care Organizations* (American Hospital Publishing, Inc., Chicago, 1997) p. 3

[59] see P.F. Drucker 'What Business Can Learn from Nonprofits' *Harvard Business Review* July-August 1989, pp 90–91

[60] see, for example, Colin Coulson-Thomas *Creating Excellence in the Boardroom A Guide To Shaping Directorial Competence and Board Effectiveness* (McGraw-Hill Book Co., London, 1993) pp 6–9 which identifies and lists the failures and inadequacies of private sector 'corporate governance'

[61] Drucker, op. cit., pp 90–91

[62] see R.D. Herman and R.D. Heimovics *Executive Leadership in Nonprofit Organizations: New Strategies For Shaping Executive-Board Dynamics* (Jossey-Bass, San Francisco, 1991)

their leadership requirements'.[63] Board performance can only be understood and improved in relation to the rest of the organisation. Herman and Heimovics describe and analyze the unique environmental (that is, the legal, political, economic, and philanthropic) context of nonprofit organizations: because nonprofit organisations are especially open (that is, affected by their environments) and dependent on external resources, leadership requires constant interaction with the surrounding environment:

> Successful leadership requires continually organizing the changing set of interests so that useful work is achieved. New strategies challenge board relationships and relations between the board and the chief executive. New funding opportunities mean new alliances and realigned priorities. Remaining open to change and being able to respond quickly and effectively is critical to the leadership of nonprofit organizations.[64]

There is a real issue of accountability when voluntary organisations are spending public money on public services; they are also expected to remain distinct from government:

> This independence is difficult to achieve to the extent that nonprofit organizations remain resource-dependent upon government. There have been many warnings that the nonprofits may be too willing to compromise their independent, private status and roles as alternatives to and critics of government by aggressively seeking government monies.[65]

The policy-management/administration/executive distinction (in Carver's terms ends/means distinctions) appears to correspond sufficiently to reality to be appealing. It is possible to conceptually or verbally to separate these activities. However, in practice, the two cannot always be clearly separated so clearly as now enunciated in the statutory 'new model' and indeed in the *Governance & Hospital Boards Discussion Document* (Department of Health and Children, June 1999). A classical expression of this sharp division in respect of statutory health agencies is to be found in the Dáil debate introducing the Health (Amendment) Bill 1996 (which when it became an Act has been applied 'in an administrative way' to voluntary bodies): The Minister for State, Mr. O'Shea, stated

> All modern organisations, whether public or private must have clear lines so that each level understands its role. A board which interferes in operational matters cannot perform its functions in an adequate way as it will

[63] ibid, p. xii

[64] ibid, p. 29

[65] ibid, pp 32–3

lose sight of the broader issues and strategy with which it must be concerned. A chief executive officer who moves into an arena which is proper to the board may neglect his or her main objective which is to implement the policy decisions taken by the board. The Bill gives effect to this by specifying the functions to be performed by board members and chief executive officers respectively.[66]

Chait and Taylor suggest that nonprofit boards will be more effective if they understand that their role differs at different policy levels. They distinguish six levels—major, secondary, functional, minor, standard operating procedures, and rules. A board's role also varies with the stages of policy development, which are characterised as defining policy objectives, formulation, implementation, and evaluation. Chait and Taylor conclude that a board's attention 'should be concentrated on developing higher level policy objectives and statements and then, on a selective basis, on executing and monitoring important policies'.[67] As Herman and Heimovics observe

> The trouble comes in applying the generally accepted principle in specific circumstances. The problems, opportunities, and changing conditions that any nonprofit organization faces do not come labeled as 'major policy' or 'administrative means' . . . The rapidity and ambiguity of change make simple policy-administration and ends-means standards impossible to consistently implement.[68]

It is more realistic to see the Chief Executive Officer (and senior managers) as a focus of leadership in voluntary organisations and as sharers in the governance responsibilities of the Board.[69]

Herman and Heimovics argue that 'the worst illusion ever perpetrated in the nonprofit field is that the board of directors makes policy and the staff carries it out. This is just not so':[70] policy/administrative distinctions are both impossible and unproductive:

> Such distinctions are, in practice, impossible, because policy is meaningless except as it is actually implemented. Distinctions of what is policy and what is administrative implementation will change as circumstances change. Spending time and effort on classifying possible future events as policy or administration may often be less productive than getting on with the job.[71]

---

[66] Mr. Brian O'Shea, T.D., Minister of State, *Dáil Éireann Parliamentary Debates* 23 May 1996, Col. 222

[67] see R.P. Chait and B.E. Taylor 'Charting The Territory of Nonprofit Boards' *Harvard Business Review* Vol. 67, No. 1, 1989, pp 44–54

[68] Herman and Heimovics, op. cit., p. 44

[69] ibid, p. 54

[70] quoting Brian O'Connell, Herman and Heimovics, op. cit., p. 58

[71] Herman and Heimovics, op. cit., p. 58

There is need for 'developing effective consensus decision making' and Herman and Heimovics state that the Chief Executive Officer's role is to encourage 'consensual decision making on the important issues as they arise'.[72]

The two 'models' considered here, statutory and voluntary, will have in common the fact that they are the products of conscious design and that they seek to take account of environmental needs and the stages of development now attained by Irish hospitals. They will both require to adhere to accredited standards for governance and to involve Board members in induction, training and education and to take responsibility for the Board's work through a programme for Board development. They will contrast in a number of other important ways especially relating to their resource dependence upon the Department of Health and Children: the strategies they adopt for dealing with this resource dependence will be different. A Ministerially appointed Board, ultimately, will not be in a position to seek 'to change the legal framework or legitimacy of the environment by political action when required if not conducive to the values of voluntary governance'.[73] This underlines the major difference between the statutory 'new model' and the voluntary 'new model': who sets the organisational goals? The statutorily appointed board must adhere to Ministerial or Departmental goals while the voluntary board 'adds value' to the health service 'by providing an independent citizen voice in determining the most effective use of public resources. Such boards can add enormously to the process of identifying and examining the most significant issues facing the organisation from the patients (or potential users of the service) perspective'.[74] One board gives public service on behalf of the Minister and the State, while the other board gives public service by giving voice to the citizens which require the service—a voice which is distinct from that of the State.

---

[72] ibid, pp 58–9

[73] see outline of possible strategies for dealing with resource dependence in Chapter 4 above, p. 158; of course both 'models' may share some of the strategies outlined

[74] see Chapter 4, above, p. 158

CHAPTER 7

Conclusions

'Over the door to the non-profit's boardroom there should be an inscription in big letters that says: Membership on this board is not power, it is responsibility'

PETER F. DRUCKER *Managing The Non-profit Organization Practices and Principles* (Butterworth–Heinemann,, Oxford paperback edition, London, 1992) p. 124

1. INTRODUCTION

The previous chapter has drawn attention to the distinctions which require to be made in public policy between boards of governance which derive their appointment from the State as opposed to appointment by a voluntary body. It suggested that a 'citizen based voluntarism' needs to be distinguished from the public service citizens may give on behalf of the Minister who appoints them to a board. There are fundamental questions of public philosophy and policy to be addressed if this distinction is made and if the 'citizen based voluntarist' approach is to be facilitated and encouraged. This chapter will focus upon the implications for governance of the voluntarist philosophy based on citizenship described in this study as contrasted with the 'managerialist' approaches which now predominate in the Irish public service. It will present an overall summary of the study.

2. MANAGERIALIST VERSUS CITIZENSHIP BASED APPROACHES

The 'new voluntarism', which finds its legitimating philosophy in the norms and values of active citizenship in a pluralist democratic republic, might be characterised under the following six headings:

1) VALUES

   Voluntary organisations must be explicit about the values they promote in the more open, accountable democratic culture which will pervade the public, private and voluntary sectors of society in the future; it is no longer either acceptable or effective to operate on assumed, unexamined or covert values.

2) DIVERSITY

   Voluntary organisations in the future will be vehicles for the expression of diverse interests in a pluralist society as opposed to representing a dominance by Catholic or religiously inspired voluntary initiative; they will also be the means for diversity in the provision of services and, for both reasons, they are essential in a pluralist society.

3) POWER

   Voluntary organisations are a means of participatory democracy and are thus an expression of citizen power as they seek to relate to their environment and to the statutory authorities and the structures of representative democracy; through mobilisation of resources, such as legitimacy (based upon citizenship rights and obligations, duties and responsibilities), voluntary organisations will seek to forge new relationships with Governmental agencies, and with other bodies both statutory and voluntary in order to pursue their objectives.

4) SOCIAL CAPITAL

Voluntary organisations will be increasingly seen as the seed-bed for the development of the civic virtues essential to active citizenship and to the formation of the social capital essential to democratic society; voluntary action will be the key means for the acquisition of the skills required for democratic participation and for the development of the bonds of solidarity and of the social obligations of citizenship.

5) PUBLIC BENEFIT

Voluntary organisations will be evaluated by society in terms of the benefits they bring to the public through the services they provide or through the opportunities for others which they create; they will be committed to accountability to all stakeholders in the services in which they are involved and will be measured by their ability to express and meet needs often by giving a voice to minorities or to those who are unable to speak for themselves

6) PARTNERSHIP

Voluntary organisations will seek to be fuller partners with statutory agencies in providing services; by adding value to the statutory services and by doing what the State is often unable to do (such as providing choice, identifying new needs, experimenting with new forms of provision, upholding unpopular needs or causes or meeting specialised needs) they will provide a basis for active partnerships with statutory bodies.

If these characteristics of the 'new voluntarism' are to flourish the nature of Irish public services must reflect an overall framework for voluntary-statutory relationships based upon an agreed democratic philosophy of active citizenship.[1]

[1] in a key international comparative study of voluntary organisations Ireland emerges as does every one of the Western European countries, (except Spain and Finland), as a 'public sector—dominant country' where the major source of voluntary revenue is not fees and payments but public sector grants and contracts; this is especially marked where the voluntary sector is large and extensive, as in Ireland, Netherlands, Belgium and Israel; see L.M. Salamon, H.K. Anheier *The Emerging Sector Revisited A Summary Revised Estimates* The Johns Hopkins Comparative Nonprofit Sector Project, Phase II, (The Johns Hopkins University, Baltimore, MD, 1999) pp 11–12

In facing the challenge of renewal voluntary organisations, in the developed world generally, as well as in Ireland in particular

are in heightened danger of losing touch with their citizen base. On the one hand, many of these organizations have long since been transformed into large bureaucracies seemingly indistinguishable from the government bureaus with which they interact; on the other hand they face a growing danger of becoming even more like the business firms with which they frequently compete.[2]

To preserve and regain 'the sector's true identity and core values' Salamon and Anheier recommend that a 'serious effort' be made 'to reinvigorate the nonprofit sector on a regular basis'. This can be done

through regular strategic planning, through improved training and management models that reflect the central values this set of institutions is supposed to promote and through a critical dialog that engages a wide range of societal actors in a discussion of the sector's appropriate social role.[3]

Attention should, therefore, be given to the underlying philosophy that has undergirded public service reforms, in Ireland in the 1990s such as those described in Chapter 2 for Irish healthcare, which impact so influentially on the voluntary sector especially in relation to governance and management.

It has been noted that the 1990s in the western world generally have been challenging years for theory builders in the fields of public administration and public policy and that two central themes have emerged in governmental reform in democratic societies: managerialism and governance.[4]

Public administration and public policy is 'about our collective social experience as much as it is about the delivering of public programs. This view reflects a concern for the social construction of meaning in the context of our civic life'.[5] This study has sought to provide a normative base for voluntary action which legitimises the

[2] Salamon and Anheier, 1999, op. cit. p. 18

[3] ibid, p. 18

[4] see G. Marshall 'In Search of Commensurability: Writings in Public Management in an Era of Governmental Reform' *Public Administration Review* Vol. 58, No. 3, May/June 1998, pp 274–279; for the development of managerialism—the introduction of managerial techniques common to the private commercial sector and the development and operation of market (or market like) mechanisms—within the Irish public services in the 1990s see Neil Collins and Patrick Butler 'Public Services in Ireland: social marketing management' in *Political Issues in Ireland Today* ed. N. Collins (Manchester University Press, Manchester, 1999) pp 33–45

[5] Marshall, op. cit., p. 274

voluntary sector's role in the governance process. Public governance and management of services, such as health, has to be shared between statutory authorities and voluntary organisations and this requires a democratic framework which legitimates both the voluntary actions of citizens in a participatory democratic society and the exercise of statutory powers on behalf of citizens through the representative structures of democratic society: public policy should be formulated, implemented and evaluated through effective partnerships between the voluntary and public sectors.[6] A participatory model of public management embraces both sectors in collaborative action in meeting and serving the public interests of citizens.

It has been noted that while the reform movements associated with the New Public Management

> vary in depth, scope, and success by country, they are remarkably similar in the goals they pursue and the technologies they utilize. Each movement is drawn to maximise productive and allocative efficiencies that are hampered by 'bureau-pathology' that is, public agencies unresponsive to the demands of citizens, led by bureaucrats with the power and incentives to expand their administrative empires and 'policy spaces'. While control of administrative bureaucracies by political leadership is a traditional concern in representative governments and the target of many waves of innovations, the institutional reforms associated with the New Public Management are unprecedented in the formal separation between policy making and service delivery.[7]

The normative models used whereby institutions are designed to solve problems and provide goods and services have formative effects on society: there is a need for vigilance about the effects of various institutional arrangements on the relationships and processes that are necessary for the health of democracy. The active engagement of citizens is a key barometer of healthy democracies. The quest is for an inclusive democratic polity in which all citizens have full rights, duties and obligations and a sense of belonging because of active participation as an equal partner entitled to the benefits and burdens society offers.[8] The long established belief that private sector practices and technolo-

[6] see the important symposium 'Leadership, Democracy and the New Public Management' *Public Administration Review* Vol. 58, No. 3, May/June 1998, pp 189–237

[7] see Linda Kaboolian 'The New Public Management: Challenging the Boundaries of the Management vs Administration Debate' *Public Administration Review* Vol. 58, No. 3, May/June 1998, p. 190

[8] see Rita Mae Kelly 'An Inclusive Democratic Polity, Representative Bureaucracies and the New Public Management', ibid, pp 201–208

gies are superior to those used in the public sector, or in the voluntary sector, is rooted in market driven management: this has led to the view that 'management is management' whether in the public, private or nonprofit sectors giving rise to a 'managerialist ideology' or 'manageri-alism'.[9] As Terry and others have warned this ideology conflicts with democratic norms and theory which focuses upon citizenship; what is required is a public service with public managers who are 'trustworthy, ethical agents who administer the public's business with the common good in mind'.[10] If private sector assumptions predominate values such as fairness, justice, representation or participation are heavily discount-ed against performance indicators of efficiency and of a financial kind in a 'market model' of the world. As Kelly observes of public services: 'procedural due process, substantive rights, equity, and protection of minority rights as well as equal opportunity and equality among citizens are values that have precedence over efficiency'.[11]

Kelly seeks the advancement of an inclusive democratic polity working within the Constitution and a republican form of government:

> It is a society in which the people share, as Alexis de Tocqueville, Vincent Ostrom, and Harold Lasswell have suggested, a body of common knowledge grounded in a shared community of understanding with a degree of trust in each other and in the political system, of which the government is an important but not the total part. There is also basic clarity about the place: its material conditions, technological levels, and the nature of national goals. Rules and rule-ordered relationships are public and accessible to all citizens.[12]

Simply put, we cannot equate customers/consumers with citizens: approaches which seek responsiveness to customers/consumers are not the same as providing a means of being accountable to the citizenry or

[9] for this ideology see the very important work by Christopher Pollitt *Managerialism and the Public Service: The Anglo-American Experience*, Second Edition (Blackwell Publishers, Oxford, 1993) and L.D. Terry 'Administrative Leadership, Neo-Managerialism, and the Public Management Movement' *Public Administration Review* May/June 1998, Vol. 58, No. 3, pp 194–200

[10] Terry, op. cit., p. 198; see also Philip Selznick *The Moral Commonwealth: Social Theory and The Promise of Community* (University Press of California, Berkeley, CA, 1992)

[11] Rita Mae Kelly 'An Inclusive Democratic Polity, Representative Bureaucracies, and the New Public Management' *Public Administration Review* Vol. 58, No. 3, May/June 1998, p. 201

[12] Rita Mae Kelly 'An Inclusive Democratic Polity, Representative Bureaucracies, and the New Public Management', op. cit., p. 202; Lasswell was an important democratic theorist and Vincent Ostrom has written *The Meaning of Democracy and the Vulnerability of Democracy: A Response to Tocqueville's Challenge* (University of Michigan Press, Ann Arbor, MI, 1997)

providing avenues and scope for citizen participation and responsibility in all the key domains and services that impinge on their lives.

As Mintzberg has written in a key article in the *Harvard Business Review* managerialist assumptions 'collapse in the face of what most government agencies do and how they have to work'. He goes on to state that the 'belief that politics and administration in government—like formulation and implementation in corporate planning—can be separated is another old myth that should be allowed to die a quiet death'.[13] Mintzberg's critique of the myths of 'the Management movement', which imply that public services must become more like business, draws attention to the fundamental distinctions between 'citizens' and 'customers'. As Mintzberg states we all wear different 'hats' in society as customers, clients, citizens and subjects but in respect of relationships with public services 'most important, I am a citizen, with rights that go far beyond those of customers or even clients'.[14] He argues that government activities concern 'citizens' much more than 'customers' and that only 'in limited spheres is direct customer service a job for the state'. In Mintzberg's view only rarely does 'the kind of management that now inundates us' apply to public services.[15] Three assumptions underlie 'the Management view of management':

- particular activities can be isolated—both from one another and from direct authority (principal-agent relationship)

- performance can be fully and properly evaluated by 'objective' measures[16]

- activities can be entrusted to autonomous professional managers held responsible for performance ('let the managers manage')

[13] H. Mintzberg 'Managing Government Governing Management' *Harvard Business Review* May/June 1996, p. 79

[14] ibid, p. 77; see also T. O'Sullivan 'Consumerism in the Health Services' *Administration* Vol 46 No 1, Spring 1998, pp 14-28, for valuable critique

[15] ibid, p. 78; Mintzberg's critique is an essential corrective to the uncritical acceptance of managerialist ideology as popularly propagated in, for example, D. Osborne, T. Gaebler *Reinventing Government How The Entrepreneurial Spirit is Transforming the Public Sector* (London, 1993)

[16] Mintzberg observes: 'Many of the activities are in the public sector precisely because of measurement problems: if everything was so crystal clear and every benefit so easily attributable, those activities would have been in the private sector long ago' ibid, p. 79; a recent death notice in *The Irish Times* asked the pertinent question 'How do you measure or praise the kindness and care of doctors, nurses and auxiliary staff in St. Luke's [Hospital] over five years and St. Vincent's [Hospital] in the closing weeks of a brave and very gentle lady's life?' *The Irish Times*, 19 August 1999

It is these assumptions that collapse in public services; as Mintzberg asks 'how many politicians are prepared to relinquish control of how many of their policies? And how many policies in government today can simply be formulated in one place to be implemented in another, instead of being crafted in an iterative process involving both politics and administration?'[17] Mintzberg states baldly when 'Management is allowed to take over, it drives everyone crazy. And no one more so than the 'customer' who ends up getting the worst of it'; the 'obsession with Management belies a good deal of the reality out there'.[18] Another major critique of private sector management as applied to 'core public services' such as health, education and welfare services, has been developed by David McKevitt in his international study *Managing Core Public Services* published in 1998: McKevitt distinguishes between 'citizen-clients' and the 'consumer model' and develops a conceptual structure for the public management of 'core public services' different from that drawn from private sector management.[19] The importance of 'citizen voice' in core public services emerges for McKevitt's review of public service reforms in a wide range of countries.

Mintzberg identifies five models for managing government and a motto which sums up the approach involved:

(i)   the Government—as—Machine Model
       Motto 'Control, Control, Control'

(ii)   the Government—as—Network Model
       Motto 'Connect, Communicate, Collaborate'

(iii) the Performance—Control Model
       Motto 'Isolate, Assign, and Measure'

(iv) the Virtual—Government Model
       Motto 'Privatize, Contract, and Negotiate'

(v)   the Normative—Control Model
       Motto 'Select, Socialize, and Judge'

---

[17] ibid, p. 79

[18] ibid, p. 80

[19] see D. McKevitt *Managing Core Public Services* (Oxford, 1998); the 'core public services' are 'non-marketable' services see especially Chapter 3 'Service Delivery—Meeting Citizen Needs' for discussion of 'the language of service delivery' pp 37–67, where McKevitt notes that the 'language of consumerism' can 'obscure the importance of citizenship and its relationship to the modern social democratic state' p. 39

It is significant that the move to the Performance—Control Model, implied in Irish public service reform, actually reinforces, as Mintzberg points out, the 'old machine model'

> . . . the performance model decentralizes in order to centralize; it loosens up in order to tighten up. And tightening up comes at the expense of flexibility, creativity, and individual initiative. Thus the brave new world of public management all too often comes down to nothing more than the same old machine management—new labels on the old bottles.[20]

Mintzberg rightly notes that there is 'no one best model' because government 'is an enormously eclectic system, as varied as life itself (because it deals with almost every conceivable facet of life)'; he believes, however, that 'we sorely need a major shift of emphasis to the normative model'.[21] This model is rooted in values and beliefs and in the concept of public service; it has five key characteristic elements

● Selection: people are chosen by values and attitudes rather than just credentials

● Socialization: this element ensures a membership dedicated to an integrated social system

● Guidance: guidance is by accepted principles rather than by imposed plans, by visions rather than by targets

● Responsibility: all members share responsibility. They feel trusted and supported by leaders who practice a craft style of management that is rooted in experience. Inspiration thus replaces so-called empowerment

● Judgement: performance is judged by experienced people, including recipients of the service, some of whom sit on representative oversight boards

This model allows for radically different 'microstructures: more missionary, egalitarian, and energized; less machinelike and less hierarchical'.[22] Mintzberg argues that this 'model' applies especially to healthcare and education 'which can never be better than the people who deliver them':

---

[20] Mintzberg, op. cit., p. 81

[21] ibid, p. 82

[22] ibid, p. 81

We need to free professionals from both the direct controls of government bureaucracy and the narrow pressures of market competition. That is why nonownership [i.e. control by self-selecting and often very diverse boards of directors, not-for-profit organisations] and some co-operative ownership seem to work so well in those areas.[23]

In respect of Irish healthcare, and indeed of other organisational fields such as education, much may be learned from theories of management for multinational corporations in respect of 'differentiated networks' which involve integration based upon agreed norms.[24] A highly centralised and uniform approach suffocates innovation and energy in large multinational enterprises; as in a large multinational corporation so also in a large and complex national healthcare system. It is possible to conceptualise healthcare providers as a highly differentiated network which might be normatively integrated. This concept facilitates the independence and autonomy of voluntary organisations and yet integrates services with the degree of policy direction and evaluation of outcomes required by the central statutory authority. An analogy might be drawn between the world headquarters and the national subsidiaries of a multinational corporation.

The work of Mintzberg and McKevitt raises questions about the direction of public service reform in Ireland. As Kelly observes 'The question of *who* is and should be represented in a democracy, *how* they are represented, and *who* should have standing on which issues is critically important.'[25]

If we limit our understanding of public services to that of efficiency in delivering goods and services we also restrict the range of concerns that are viewed as a legitimate for debate and collective action. Voluntary organisations in a democratic society add value because they provide a form of what Kelly describes as 'representative bureaucracies' which provide substantive representation (that is citizens acting for others) for citizens.[26] In addition 'descriptive representation' for

[23] ibid, p. 82; Mintzberg states that both business and government can learn a great deal from the nonprofit organisations, p. 83

[24] see especially N. Notria, S. Ghoshal *The Differentiated Network Organizing Multinational Corporations For Value Creation* (Jossey-Bass Publishers, San Francisco, 1997); I am indebted to Professor John Murray, Trinity College, Dublin for this reference

[25] Kelly, op. cit., p. 203

[26] Kelly, op. cit., describes the three most common forms of substantive representation (1) *the trustee*, someone who uses his or her discretion to make decisions on behalf of and in the best interests of the represented (2) *the delegate*, someone who seriously attempts to discern the desires of the represented and (3) *the politico*, someone who acts to maximise a political position or status

different kinds of citizens, groups or minorities is very important, as the literature demonstrates, as for example when 'women and minorities are in the decision-making and implementing structures, more women and minorities are hired, their concerns are more likely to be addressed, their material well-being rises, and their sense of the fairness and justice of the polity increases . . .' Being there 'matters'.[27] The capacity of active citizens to act in a voluntary capacity on governing boards in the interests of, and in the service of, others is a resource which must be encouraged, facilitated and developed. The richness of the theoretical perspectives of Robert K. Greenleaf in this regard in respect of 'trustees as servants', the 'institution as servant' and 'the servant leader' applies especially to voluntary organisations, such as public voluntary hospitals, but is insightful also for all institutions and their governing boards.[28] The relatively simple notion of the formal elected representatives in the Oireachtas or indirectly through Health Boards holding the bureaucracy accountable for delivering goods and services such as healthcare is both impoverished and inadequate for citizens in a pluralist democracy. An inclusive democratic polity requires more than satisfied customers but that is what is on offer at best under the current policy environment in the Irish health service:

> The philosophy of contracting and much of the New Public Management rest on the principal-agent relationship. In this relationship the government manager clearly articulates the policy, sets performance standards, and chooses in a competitive market an agent who will faithfully act on the government's behalf to deliver the goods and services so that the outcome sought will be attained. The feasibility of implementing this logic depends on the directness and clarity of the following: the policy to be implemented, the lines of responsibility, and the performance standards. It depends, most basically, on the extent to which politics and administration can indeed be separated, and on the actual existence of a competitive marketplace in the public sector.[29]

Even if these conditions are met the question is 'how are citizens' wishes to be incorporated and represented in the delivery and implementation process? Would it not require some thought as to what structures or mechanisms would in the end persuade them that the choice

---

[27] Kelly, op. cit., p. 204

[28] see R.K. Greenleaf's seminal essays 'The Servant Leader' 'The Institution as Servant' and 'Trustees as Servants' which are republished in R.K. Greenleaf *Servant Leadership A Journey into the Nature of Legitimate Power and Greatness* (Paulist Press, New York, 1991)

[29] Kelly, op. cit., p. 205

was just, fair and appropriate when their elected officials are no longer directly involved?'[30] One possible answer is through having 'descriptive representatives' by the use of voluntary organisations, who have some potential for representing citizen views in the bureaucracy or in the contracting agency. As Kelly comments 'being there' in some form should be one of the 'taken for granted' elements of an inclusive democratic polity wherever and whenever possible.[31]

Kelly agrees with Putnam's conclusions 'that democratic institutions cannot be built from the top down (or at least not easily). They must be built up in the everyday traditions of trust and civic virtue among its citizens'. The Putnam thesis that civic communities based on high levels of political interest, social equality, interpersonal trust, and voluntary association lead to higher probabilities of effective governance and democracy is a challenge to managerialism in the delivery of public services. If it is accepted then voluntary action by citizens is crucial; as Kelly concludes

> Representative bureaucracies and contracting agencies that incorporate descriptive, symbolic and substantive representation of diverse citizens not only promote a more inclusive democratic polity they also promote more efficient and effective decision making by government when market imperfections exist.[32]

As Vincent Ostrom has written

> It is within families and other institutional arrangements characteristic of neighbourhood, village, and community life that citizenship is learned and practised for most people most of the time. The first order of priority in learning the craft of citizenship as applied to public affairs needs to focus on how to cope with problems in the context of family, neighbourhood, village and community. This is where people acquire the rudiments for becoming self-governing, by learning how to live and work with others.[33]

What makes public administration and public management *public* and thus distinctive is that politics of the most fundamental sort is at the heart of the enterprise. It is the politics of fulfilling, maintaining, and enhancing the character of a democratic and republican regime. Institutional design and redesign are at the heart of the public manage-

---

[30] ibid, p. 206

[31] ibid, p. 206

[32] Kelly, op. cit., p. 207; see also David Putnam *Making Democracy Work: Civic Traditions in Modern Italy* (Princeton University Press, Princeton, NJ, 1993) p. 172

[33] V. Ostrom *The Meaning of Democracy and the Vulnerability of Democracies A Response To Tocqueville's Challenge* (The University of Michigan Press, Ann Arbor, 1997) p. x

ment enterprise; politics and the logic of governance that stems from democratic politics should be at the core of institutional design efforts rather than economics (and the logic of governance of that stems from economic models).[34]

As Christopher Pollitt observes

> If it were possible significantly to increase the direct participation of the public in the design, delivery and assessment of public services, then politicians would have to reckon with a new, informal and highly legitimate source of opinion on 'what should be done'. So, too would the professional (and other) providers. This would not be the consumerism of the new right, but the active participation of users and taxpayers in the running of everyday services—a real cultural shift.[35]

One advocate of such a shift argues that

> the practice of public administration must be expanded to civic and voluntary associations that mediate between individuals and the state. These associations may thus be transformed into lively democratic laboratories for civic engagement and responsibility.[36]

3. SUMMARY

This book has sought to provide an explicit framework for voluntary action in Irish society based upon a democratic theory of active citizenship in a pluralist society as outlined in Chapter 3. Whether this is a convincing philosophical justification is ultimately a matter for agreement or disagreement about fundamental values. As an answer to the key question behind this inquiry it draws considerable strength from a major conclusion of Robert Putnam in his seminal empirical study *Making Democracy Work*:

> Effective and responsive institutions depend, in the language of civic humanism, on republican virtues and practices. Tocqueville was right: Democratic government is strengthened, not weakened, when it faces a vigorous civil society.

[34] see Brian J. Cook 'Politics, Political Leadership, and Public Management' *Public Administration Review* Vol. 58, No. 3, May/June 1998, p. 29

[35] C. Pollitt *Managerialism and the Public Services: The Anglo-American Experience* (Second Edition, Blackwell Publishers, Oxford, 1993) p. 195; Pollitt outlines some alternatives to managerialism such as Public Service Orientation and Public Management which would be more congenial to the citizen-based approach through voluntary action see J. Steward and M. Clarke 'The Public Service Orientation: issues and dilemnas' *Public Administration*, Vol. 65, No. 2, Summer 1987, pp 161–178 and C. Ventriss 'Towards a Public Philosophy of Public Administration: a civic perspective of the public' *Public Administration Review* Vol., 49, No. 2, March-April, 1989, pp 173–9

[36] Ventriss, op. cit., p. 176

On the demand side, citizens in civic communities expect better government and (in part through their own efforts), they get it. They demand more effective public service and they are prepared to act collectively to achieve their shared goals. Their counterparts in less civic regions more commonly assume the role of alienated and cynical supplicants. On the supply side, the performance of representative government is facilitated by the social infrastructure of civic communities and by the democratic values of both officials and citizens. Most fundamental to the civic community is the social ability to collaborate for shared interests.[37]

This study has also sought to clarify the definition of what constitutes a 'voluntary' agency generally as well as in the Irish health services. It proposes that voluntary organisations in order to be voluntary should display all of the criteria used in the internationally recognised structural—operational definition of the Johns Hopkins Comparative Nonprofit Sector Project: such organisations require an institutional or formal organisational form; they are required to be separate from government; they must be non-profit distributing; they must be self-governing and they must have a meaningful degree of voluntary participation.[38] The distinctive characteristics of such organisations in terms of their expression of values and their contribution to the formation of social capital through active citizenship have been described. These voluntary organisations are eligible to be partners in public service to the extent that they provide public goods or services.

The quality of such partnerships between voluntary and statutory agencies is a matter of great importance in respect of public philosophy and public policy. Based upon clear distinctions as to what constitutes voluntary organisations it is suggested that the State should have a public policy to foster the development of voluntary organisations as central means whereby citizens may actively participate in, and govern, the benefits and services they require.

It has been increasingly recognised that the development of genuine voluntary/statutory partnerships is essential to the full development of the voluntary sector: such partnerships must aspire to a level of equality between the partners and a recognition that each partner has a degree of autonomy in its own sphere of action. Voluntary organisations, in such partnerships, must share in the planning and policy-

[37] Robert D. Putnam *Making Democracy Work Civic Traditions in Modern Italy* (Princeton University Press, Princeton, N.J., 1993) p. 182

[38] see F. Donoghoe 'Defining The Nonprofit Sector: Ireland' Working Paper No. 28 *The Johns Hopkins Comparative Nonprofit Sector Project* (Institute for Policy Studies, The Johns Hopkins University, Baltimore, 1998) and p. 55 above

making process, the decision-making and the evaluation/review processes, as well as being responsible for implementation of planned services.[39] The case study in Chapter 5 underlies the lack of clarity in Irish health policy as to the definition and role of voluntary hospitals and this led to a confirmation of a 'dependent partnership' approach by the State eroding a great deal of the positive influence of the voluntary leadership of the Hospital. This has made the challenge of developing the Hospital to achieve a distinctive role, as a public *voluntary* hospital in 'active partnership', much more difficult; it is probably impossible to achieve without a significant change in public policy and in the approach of the statutory authorities. This provides an example where social capital is depleted by the effects of statutory actions on voluntary organisations. Changes in public policy to support voluntary action, as we have seen, will require that 'managerialist' approaches to the governance and delivery of public services will need to be modified in the light of citizenship requirements. It is suggested that 'active partnership' models should replace 'dependent partnership' models as described in Chapter 2 above and that the pursuit of more co-operative and collaborative relationships will ultimately maximise the advantages identified for service planning and minimise the disadvantages identified and experienced by voluntary organisations to date.[40] The study has indicated that a wider repertoire of models and approaches is available for voluntary and statutory relationships than has been recognised in policy so far and that an 'active partnership' model is more consistent with a policy of developing voluntary organisations (and thereby building social capital) than the 'dependent partnership' model used to date in service planning.

This book presents for voluntary organisations and in particular for public voluntary hospitals, a 'usable theory' to provide a framework for designing governance and management arrangements.[41] It is argued that this approach will help preserve the voluntary character of such organisations and provides a richer basis for their development than

---

[39] see for examples of arguments being made in this direction in Irish healthcare, R. Mulvihill *Voluntary-Statutory Partnership in Community Care of the Elderly* (National Council for the Elderly, Dublin, 1993); *A Study of Partnership between Voluntary and Statutory Sectors in Palliative Care in Ireland* (Policy Research Centre, National College of Ireland, for The Irish Hospice Foundation, 1999)

[40] see Chapter 2 above, pp 68-71

[41] see Chapter 4 above pp 150-160

simply importing the 'corporate' or 'managerialist' model which has been advanced by statutory authorities during the 1990s.

Governance and management has become a key policy concern in the relationships between the State and voluntary organisations in Ireland.[42] It is hoped that this book has made a contribution to a new policy framework for developing relationships between the State sphere of responsibilities and the voluntary sphere of citizen rights, duties and responsibilities in the light of the public discourse which ought to surround the White Paper which is to follow the 1997 Green Paper *Supporting Voluntary Activity A Green Paper on the Community and Voluntary Sector and its Relationship with the State.*

---

[42] this is not restricted, of course, to healthcare see in education, for example, John Walshe *A New Partnership in Education From Consultation To Legislation in the Nineties* (Institute of Public Administration, Dublin, 1999) Chapter 4 'The Governance of Schools'; also Education Act, 1998, Part IV 'Boards of Management' and Universities Act, 1997, Chapter II 'Governance'

A Personal Reflection Upon Theory, Method and Data

This study developed because of my involvement in very concrete problems and issues relating to the governance and management of a newly merged public voluntary hospital. The research was a response to my attempts to understand or to explain what was really going on underneath the surface of the problems and issues encountered by the hospital from 1996. The M.Sc. Programme in Health Services Management which I began in 1997 at Trinity College, Dublin, provided an opportunity to try to discover what ought to have been going on, why what was happening was occurring, and how voluntary and statutory bodies might relate more effectively and the bearing of these crucial relationships on governance and management.

The difficult and lengthy process prior to the merger of the three hospitals in 1996 had given rise to a range of issues concerning the role of voluntary organisations in healthcare and their continuing relevance as the Irish healthcare system evolved. Were such organisations outmoded or could a fresh expression of their legitimacy be articulated? If they had a legitimate place and this found expression in public policy what relationships were possible between voluntary and statutory bodies and what effect do these relationships have upon the way voluntary organisations might be governed and managed? It appeared to me that the general findings of research in seeking answers to these questions in the field of healthcare would have a broader relevance and perhaps a more general application to voluntary action in other key domains in society.

It has been well stated that 'the research process is not a clear-cut sequence of procedures following a neat pattern but a messy interaction between the conceptual and empirical world, deduction and induction occurring at the same time'.[1] The 'messy interaction' was

---

[1] F. Bechhofer 'Current Approaches to Empirical Research: Some Central Ideas' in *Approaches To Sociology* ed. J. Rex (London, 1974) p. 73 quoted in John Gill and Phil Johnson *Research Methods For Managers* Second Edition (London 1997) p. 2; this later book was my main guide as to methodology and is an excellent companion for researchers in the field of management studies

269

essential as I sought theories, or models, or concepts which would be practical and usable in the concrete circumstances of the Irish health services: Gill and Johnson were helpful here reminding us that 'there is nothing so practical as a good theory' and of the importance of 'clearly utilizable research'.[2]

In order to evaluate the operation of the Board of the hospital the immediate question which arose concerned the meaning attached to 'voluntary' and whether there was a clear understanding of the 'voluntary' concept in health policies and in the relationships between statutory and voluntary organisations in the Irish health system. It quickly emerged that policy lacked clarity in this regard and this led to a detailed review of the remarkable and growing literature concerning the voluntary or 'third sector' seeking answers to the first part of the research question which began to crystallise: is there a convincing philosophical justification for voluntary action in society which would undergird the legitimacy of voluntary organisations and their involvement in public services such as health or for that matter other key fields such as education.[3]

Seeking an answer to this question led to a review of the theories of voluntary action which have emerged particularly since the 1970s. These theories, as briefly summarised in Chapter 3 above, help to explain why voluntary action occurs but they do not provide either a satisfying philosophical justification or a normative case of sufficient power and both of these, it seems to me, are essential to provide the necessary degree of legitimacy for voluntary organisations in a democratic society. There is a need for theory to evaluate as well as to explain: at a practical level the hospital, as a voluntary hospital, was having real difficulties explaining or being accepted as having a legitimate organisational form. This led to the first chapter which I drafted which concerned the place of voluntary associations in both classical and recent democratic theory which has become Chapter 3 above. The norms and values associated with active citizenship in a pluralist democracy offered a basis by which all institutions in a democratic

---

[2] Gill and Johnson, op. cit., p. 23, p. 2

[3] the discovery of the extensive literature on the nonprofit or 'third sector' was a major source of surprise and illumination and much of it was very recent dating from the late 1970s; many practitioners in the Irish voluntary sector are probably quite unaware of how extensively the international and national academic and policy communities have focussed upon voluntary sector studies—I certainly was!

society might be evaluated: a good question to ask of our institutions whether voluntary or statutory is whether they promote or frustrate active citizenship by all the diverse groups in our society?

The excursion into political theory proved to be both exciting and challenging. I had graduated with a degree in Modern History and Political Science in 1971 when there had been a predominant emphasis on political science as an empirically based discipline explaining the predominance of elites in democracies amongst a passive citizenry.[4] What was exciting now in the late 1990s was to discover what has been termed 'the communitarian turn in contemporary moral, social and political theory' which re-emphasises the importance and role of voluntary organisations (which had been present in the classical works of Alexis de Tocqueville and J.S. Mill but neglected in the work of the emergent discipline of political science until very recently): this 'communitarism liberalism' which characterises so many of the key democratic theorists which have come to the fore in the 1980s and 1990s has led to a central focus upon civil society and on citizenship.[5] I present a normative statement for the legitimacy of voluntary action based upon this recent work in Chapter 3 above.

This initial statement of the democratic legitimacy of voluntary action renewed my confidence that the search for improved voluntary and statutory relationships was important in health policy (as in other areas of public policy). The publication of the Green Paper *Supporting Voluntary Activity* in 1997 provided further evidence that 'active citizenship' and the legitimacy of voluntary organisations were emerging and vital themes in Irish public policy generally. In the new hospital in 1998 relationships with the statutory authorities entered a crisis as described in the case study in Chapter 5 above. As a member of the Board of the hospital I was now operating on two levels at least: as an active member of the Board grappling with a developing crisis which was difficult to understand as it unfolded and as a researcher seeking to place in a more 'global' context the 'local' experiences of the hospital. The exploration turned now to trace how voluntary hospitals had reached

[4] this view was just beginning to be challenged and one of the most memorable books I read before my degree in 1971 was Peter Bachrach's *The Theory of Democratic Elitism A Critique* first published 1967 (University of London Press Ltd., London, 1969); this book is still powerfully relevant

[5] for quotations see Philip Selznick *The Moral Commonwealth Social Theory and the Promise of Community* (University of California Press, Berkeley and London, 1992) p. xi; Selznick's book provides an important theoretical overview and statement

the stage they had by the late 1990s: a stage characterised by rapid implementation of new policy (the development of new tiers of statutory authorities under the new Eastern Regional Health Authority in particular was now well underway) and by lack of clarity in the policy about the possible distinctive roles of voluntary organisations and in particular public voluntary hospitals. It was important to set the relationships between voluntary hospitals and the State into a historical context. Chapter 1, above, was drafted and the historical approach and method applied here helped to set the problems of the late 1990s into an understandable context: the predominance of voluntary action in healthcare under the auspices of the churches (especially that of the Catholic Church in such a hugely homogenous Catholic society as Irish society was and is) helped to explain the absence of a secular public philosophy concerning voluntary action and citizen participation in the Republic. As the health service developed under State auspices and the influence of the churches, (and especially that of the Catholic Church) waned the public voluntary hospitals became increasingly vulnerable; they appeared as reluctant and awkward building blocks of an integrated and more centrally controlled health system. It seemed to me that if public voluntary hospitals were to have a healthy future the explication of the democratic legitimacy of voluntary action assumed an even more urgent form against this historical background.

So as the research progressed it became increasingly a 'multi-method' study: I had been guided to discover the literature on the voluntary sector, I had rediscovered political theory and its relevance to public policy, in this case health policy, and I was using historical and comparative approaches to trace the experiences of the relationships of voluntary and statutory bodies in Ireland and in the United Kingdom. Now I had to turn to policy analysis as it became important to describe and analyse in some detail the policy environment in Irish healthcare in the 1990s. This became Chapter 2 above. Indeed the environment in which voluntary bodies operate became a very important theme of the study: it had not figured much in the hospital as our thinking had been focussed upon merging and moving the hospital throughout the 1990s. Yet as the policy was analysed, and the literature from both organisation theory and voluntary organisations and their governance and management was reviewed, the organisation—environment linkage emerges as central to understanding organisational development. Voluntary organisations and, in particular, public voluntary hospitals are highly resource dependent and the implications of this key characteristic for their governance and management became clearer as the study developed. However the policy analysis of key concepts such as 'partnership'; and 'service planning' revealed that it is possible to imagine and describe from the literature a range of alternative models and approaches for voluntary-statutory relationships which would provide a more developmental context for voluntary organisations (than that experienced to date in Ireland by voluntary health providing agencies) and which yet would take account of their high resource dependence on the State. A 'usable' theory (if the legitimacy of such organisations were to be based upon the key concept of 'active citizenship') might be built which would have the very practical result that the destructive tensions experienced in relation to the operation of service planning (as described in the case of the hospital in Chapter 5) might be replaced by collaborative and 'active partnership' approaches. This could lead to public goods and services, such as healthcare, being delivered by and to citizens in a context which makes effective and optimises the complementary roles of voluntary and statutory agencies.

The implications for governance and management of voluntary healthcare organisations that stemmed from voluntary and statutory relationships appeared to me to be profound. As described in Chapter 2 above the relationships may range over a wide typology involving competition, co-operation, conflict and collaboration.[6] A detailed review of the prescriptive literature on governance and management was next undertaken to describe what models were available and whether they applied to voluntary organisations and to public voluntary hospitals. When combined with key insights from organisation theory it became possible to outline the elements of a 'usable theory' for governance and management of public voluntary hospitals in Chapter 4 above. Such a theory seeks to account for both the environmental constraints and the essential attributes of voluntary organisations and to offer a practical framework for the future.

It was now very important to test the conclusions (hypotheses?) drawn from the historical context, the policy analysis, political theory, and the organisation and management literature in the context of a detailed narrative of the experiences of the first Board of the Hospital. Boards have proved particularly elusive to study and the literature

---

[6] an important contribution to such a typology is found in *Government and The Third Sector Emerging Relationships in Welfare States* eds. B. Gidron, R.M. Kramer, L.M. Salamon (Jossey-Bass Publishers, San Francisco, 1992) pp 16–20 based on four models: 'Government Dominant'; 'Dual'; 'Collaborative' and 'Third Sector Dominant'

provided no obvious model for this case study; there are no similar descriptions of the operation of boards of Irish hospitals to that now provided in chapter 5 above. However, there are great risks of subjectivity in reporting on a Board on which the reporter sits as a member. Despite these risks it was important to try because of the unique access to the experiences of the Board through being a member and to counter the risks as best one could: the case study was done in the context of the overall research (I only drafted what became Chapter 5 from June 1999). In short it provided a unique opportunity to review the main conclusions (hypotheses?) based upon the theory and the literature in the light of the very detailed empirical evidence provided by a functioning board to which one had access.[7]

The risks were countered by careful description from actual documents or records contemporary with the events to which they relate; little use was made of interview material by key informants in respect of the details of the case as much of what might be said so close to the events might be self-serving or exculpatory. The detailed interviews undertaken were designed and used to provide perceptions, views or insights into the wider issues of the study as reported in Chapter 6. The research was undertaken not to apportion blame but to produce understanding and a sound basis for improvements in governance and management and in voluntary and statutory relationships. The risks were further reduced by using the more objective and agreed criteria of the Charter of the Hospital as well as the prescriptive literature to evaluate the developments in the case study. This basis only became clear after an initial narrative on the Board 1996–1999 was drafted using a methodology akin to contemporary history but obviously subject to the experiences and bias of the author. These could be modified (at least!) by the approach adopted in Chapter 5.[8]

It was important to provide as far as possible evidence-based and full descriptions of events so recently lived through and this helps to preserve a historian's objectivity albeit only in the imperfect form possible for a participant observer. It will be open to those with other

[7] the central idea that in case studies we must 'locate the global in the local' is argued by Jacques Hamel with Stephanie Dufour, Domenci Fortin *Case Study Methods* Qualitative Research Methods Series, Vol. 32, (Sage Publications, London, 1993) p. v; pp 34–40

[8] I gladly acknowledge the guidance and advice of my supervisor, Ms Gemma Donnelly-Cox, for identifying the approach used in the case study

perspectives and perhaps with access to other sources of evidence, (and perhaps other questions to answer) to describe the experiences in other ways.[9]

In order to reflect on the relationships between voluntary and statutory bodies and upon their implications for governance and management a range of six detailed in-depth interviews involving nine key informants (of which five were from the statutory side being officials of the Department of Health and Children and one from an Eastern Health Board background who also was a former public representative) were conducted.[10] The interviews were used to present the 'real life' spectrum of views by those most keenly involved in the day to day voluntary-statutory relationship upon the key themes of legitimacy, relationships, governance and management, 'partnership' and service planning.

It emerged that the pervasive 'managerialist ideology' which has informed Irish public service reform is central to understanding how Irish statutory authorities are now seeking to relate to voluntary agencies in the health services (and generally probably in other services). The study concludes by indicating the key characteristics of what may be termed the 'new' voluntarism and by suggesting that a reorientation around citizenship is required in both public and voluntary sectors: the role of the voluntary sector cannot be properly understood or developed without a better understanding of the role of the statutory sector.[11] A further reorientation in the reform of the public sector towards citizens rather than towards customers is suggested.

---

[9] The Adelaide and Meath Hospital, Dublin, Incorporating The National Children's Hospital has a policy of safeguarding hospital archives and employs a Hospital Archivist; it is hoped that all the relevant material for studies of the Hospital and its activities will be available to researchers in due course.

[10] the methodology employed for the interviews owed a great deal to Chapter 5 'The Open-Ended Semistructured Interview: An (Almost) Operational Guide' by Dean Hammer and Aaron Wildarsky in A. Wildarsky *Craftways On the Organisation of Scholarly Work* (Transaction Publishers, New Brunswick (USA) and London, 1989) pp 57–101; the interviews were recorded, transcripts sent for approval to the interviewees and signed and approved by them before use.

[11] see *Government and Voluntary Organizations A Relational Perspective* eds. S. Kulnle and P. Selle, (Avebury, Aldershot, Hants, 1992), p. 31–2, for a similar conclusion when they state that the dynamics which inform government and voluntary sectors 'would argue that one cannot understand either organizational characteristics or the values expressed by the voluntary sector without simultaneously taking into account their relationship with government'

I have been on a personal journey from late 1997 when I began to reflect seriously about this subject and it has been a journey characterised by new discoveries for me personally and by increasing understanding provided by a wide range of disciplines which now seem to me to be essential to voluntary sector studies. I started by seeking to help a hospital facing difficult issues. I hope the study will help chart a way forward in voluntary hospital governance and management. In addition however, I have reached a point where it seems to me to be crucial to reform Irish public policy and health service provision around a vision of a fully democratic society of active committed and voluntary citizens.

Sources and Bibliography

A.   SOURCES

1.   *Official Publications: Ireland and European Union*

2.   *Sources Used in Case Study; Chapter 5*

3.   *Interviews*

B.   BIBLIOGRAPHY

A. SOURCES

1. Official Publications: Ireland, United Kingdom of Great Britain and Northern Ireland and European Union

Access To Information held by the Department of Health and Children A Manual prepared in accordance with Section 15 of the Freedom of Information Act, 1997, (Department of Health and Children, April 1998)

Better Local Government A Programme for Change (Department of the Environment, Stationery Office, Dublin, 1996)

W. Beveridge *Social Insurance and Allied Services* (November 1942 Cmd 6404 (London, 1942)

'Board/Governance Proposals For Changes in Establishment Order' Department of Health and Children, n.d. [1997]

Building Real Partnership Compact Between The Government and the Voluntary and Community Sector in Northern Ireland (Northern Ireland Office, December 1998)

Communication From the Commission on Promoting The Role of Voluntary Organisations and Foundations in Europe (Office for Official Publications of the European Communities, Luxembourg, 1997)

Delivering Better Government Strategic Management Initiative Second Report to Government of the Co-ordinating Group of Secretaries A Programme of Change for the Irish Civil Service (Government Publications, Dublin 1996).

M. Dixon, A. Baker *A Management Development Strategy for the Health and Personal Social Services in Ireland* (Commissioned and Published by the Department of Health, 1996)

Enhancing The Partnership Report of The Working Group on the Implementation of The Health Strategy in Relation to Persons with a Mental Handicap (Department of Health [1997])

'*General Hospital Development Plan*' Public Statement by Mr. Brendan Corish, TD, Minister for Health, 1973 (Typescript issued by Department of Health)

Governance & Hospital Boards Discussion Document (Department of Health & Children, June 1999)

'Governance Issues Position Paper' Department of Health and Children, July 1997

Health Act, 1970

Health Act, 1970 (Section 76) (Adelaide and Meath Hospital, Dublin, Incorporating The National Children's Hospital), Order 1996

Health (Amendment) (No. 2) Act, 1996

Health (Amendment) (No. 3) Act, 1996

Health The Wider Dimensions A Consultative Statement on Health Policy (Department of Health [1986])

Health (Eastern Regional Health Authority) Act, 1999

Health for All By the Year 2000 World Health Organisation, 1985

Interim Report of the Task Force on the Eastern Regional Health Authority, June 1997 (The Department of Health, 1997)

Management Reporting and Control, Service Planning and the Financial Position of the Adelaide and Meath Hospital, Dublin, Incorporating The National Children's Hospital, (The Deloitte and Touche Consultants Report to the Minister for Health and Children, December 1998)

National Economic and Social Council *Some Major Issues in Health Policy* (Stationery Office, Dublin, 1976)

Partnership 2000 For Inclusion, Employment and Competitiveness, (Stationery Office, Dublin, 1996)

Public Health in Europe, Employment and Social Affairs Series of European Commission (Office for Official Publications of the European Communities, Luxembourg, 1997)

Report of the Commission on Health Funding September 1989 (Stationery Office, Dublin 1989)

Report of the Committee on Fundraising Activities for Charitable and Other Purposes, (Stationery Office, Dublin, 1990)

Report of the Constitution Review Group (Stationery Office, Dublin, 1996)

Report of The Tribunal of Inquiry into The Blood Transfusion Service Board (Stationery Office, Dublin, 1997)

Shaping A Healthier Future A Strategy For Effective Healthcare in the 1990s (Department of Health, Stationery Office, Dublin [1994])

Sharing in Progress National Anti-Poverty Strategy, (Stationery Office, Dublin [1997])

St. James's Hospital Board (Establishment) Order, 1971 (Amendment) Order, 1998, Statutory Instrument S.I. No. 538 of 1998

Supporting Voluntary Activity A Green Paper on the Community and Voluntary Sector and its Relationship with the State (Stationery Office, Dublin [1997])

The Freedom of Information Act, 1997

The Hospital Federation and Amalgamation Act, 1961

The New NHS Modern Dependable, (UK White Paper, The Stationery Office, London, 1997)

The Public Service Management Act, 1997

Working For Health and Well-Being Strategy Statement 1998–2001 (Department of Health and Children, 1998)

2. Sources Used in Case Study: Chapter 5

(i)   *Newspapers*

   Irish Medical News
   Irish Medical Times
   The Belfast Telegraph
   The Church of Ireland Gazette
   The Irish Independent
   The Irish Times
   The Sunday Business Post
   The Sunday Independent
   The Sunday Times
   The Sunday Tribune

(ii) *The Adelaide and Meath Hospital, Dublin, Incorporating The National Children's Hospital*

   Board Files, Minutes and Correspondence

   Charter of The Adelaide and Meath Hospital, Dublin, Incorporating The National Children's Hospital (Printed by Authority of the Board of the Hospital, 1996)

   Dr. D. McCutcheon 'Letter to All Staff', 3 March 1999

   Guide To Governance and Management of the Hospital Volume 1; September 1998 (Produced by the Strategic Planning Committee of the Board for the information of staff

   Letters of Determination issued by the Department of Health and Children for 1998 and 1999.

   'Letter To Staff of the Adelaide and Meath Hospital, Incorporating The National Children's Hospital' from the

Hospital President, Most Rev. Dr. Walton Empey, Archbishop of Dublin, 19 January 1999

Medical Board Press Release, 15 December 1998

'Minister Failing New Hospital and People of Tallaght' Press Statement, Mrs. Rosemary French, Chairman, The Adelaide and Meath Hospital, Dublin, Incorporating The National Children's Hospital, 13 December 1998

Pulses—The Hospital Newsletter

Service Plans for the Hospital for 1998 and 1999

Terms of Reference of the 'Troika' January 1999

(iii) *The Adelaide Hospital Society*

Board Files, Minutes and Correspondence

'Heads of Agreement' Kennedy-Kingston Working Group May 1993

Submission To The Interdepartmental Working Party on Abortion (The Adelaide Hospital Society, March 1998)

Terms of Reference For the Kingston Working Group From The Minister for Health, Dr. O'Hanlon, July 1990

The Adelaide Hospital: Symbol and Expression of a Plural Society (Submission by The Adelaide Hospital Society To The Forum for Peace and Reconciliation, 1994)

(iv) *Parliamentary Records*

'Cost Overruns at Tallaght Hospital' Paper From Department of Finance to Committee on Public Accounts, Dáil Éireann, March 1999

Dáil Éireann, Parliamentary Debates

Seánad Éireann, Parliamentary Debates

(v) *Press Statements and Media Interviews*

Joint Press Statement by Hospital Board and the Department of Health and Children, 18 December 1998

Press Statement, Department of Health and Children, 9 December 1998

Press Statement 'Shatter Calls for More Funding for Tallaght Hospital' 29 April 1998 issued by Fine Gael National Press Office, Leinster House

Statement by Mr. Brian Cowen TD, Minister for Health and Children re 'Tallaght Hospital' 14 December 1998

Transcript of Interview between Dr. David McCutcheon and Pat Kenny on 'Today with Pat Kenny' RTE Radio I, 15 March 1999

Transcript of Interview Between Minister Brian Cowen and Pat Kenny, RTE Radio I, 22 January 1999

Transcript of 'Today with Pat Kenny' Re 'Tallaght Hospital' RTE Radio I, 23 March 1999

Transcript 'Tallaght Hospital Report' on 'Morning Ireland' RTE Radio I, 10 December 1998

(vi) *Published Sources*

A. Aughey 'Obstacles to Reconciliation in the South' in *Building Trust in Ireland* Studies Commissioned by the Forum for Peace and Reconciliation, (The Blackstaff Press, Belfast, 1996)

D. McConnell 'Regions and Minorities—the Adelaide Hospital— the last Protestant general teaching hospital in the Republic of Ireland' in *Culture in Ireland—Regions: Identity and Power* Proceedings of the Cultures of Ireland Group Conference 27–29 November 1992, ed. P. O'Drisceoil (The Institute of Irish Studies, The Queen's University of Belfast, 1993)

P. Gatenby *Dublin's Meath Hospital 1753–1996* (Town House, Dublin, 1996)

Management Reporting and Control Service Planning, and the Financial Position of the Adelaide and Meath Hospital, Dublin, Incorporating The National Children's Hospital, (The Deloitte and Touche Consultants Report to the Minister for Health and Children, December 1998)

D. Mitchell *A 'Peculiar' Place the Adelaide Hospital, Dublin, Its Times, Places and Personalities 1839 to 1989* (Blackwater Press, Dublin [1989])

Tallaght Hospital Architectural Competition ed. Neil Steedman (Tallaght Hospital Board, n.d. [1986])

'The Thing Called Ethos: What exactly does the Adelaide Hospital mean when it talks about 'ethos'? *The Consultant* February 1993

3. Interviews

Interviews were conducted by the author with the following:

1) Dr. David McCutcheon, former CEO of The Adelaide and Meath Hospital, Dublin, Incorporating The National Children's Hospital, 31 March 1999

2) Mr. Jerry O'Dwyer, Secretary-General, The Department of Health and Children, 25 May 1999

3) Mr. Gerry Brady, Vice-Chairman of the Board of The Adelaide and Meath Hospital, Dublin, Incorporating the National Children's Hospital, 1996–1999; Chairman of the Meath Hospital Foundation, 9 June 1999

4) Mr. Nicholas Jermyn, CEO, St. Vincent's University Hospital and Acting CEO of The Adelaide and Meath Hospital, Dublin, Incorporating The National Children's Hospital, 14 June 1999

5) Group Interview with Ms Angela Fitzgerald, Mr. Tony Morris, Mr. Vincent Barton and Mr. Denis O'Sullivan of The Department of Health and Children, 18 June 1999

6) Mrs. Rosemary French, Chairman of The Adelaide and Meath Hospital, Dublin, Incorporating The National Children's Hospital, 29 June 1999

Tapes of the interviews and transcripts approved by those interviewed will be placed in the archives of The Adelaide and Meath Hospital, Dublin, Incorporating The National Children's Hospital.

B BIBLIOGRAPHY

Note: Books are cited by place and date of publication only except where it is important to note the publishers of special interest publications or where no place of publication is given.

A Beveridge Reader, eds. K and J. Williams, (London, 1987)

Administration Yearbook and Diary 1999 (Institute of Public Administration, Dublin 1998)

M. Adshead and B. Quinn 'The Move From Government to Governance: Irish development policy's paradigm shift' *Policy & Politics* Vol 26 No 2, 1998

A Healthier Future? Managing Healthcare in Ireland eds. E. McAuliffe and L. Joyce (Dublin, 1998)

J.A. Alexander, L. Morlock, B. Gifford 'The Efforts of Corporate Restructuring on Hospital Policymaking' *Health Services Research* Vol. 23, No. 2, 1998

J.A. Alexander, B.J. Weiner 'The Adoption of the Corporate Governance Model by Nonprofit Organisations' *Nonprofit Management & Leadership*, Vol. 8, No. 3, Spring 1998

R.C. Andringa, T.W. Engstrom *Nonprofit Board Answer Book Practical Guidelines for Board Members and Chief Executives* (National Center For Nonprofit Boards, Washington, DC, 1997)

H.K. Anheier 'Voluntary Action Studies: What are the issues' in *Voluntary Action in Ireland North and South: Report of a Research Symposium* ed. A. Williamson (Association for Voluntary Action Research in Ireland, Centre for Voluntary Action Studies, University of Ulster, Coleraine, 1998)

An Introduction to the Voluntary Sector, eds J. Davis Smith, Colin Rochester, Rodney Hedley (London, 1995)

A Study of Partnership between Voluntary and Statutory Sectors in Palliative Care in Ireland (Policy Research Centre, National College of Ireland for the Irish Hospice Foundation, 1999)

C.M. Arensberg and S.T. Kimball *Family and Community in Ireland* (Cambridge, Mass., 1968)

A Study of Partnership Between Voluntary and Statutory Sectors in Palliative Care in Ireland (Policy Research Centre, National College of Ireland for The Irish Hospice Foundation, 1999)

P. Bachrach *The Theory of Democratic Elitism A Critique* (London, 1969)

Derek Bacon 'Social Capital and Civil Society: the contribution of voluntary action' unpublished presentation to the AVARI/CVAS Research Forum, 2 June 1999 (Centre for Voluntary Action Studies, University of Ulster, Coleraine)

Derek Bacon '*Splendid and Disappointing*' *Churches Voluntary Action and Social Capital in Northern Ireland* (Centre for Voluntary Action Studies, University of Ulster, 1998)

M. Baker *Making Sense of the New NHS White Paper*, (Radcliffe Medical Press, Abington 1998)

B. Barber *Strong Democracy: Participatory Politics for a New Age* (Berkeley CA, 1984)

T.A. Barocci *Non-Profit Hospitals: Their Structure, Human Resources, and Economic Impact* (Boston, 1981)

R. Barrington *Health, Medicine and Politics in Ireland 1900–1970* (Dublin, 1987)

R. Barrington 'The Future Political, Legislative and Social Framework of the Health Services' in *The Irish Health System in the 21st Century*, eds. A.L. Leahy and M.M. Wiley, (Dublin, 1998)

A. Ben-Ner and T. Van Hoomissen 'Nonprofit Organizations in the mixed economy: a demand and supply analysis' in *The Nonprofit Sector in the Mixed Economy* eds. A. Ben-Ner and B. Gui (University of Michigan Press, Michigan, 1993)

P. Berger, R. Neuhaus, *To Empower People: The Role of Mediating Structures in Public Policy*, (American Enterprise Institute for Public Policy Research, Washington D.C., 1977)

Isaiah Berlin 'John Stuart Mill and the Ends of Life' in J.S. Mill *On Liberty in Focus*, ed. J. Gray and G.W. Smith, (London, 1991)

Isaiah Berlin *The Proper Study of Mankind An Anthology of Essays*, eds. H. Hardy, R. Hausheer, (Pimlico, London, 1998)

William Beveridge *Voluntary Action, A Report on the Method of Social Advance* (Allen & Unwin, London, 1948)

David Billis *Sliding Into Change: the future of the voluntary sector in the mixed organisation of welfare*, (Centre for Voluntary Organisations, London School of Economics, London 1993)

D. Billis *Organising Public and Voluntary Agencies*, (London, 1993)

T. Blair *The Third Way New Politics for the New Century*, (The Fabian Society, London, 1998)

C. Braithwaite *The Voluntary Citizen: an enquiry into the place of philanthropy in the community* (London, 1938)

H. Brody *Inishkillane* (Harmonsworth, 1974)

H. Brogan *Tocqueville*, (Collins/Fontana, 1973)

John Brooke 'Sir Lewis Bernstein Namier 1888–1960' *Brief Lives Twentieth Century Pen Portraits From The Dictionary of National Biography Selected by Colin Matthew* (Oxford, 1997)

A. Brown *Modern Political Philosophy Theories of the Just Society*, (London 1986)

P. Brown and G. Chadwick 'Management and the Health Professional' in *Reflections on Health Commemorating Fifty Years of the Department of Health 1947–1997* ed. J. Robins (Department of Health, Dublin, 1997)

Terence Brown *Ireland A Social and Cultural History 1922–1985*, Third Impression with added postscript, (London 1985)

A. Bryman and R.G. Burgess, *Analyzing Qualitative Data*, (Routledge, London 1994)

John P. Burke 'Reconciling Public Administration and Democracy: The Role of the Responsible Administrator' *Public Administration Review* Vol. 49, No., 2, March/April 1989

Business Research Methods: Strategies, Techniques and Resources, (eds.) T. Brannick, W.K. Roche (Dublin, 1997)

E. Callan *Creating Citizens Political Education and Liberal Democracy* (Oxford, 1997)

M. Canovan *Hannah Arendt A Reinterpretation of Her Political Thought* (Cambridge, 1992)

M. Canovan 'Hannah Arendt: Republicanism and Democracy' in *Liberal Democracy and its Critics* eds. A Carter and G. Stokes (Cambridge, 1998)

A. Carter 'Václav Havel: Civil Society, Citizenship and Democracy' in *Liberal Democracy and its Critics*, eds. A. Carter and G. Stokes, (Cambridge, 1998)

J. Carver *Boards That Make A Difference: A New Design for Leadership in Nonprofit and Public Organisations*, Second Edition, (Jossey-Bass, San Francisco, 1997)

R.P. Chait and B.E. Taylor 'Charting The Territory of Nonprofit Boards' *Harvard Business Review* Vol. 67, No. 1, 1989

Civil Society and the State: New European Perspectives, ed. John Keane (Verso, London, 1988)

A. Clifford *The Mater Hospital (Belfast) and the National Health Service Past, Present and Future* (Athol Books, Belfast, 1990)

Davis Coakley *The Irish School of Medicine Outstanding Practitioners of the 19th Century*, (Dublin, 1988)

Davis Coakley *Robert Graves Evangelist of Clinical Medicine*, (Dublin, 1996)

D. Coakley *Irish Masters of Medicine*, (Dublin, 1992)

N. Coates 'A model for consulting to help effect change in organisations', *Nonprofit Management and Leadership*, Vol. 8, No. 2, Winter 1997

J.L. Cohen and A. Arato *Civil Society and Political Theory*, (Cambridge, Mass, 1992)

J. Cohen and J. Rogers *Associations and Democracy*, (London, 1995)

James S. Coleman 'Social Capital in the Creation of Human Capital' *American Journal of Sociology* 94, (1988)

Neil Collins and Patrick Butler 'Public Services in Ireland: social marketing management' in *Political Issues in Ireland Today* ed. N. Collins (Manchester, 1999)

S. Conroy 'Governance—Where The Dream Starts and the Buck Stops' in *A Healthier Future? Managing Healthcare in Ireland* eds. E. McAuliffe and L. Joyce (IPA, Dublin, 1998)

Brian J. Cook 'Politics, Political Leadership and Public Management' *Public Administration Review*, Vol. 58, No. 3, May/June 1998

J. Cooney *John Charles McQuaid Ruler of Catholic Ireland* (Dublin, 1999)

J.M. Costan 'A Model and Typology of Government—NGO Relationships' *Nonprofit and Voluntary Sector Quarterly* Vol. 27, No. 3, 1998

Colin Coulson-Thomas *Creating Excellence in the Boardroom A Guide To Shaping Directorial Competence and Board Effectiveness* (London, 1993)

A. Crawford 'Review Article 'The Spirit of Community: Rights, Responsibilities and the Communitarian Agenda" in *Journal of Law and Society*, Vol. 23, No. 2, June 1996

J. Curry *Irish Social Services*, (2nd edition, Dublin, 1993)

B. Curtin and T. Varley 'Community Action and the State' in *Irish Society: Sociological Perspectives* eds. P. Clancy et al (Dublin, 1995)

R. Dagger *Civic Virtues Rights, Citizenship and Republican Liberalism* (New York, 1997)

Robert A. Dahl *On Democracy* (New Haven and London, 1998)

M.E. Daly 'An Atmosphere of Study Independence': The State and the Dublin Hospitals in the 1930s in *Medicine, Disease and the State in Ireland, 1650–1940* eds. G. Jones and E. Malcolm (Cork, 1999)

Jennifer D'Arcy 'Citizenship and *Irish Social Policy*' in *Irish Social Policy in Context* eds. G. Kiely, a. O'Donnell, P. Kennedy, S. Quin (University College Dublin Press, Dublin, 1999)

G. Davis 'Rethinking Policy Making: a new role for consultation?' *Administration* Vol. 45, No. 3, (Autumn 1997)

N. Deakin 'What Does Contracting do to Users?' in *Voluntary Agencies Challenges of Organisation and Management*, eds. D. Billis and M. Harris (London, 1996)

J. Deffenbaugh 'Understanding the Roles of NHS Trust Board Members' *Journal of Management in Medicine* Vol. 10, No. 2, 1996

R.H. deHoog 'Competition, Negotiation or Cooperation Three Models for Service Contracting' *Administration & Society* Vol. 22, No. 3, 1990

Kathryn G. Denhardt 'The Management of Ideals: A Political Perspective on Ethics' *Public Administration Review* Vol. 49, No. 2, March/April 1989

N.K. Denzin Y.S. Lincoln, *Handbook of Qualitative Research*, (Sage Publications, London, 1994)

Bishop Dignam *Social Security: Outlines of a Scheme of National Health Insurance* (Sligo, 1945)

Dimensions of the Voluntary Sector How is the Voluntary Sector Changing? (Charities Aid Foundation, London, 1995)

G. Donnelly-Cox, G. Jaffro *The Voluntary Sector in the Republic of Ireland Into The Twenty-first Century* The AVARI Research Monograph Series, (Association for Voluntary Action Research in Ireland, Centre for Voluntary Action Studies, University of Ulster, Coleraine, 1999)

G. Donnelly-Cox, G. MacKechnie 'Management Education for the Irish Voluntary Sector: First Steps in Program Design', unpublished paper, School of Business Studies, Trinity College Dublin, 1998

F. Donoghue *Defining The Non Profit Sector: Ireland.* Working Paper of The John Hopkins Comparative Non Profit Sector Project, No. 28, edited by Lester M. Salamon and Helmut K. Anheier (The John Hopkins Institute for Policy Studies, Baltimore, 1998)

F. Donoghue, H.K. Anheier, L.M. Salamon *Uncovering The Nonprofit Sector in Ireland Its Economic Value and Significance* The Johns Hopkins comparative Nonprofit Sector Project, Phase II (Johns Hopkins University/National College of Ireland, Dublin, 1999)

James Douglas 'Political Theories of Nonprofit Organisation' in *The Nonprofit Sector A Research Handbook,* ed. W.W. Powell (New Haven and London, 1987)

D.J. Duca *Nonprofit Boards: Roles, Responsibilities, and Performance,* (John Wiley, New York, 1996)

G.W. Dunleavy *Douglas Hyde: A Maker of Modern Ireland* (Berkeley CA, 1991)

P.F. Drucker *Managing the Non-Profit Organisation Practices and Principles,* (Butterworth-Heinemann, Oxford, 1990, paperback edition, 1992)

P.F. Drucker 'What Business Can Learn From Nonprofits' *Harvard Business Review* July-August 1989

T.S. Eliot 'The Dry Salvages' in T.S. Eliot *The Complete Poems and Plays* (London, 1969)

K.T. Elsdon with J. Reynolds and S. Stewart, *Voluntary Organisations Citizenship, Learning and Change,* (NIACE and Dept. of Adult Education, University of Nottingham, 1995)

J.B. Elshtain *Democracy on Trial,* (New York, 1995)

R.M. Emerson 'Power-Dependence Relations' *American Sociological Review,* Vol. 27, No. 1, 1962

M. Passerin d'Entrèves *The Political Philosophy of Hannah Arendt* (London and New York, 1994)

A. Etzioni *The Active Society: A Theory of Societal and Political Processes,* (London 1968)

A. Etzioni *The Spirit of Community Rights Responsibilities and the Communitarian Agenda,* (New York, 1994, London 1995)

A. Etzioni *The New Golden Rule Community and Morality in a Democratic Society,* (London, 1997)

W.M. Evan *Organisation Theory Research and Design* (New York, 1993)

P. Faughan 'A Healthy Voluntary Sector: Rhetoric or Reality?' in *Reflections on Health Commemorating Fifty Years of The Department of Health 1947–1997*, ed. J. Robins (Department of Health, 1997)

P. Faughnan, M. Healy *The Voluntary Sector and the State*, (CMRS, Dublin, 1992)

E. Ferlie, L. Ashburner, L. Fitzgerald 'Corporate Governance and the Public Sector: Some Issues and Evidence from the NHS' *Public Administration*, Vol. 73, Autumn 1995

J.M. Ferris and E. Graddy 'Contracting Out: For What? With Whom?' *Public Administration Review* Vol. 46, 1986

J.M. Ferris 'Coprovision: Citizen Time and Money Donations in Public Service Provision' *Public Administration Review* Vol. 44, No. 4, July/August 1984

J.M. Ferris 'The Double-Edged Sword of Social Service Contracting: Public Accountability Versus Nonprofit Autonomy' *Nonprofit Management & Leadership* Vol. 3, No. 4, Summer 1993

M. Festenstein 'Contemporary Liberalism' in *New Political Thought An Introduction* ed. A. Lent (London, 1998)

Angela Fitzgerald, Fergal Lynch 'Casemix Measurement: Assessing The Impact in Irish Acute Hospitals' *Administration*, Vol, 46, No. 1, Spring 1998

R.F. Foster *Modern Ireland 1600–1972* (London, 1988)

E. Frazer 'Communitarianism' in *New Political Thought An Introduction* ed. A. Lent (London, 1998)

H. George Frederickson 'The Recovery of Civicism in Public Administration' *Public Administration Review* Vol. 42, No. 2, November/December 1982

Francis Fukuyama *Trust The Social Virtues and the Creation of Prosperity* (London, 1995)

W.A. Galston *Liberal Purposes Goods, Virtues, and Diversity in the Liberal State* (New York, 1991)

T. Garvin 'Patriots and republicans: an Irish evolution' in *Ireland and the Politics of Change* eds. W. Crotty and D.E. Schmitt (London, 1998)

T. Garvin 'The Politics of Denial and Cultural Defence: the Referendums of 1983 and 1986 in context' *The Irish Review*, No. 3, 1988

K. Gaskin and J. Davis Smith, *A New Civic Europe? A Study of the Extent and Role of Volunteering*, (Volunteer Centre, UK, 1995)

Peter Gatenby, *The School of Physic Trinity College Dublin A Retrospective View*, (Faculty of Health Sciences, Trinity College, Dublin, 1994)

E. Gellner *Conditions of Liberty Civil Society and its Rivals*, (London, 1994)

A. Giddens, *Beyond Left and Right; The Future of Radical Politics*, (Cambridge, 1994)

A. Giddons *The Third Way The Renewal of Social Democracy*, (Cambridge, 1998)

J. Gill, P. Johnson, *Research Methods for Managers*, (2nd edition, London, 1997)

F. Gladstone *Voluntary Action in a Changing World*, (Bedford Square Press, London, 1979)

Mary Ann Glendon *Rights Talk: The Impoverishment of Political Discourse* (New York, 1991)

Government and The Third Sector Emerging Relationships in Welfare States eds. B. Gidron, R.M. Kramer, L.M. Salamon (San Francisco, 1992)

Government and Voluntary Organizations A Relational Perspective, eds. Stein Kuhnle and Per Selle (Avebury, Aldershot, Hants, 1992)

J. Gray *Liberalism Second Edition*, (Open University Press, Buckingham, 1995)

J.M. Greenfield *The Non Profit Handbook*, 2nd edition, (Chicester-Wiley, New York, 1997)

R.K. Greenleaf *The Power of Servant Leadership*, ed. L.C. Spears (Barrett-Koehler Publishers, San Francisco, 1998)

Robert K. Greenleaf *Servant Leadership A Journey into the Nature of Legitimate Power and Greatness* (Paulist Press, New York, 1991)

K.A. Gronbjerg 'Managing Grants and Contracts: the Case of Four Nonprofit Social Srvice Organization' *Nonprofit and Voluntary Sector Quareterly* Vol. 20, No. 1, 1991

Richard Gutch *Contracting Lessons From The US* (NCVO Publications, London, 1992)

A. Gutmann *Democratic Education* (Princeton, N.J. 1987)

R. Hadley and S. Hatch *Social Welfare and the Failure of the State*, (London, 1981)

J.A. Hall (ed.) *Civil Society Theory History Comparison*, (Cambridge, 1995)

P.D. Hall, *Inventing The Nonprofit Sector and other Essays on Philanthropy, Voluntarism, and Nonprofit Organizations* (Baltimore, MD, 1992)

C. Ham 'Priority Setting: Political Issues' in *Fixing Health Budgets: Experience from Europe and North America*, ed. F.W. Schwartz, H. Glennerster, R.B. Saltman (John Wiley, Chichester, 1996)

Jacques Hamel with Stephanie Dufour, Domenci Fortin *Case Study Methods* Qualitative Research Methods Series, Vol. 32 (London, 1993)

C. Handy *Understanding Voluntary Organisations*, (London, 1988)

C.M. Hann, E. Dunn (eds), *Civil Society: Challenging Western Models*, (London, 1996)

H. Hansmann 'Economic theories of nonprofit organisations' in *The Nonprofit Sector: A Research Handbook* ed. W.W. Powell (New Haven and London, 1987)

J. Harris *William Beveridge A Biography* first published 1977 revised edition (Oxford, 1997)

M. Harris 'Do We Need Voluntary Governing Bodies?' in *Voluntary Agencies Challenges of Organization and Management*, eds. D. Billis and M. Harris, (London, 1996)

M. Harris *The Power and Authority of Governing Bodies : three models of practice in service-providing agencies*, (Centre for Voluntary Organisations, LSE, London, 1993)

M. Harris 'Voluntary Management Committees: The Impact of Contracting in the UK' in *The Contract Culture in Public Services Studies from Britain, Europe and the USA*, eds. Perri 6, J. Kendall, (Arena, Aldershot, Hants., 1997)

M. Harris 'Instruments of Government? Voluntary sector boards in a changing public policy environment' *Policy & Politics* Vol 26 No 2, 1998

M. Harris and D. Billis, *Organising Voluntary Agencies A Guide Through the Literature*, (Bedford Square Press, NCVO, London 1985)

N. Harris *Beliefs in Society*, (Harmondsworth, 1968)

B. Harvey, *Networking in Europe A Guide to European Voluntary Organisations*, (NCVO Publications, 2nd edition, 1995)

V. Havel *Disturbing The Peace* (London, 1990)

V. Havel *Letters to Olga* (London, 1988)

292

T. Hayes, *Management, Control and Accountability in Non Profit/Voluntary Organisations*, (Avebury, Aldershot, 1996)

D. Held *Models of Democracy* 2nd Edition, (Cambridge, 1996)

B. Hensey *The Health Services of Ireland*, (Institute of Public Administration, Dublin, 4th edition, 1988)

R.D. Herman et al (eds), *The Jossey-Bass Handbook of Non-Profit Leadership and Management*, (Jossey Bass, San Francisco, 1994)

R.D. Herman, R.D. Heimovics *Executive Leadership in Nonprofit Organisations: New Strategies for Shaping Executive—Board Dynamics*, (Jossey Bass, San Francisco, 1991)

R.E. Herzlinger 'Effective Oversight: A Guide For Nonprofit Directors' *Harvard Business Review* July–August 1994

Peter A Hill 'Social Capital in Britain' British *Journal of Political Science* Vol. 29, No. 3, 1999

M.D. Higgins, 'The Space of Politics Recovered', Unpublished Paper Presented To The Policy Development Commission of The Labour Party, March 1999

P. Hirst *Representative Democracy and its Limits*, (Cambridge, 1990)

P. Hirst *Associative Democracy: New Forms of Economic and Social Governance*, (Cambridge, 1994)

P. Hirst 'Associational Democracy' in *Prospects For Democracy North, South, East, West* ed. D. Held (Cambridge, 1993)

T.P. Holland, R.A. Ritro, A.R. Kovner *Improving Board Effectiveness Practical Lessons For Nonprofit Health Care Organizations* (American Hospital Publishing Inc., Chicago, 1997)

T.P. Holland 'Strengthening Board Performance' in *Skills for Effective Management of Nonprofit Organizations* eds. R.L. Edwards, J.A. Yankey, M.A. Altpeter (National Association of Social workers, Washington, D.C., 1998)

C. Hood 'A Public Management For All Seasons?' *Public Administration*, Vol. 69, Spring 1991

C.O. Houle *Governing Boards: Their Nature and Nurture*, (Jossey-Bass, San Francisco, 1989)

M. Hudson *Managing Without Profit The Art of Managing Third Sector Organisations*, (Harmondsworth, 1995) and Second Edition published in 1999

H. Ibsen *Ghosts*, (1881)

T. Inglis *Moral Monopoly The Rise and Fall of the Catholic Church in Modern Ireland* 2nd Edition (University College Dublin Press, Dublin, 1998)

Rachel Iredale 'Public Consultation and Participation in Policy Making' in *Irish Social Policy in Context* eds. G. Kiely, A. O'Donnell, P. Kennedy, S. Quin (University College Dublin Press, Dublin, 1999)

J.C. Isaac 'Oases in the desert: Hannah Arendt on democratic politics' *American Political Science Review*, 88, 1 (March, 1994)

Issues in Voluntary and Non-Profit Management, eds. J. Batsleer, C. Cornforth, R. Paton (Open University/Addison-Wesley, London, 1992)

G. Jaffro 'Insights into the Boards of Irish Voluntary Agencies' *Administration* Vol. 46, No. 3 Autumn 1998

G. Jaffro 'The Changing Nature of Irish Voluntary Social Service Organisations', *International Journal of Public Sector Management*, Vol. 9, No. 7, 1996, pp 45–59

Estelle James 'The Nonprofit Sector in Comparative Perspective' in *The Nonprofit Sector: A Research Handbook* ed. W.W. Powell (New Haven and London, 1987)

T. Janoski *Citizenship and Civil Society A Framework of Rights and Obligations in Liberal, Traditional and Social Democratic Regimes* (Cambridge, 1998)

T.H. Jeavons 'Stewardship Revisited: Secular and Sacred Views of Governance and Management' *Nonprofit and Voluntary Sector Quarterly*, Vol. 23, No. 2, 1994

T.H. Jeavons 'When the Management is the Message: Relating Values to Management Practice in Non profit Organisations' *Non Profit Management and Leadership*, Vol. 2, No. 4, 1992

N. Johnson *The Welfare State in Transition: the Theory and Practice of Welfare Pluralism* (Brighton, 1987)

John Stuart Mill on Liberty and Other Essays, edited with an introduction and notes by John Gray (Oxford World's Classics, Oxford University Press, Oxford, 1991)

John Stuart Mill on Politics and Society, Selected and edited by G.L. Williams (Fontana/Collins, 1976)

John Stuart Mill On Liberty, edited with an introduction by G. Himmelfarb, Penguin Classics (Penguin Books, London, 1985)

L. Kaboolian 'The New Public Management: Challenging the Boundaries of the Management vs Administration Debate' *Public Administration Review* Vol. 58, No. 3, May/June 1998

E. Kane 'The Power of Paradigms: Social Science and Intellectual Contributions to Public Discourse in Ireland' in *On Intellectuals and Intellectual Life in Ireland: International Comparative and Historical Contexts,* ed. L. O'Dowd (Institute of Irish Studies, QUB and The Royal Irish Academy, 1996)

D. Kavanagh, *Political Culture,* (London, 1972)

J. Keane *Civil Society Old Images, New Visions* (Cambridge, 1998)

R. Kearney *Postnationalist Ireland Politics, Culture Philosophy* (London and New York, 1997)

Adrian J. Kearns 'Active Citizenship and Urban Governance' *Transactions of the Institute of British Geographers,* New Series, Vol. 17, No. 1, 1992

Rita Mae Kelly 'An Inclusive Democratic Polity, Representative Bureaucracies and the New Public Management' *Public Administration Review* Vol. 58, No. 3, May/June 1998

J. Kendall and H.K. Anheier, 'The Third Sector and the European Union Policy Process: An Initial Evaluation', Paper for presentation at the 1998I STR Conference, Geneva, 8–11 July 1998

J. Kendall and M. Knapp, 'A Loose and Baggy Monster: boundaries, definitions and typologies' in *An Introduction To the Voluntary Sector,* eds. J. Davis Smith, et al (London, 1995)

J. Kendall and M. Knapp *The Voluntary Sector in the U.K.* John Hopkins Nonprofit Sector Series 8 (Manchester, 1996)

P.M. Kettner, L.L. Martin 'Purchase of Service Contracting: Two Models' *Administration in Social Work* Vol. 14, No. 1, 1990

J.M. Keynes *The General Theory of Employment Interest and Money,* (London, 1936)

David Kieran 'The Role of Culture—in the Relationship Between The Statutory and Voluntary Sectors—on the Provision of Services to the Intellectually Disabled' (Unpublished M.Sc. Health Services Management Thesis, Trinity College, Dublin, 1998)

J.W. Kingdon, *Agendas, Alternatives and Public Policies,* (New York, 1995)

R. Klein *The Politics of the National Health Service* 3rd Edition (Longman, Harlow, 1995)

B. Knight, *Voluntary Action*, (Home Office, London, 1993)

R. Kramer *Voluntary Agencies in the Welfare State*, (California, 1981)

R. Kramer *Voluntary Organisations in The Welfare State: On the Threshold of The '90s* Working Paper 8 (The Centre for Voluntary Organisation, The London School of Economics and Political Science, London, 1990)

R.M. Kramer 'Voluntary Agencies and the Contract Culture: 'Dream or Nightmare?' *Social Service Review* Vol. 68, No. 1, March 1994

R. Kramer 'Voluntary Agencies and the personal social services' in *The Nonprofit Sector: A Research Handbook* ed. W.W. Powell (New Haven and London, 1987)

R.M. Kramer and B. Grossman 'Contracting for Social Services: Process management and Resource Dependencies' *Social Service Review* Vol. 61, No. 1, 1987

W. Kymlicka *Multicultural Citizenship A Liberal Theory of Minority Rights* (Oxford, 1995)

W. Kymlicka and W. Norman 'Return of the Citizen: A Survey of Recent Work on Citizenship Theory' *Ethics* Vol. 104 (January 1994)

C. Leadbetter *Civic Spirit The Big Idea for a New Political Era*, (Demos, in association with New Statesman, London, 1997)

C. Leadbetter *The Rise of the Social Entrepreneur*, (Demos, London, 1997)

J. Lee *Ireland 1912–1985 Politics and Society*, (Cambridge, 1989)

J. Lee 'Aspects of Corporatist Thought in Ireland: the Commission on Vocational Organisation 1939–43' in *Studies in Irish History* eds. A. Cosgrave and D. McCartney (Dublin, 1979)

D.J. Lewis 'Interagency Partnerships in Aid-Recipient Countries: Lessons From An Aquaculture Project in Bangladesh' *Nonprofit and Voluntary Sector Quareterly* Vol. 27, No. 3, 1998

J. Lewis 'What does Contracting do to Voluntary Agencies' in *Voluntary Agencies Challenges of Organisation and Management*, eds Billis and Harris, (London, 1996), pp 98–112

Life After Politics New Thinking for the Twenty first Century, ed., G. Mulgan (London 1997)

M. Luddy *Women and Philanthropy in Nineteenth Century Ireland*, (Cambridge University Press, 1995)

F. Lynch 'Health Funding and Expenditure in Ireland' in *A Healthier Future? Managing Healthcare in Ireland*, eds. E. McAuliffe and L. Joyce (Dublin, 1998)

J.B. Lyons *The Quality of Mercer's The Story of Mercer's Hospital, 1734–1991*, (Dublin, 1991)

E. Macadam *The New Philanthropy a Study of the Relations between the Statutory and Voluntary Social Services* (London, 1934)

I. McBride *Scripture Politics: Ulster Presbyterians and Irish Radicalism in the late eighteenth century* (Oxford, 1998)

E.M. McInnes *St. Thomas' Hospital*, Second Enlarged Edition (Trustees for St. Thomas' Hospital, London, 1990)

A. MacIntyre *After Virtue A Study in Moral Theory*, (London, 1981)

A. MacIntyre *Whose Justice? Which Rationality?* (London, 1988)

Eamonn McKee 'Church-state relations and the development of Irish health policy: the mother-and-child scheme, 1994–53' *Irish Historical Studies* Vol. XXV No. 93, November 1986, pp 159 - 194

D. McKevitt *Health Care Policy in Ireland A Study in Control*, (Hibernian University Press [Cork 1990])

D. McKevitt *Managing Core Public Services* (Oxford, 1998)

D. McKevitt 'Strategic Management in the Irish Civil Service: Prometheus unbound or Phoenix redux?' *Administration* Vol. 43, No. 4, 1996

D. McKevitt and Justin F. Keegan 'Making Sense of Strategy Statements: A User's Guide' *Administration* Vol. 45, No. 3, (Autumn 1997)

D. McKevitt and Justin F. Keegan 'Another Set of Strategy Statement: What is the Evidence on Implementation?' *Administration* Vol. 47, No. 1, (Spring 1999)

E. McLaughlin 'Ireland: Catholic Corporatism' in *Comparing Welfare States: Britain in International Context* eds A. Cochrane and J. Clarke (Sage, London, 1993)

John Macmurray *Conditions of Freedom*, (London, 1950)

[John Macmurray] *The Personal World John Macmurray on Self and Society*, selected and Introduced by Philip Conford (Floris Books, Edinburgh, 1996)

C.B. Macpherson *The Life and Times of Liberal Democracy*, (Oxford, 1977)

Making A Difference Strengthening Volunteering in the NHS, Report of the Working Group on Volunteering in the NHS, NHS Executive, September 1996

Making A Difference Strengthening Volunteering in the NHS, Annexes, NHS Executive, September 1996

Managing in the Voluntary Sector: A Handbook for Managers in Charitable and Non-Profit Organisations, ed. Stephen P. Osborne (International Thomson Business, London, 1996)

P. Mandelson, R. Liddle *The Blair Revolution Can New Labour Deliver?*, (Faber and Faber, London, 1996)

James G. March, Johan P. Olsen *Democratic Governance* (New York, 1995)

G. Marshall 'In Search of Commensurability: Writings in Public Management in an Era of Governmental Reform' *Public Administration Review* Vol. 58, No. 3, May/June 1998

Medicine, Disease and the State in Ireland, 1650–1940 eds. G. Jones and E, Malcolm (Cork University Press, Cork, 1999)

Anna Maria Meegan 'Management of Service Agreements Between Voluntary and Statutory Sectors in Irish Health Service Provision' (Unpublished M.Sc. Health Service Management Thesis, Trinity College, Dublin, 1998)

F.O.C. Meenan *St. Vincent's Hospital 1834–1994 An Historical and Social Portrait* (Dublin, 1995)

Meeting the Challenge of Change: Voluntary Action Into the 21st Century, the Report of the Commission on the Future of the Voluntary Sector, (NCVO Publications, London, 1996)

Meeting the Challenge of Change: Voluntary Action Into the 21st Century, Summary of Evidence and selected papers for the Report, (NCVO Publications,, London [1996])

M. Middleton 'Nonprofit Boards of Directors: Beyond the Governance Function' in *The Nonprofit Sector A Research Handbook*, ed. W.W. Powell, (New Haven and London, 1987),

J. Miley *A Voice For the Country Fifty Years of Macra na Feirme* (Macra na Feirme, Dublin, 1994)

J.S. Mill 'M. de Tocqueville on Democracy in America' *Edinburgh Review* LXXII, 1840 reprinted in *John Stuart Mill On Politics and Society* selected and edited G.L. Williams (Glasgow, 1976)

H. Mintzberg 'Managing Government—Governing Management' *Harvard Business Review*, May–June 1996

H. Mintzberg *Power In and Around Organizations* (Englewood Cliffs, N.J., 1983)

G. Mitchell *Deeds Not Words the Life and Work of Muriel Gahan* (Dublin, 1997)

G. Morgan *Images of Organization*, 2nd Edition (London, 1997)

C. Mouffe (ed) *Dimensions of Radical Democracy: Pluralism, Citizenship, Community*, (Verso, London, 1992)

E. Mournier *Be Not Afraid*, (London, 1951)

J.A. Muir Gray *Evidence-Based Healthcare How To make Health Policy and Management Decisions* (Edinburgh, 1997)

G. Mulgan, C. Landry, *Rethinking Charity Finance*, (London, 1994)

G. Mulgan, C. Landry, *The Other Invisible Hand: Remaking Charity for the 21st Century*, (Demos, London, 1995)

R. Mulvihill *Voluntary-Statutory Partnership in Community Care of the Elderly* (National Council for the Elderly, Dublin, 1993)

New Frontier for Full Citizenship eds. B. Reynolds and S. Healy (CMRS, Dublin, 1993)

New Political Thought An Introduction, ed. Adam Lent (London, 1998)

N. Nohria, S. Ghoshal *The Differentiated Network Organizing Multinational Corporations For Value Creation* (San Francisco, 1997)

R. O'Donnell, D. Thomas 'Partnership and Policy Making' in *Social Policy in Ireland Principles, Practice and Problems* eds. S. Healy and BN. Reynolds (Dublin, 1998)

J. O'Dwyer 'Reflections on Future Structures in the Health Services' in *The Irish Health System in the 21st Century*, eds. A.L. Leahy and M. Wiley, (Dublin, 1998)

T.O'Hara 'Current Structure of the Irish Health Care System—Setting The Context' in *The Irish Healthy System in the 21st Century*, eds. A. L. Leahy and M.M. Wiley (Dublin, 1998)

Adrian Oldfield *Citizenship and Community Civic Republicanism and the Modern World* (London and New York, 1990)

D. Osborne, Ted Gaebler *Reinventing Government How the Entrepreneurial Spirit in Transforming the Public Sector* (London, 1993)

S. Osborne *Understanding Voluntary Organisations in Contemporary Western Society*, (Aston Business School, Birmingham, 1993)

S. Osborne *Towards a Theory of the Voluntary Sector? A Review of Theories of Voluntary Action*, Working Paper No. 24 (Aston Business School, Birmingham, 1993)

V. Ostrom *The Meaning of Democracy and the Vulnerability of Democracy: A Response To Tocqueville's Challenge* (Ann Arbor, MI, 1997)

E. O'Sullivan 'Voluntary Agencies in Ireland—What Future Role?' *Administration* Vol. 47, No 4, Winter 1999-2000

T. O'Sullivan 'Changing Relationships and the Voluntary and Statutory Sectors' in A *Healthier Future? Managing Healthcare in Ireland*, eds. E. McAuliffe and L. Joyce (IPA, Dublin, 1998)

T. O'Sullivan 'The Voluntary-Statutory Relationship in the Health Services', *Administration*, Vol. 42, No. 1, Spring 1994

T. O'Sullivan 'Consumerism in the Health Services' *Administration*, Vol. 46, No. 1, Spring 1998

Fintan O'Toole 'Replacing a community of believers with one of citizens' *The Irish Times* 16 July 1999

M.A.G. " Tuathaigh 'Religion, Nationality and a Sense of Community in Modern Ireland' in *Community, Culture and Conflict Aspects of the Irish Experience*, ed. M.A.G. " Tuathaigh (Galway University Press, 1986)

D. Owen *English Philanthropy 1660–1960*, (London, 1964)

N. Pearce, S. Spencer 'Reports and Surveys Education for Citizenship: The Crick Report' *The Political Quarterly* Vol. 70, No. 2, April–June 1999

C. Perrow *Organizational Analysis: A Sociological View* (London, 1970)

C. Perrow 'Goals and Power Structures' in *The Hospital in Modern Society*, ed. E. Freidson (The Free Press of Glencoe, New York, 1963)

P. Pettit *Republicanism A Theory of Freedom and Government* (Oxford, 1997)

J. Pfeffer and G.R. Salancik *The External Control of Organizations A Resource Dependence Perspective*, (New York, 1978)

M. Polanyi *Personal Knowledge Towards a Post-Critical Philosophy* (2nd Edition, London, 1962)

C. Pollitt *Managerialism and the Public Service: the Anglo-American Experience* Second Edition (Oxford, 1993)

F. Powell *The Politics of Irish Social Policy 1600–1990*, (The Edwin Mellen Press, Lampeter, UK, 1992)

F. Powell 'The Irish Voluntary Sector and the State: the Blossoming of Civil Society or a Crisis in Identity?'' Unpublished paper presented to Sociological Association of Ireland Conference, Wexford, 8–10 May 1998

F. Powell and D. Guerin *Civil Society and Active Citizenship: the role of the voluntary sector* (Association for Voluntary Action Research in Ireland, Centre of Voluntary Action Studies, University of Ulster, Coleraine, 1999)

F. Powell, D. Guerin *Civil Society and Social Policy Voluntarism in Ireland*, (A & A Farmer, Dublin, 1997)

Walter W Powell (ed), *The Non Profit Sector: A Research Handbook*, (Yale University Press, New Haven and London, 1987)

F. Prochaska, *Philanthropy and the Hospitals of London: the King's Fund*, (Oxford, 1992)

F. Prochaska *The Voluntary Impulse Philanthropy in Modern Britain*, (London, 1988)

Progress, Values and Public Policy eds. B. Reynolds and S. Healy (CORI, Dublin, 1996)

Robert Putnam *Making Democracy Work: Civic Traditions in Modern Italy* (Princeton, N.J. 1993)

John Rawls *A Theory of Justice* (Oxford University Press paperback, 1973)

John Rawls *Political Liberalism*, paperback edition , (Columbia University Press, New York, 1996)

Mary Redmond 'Social Enterpreneurship—A New Authority?' in *Are We Forgetting Something?* eds. H. Bohan & G. Kennedy (Dublin, 1999)

Reflections on Health Commemorating Fifty Years of The Department of Health 1947–1997, ed. J. Robins (Department of Health, 1997)

Reflections on Leadership How Robert K. Greenleaf's Theory of Servant-Leadership Influenced Today's Top Management Thinkers ed. L.C. Spears (John Wiley, New York, 1995)

Religion, Education and the Constitution, ed. D.A. Lane, (The Columba Press, Dublin, 1992)

R.A.W. Rhodes 'The New Governance: Governing Without Government' *Political Studies* Vol. XLIV, 1996

J. Riley *Mill on Liberty*, (London, 1998)

W.K. Roche 'Public Service Reform and Human Resource Management' *Administration* Vol. 46, No. 2, (Summer 1998)

M. Rooff *Voluntary Societies and Social Policy*, (London, 1957)

S. Rose-Ackerman 'Altruism, nonprofits, and economic theory' *Journal of Economic Literature* Vol. 34, No. 2, 1996

M. Rowley *The Private Future: Causes and Consequences of Community Collapse in the West* (London, 1973)

H. Ruddle, F. Donoghue *The Organisation of Volunteering A Study of Irish Voluntary Organisations in the Social Welfare Area*, (Policy Research Centre, National College of Industrial Relations, Dublin, 1995)

H. Ruddle, R. Mulvihill *Reaching Out Donating and Volunteering in the Republic of Ireland The 1997/98 Survey* (Policy Research Centre, National College of Ireland, Dublin, 1999)

H. Ruddle, J. O'Connor *Reaching Out Charitable Giving and Voluntary in the Republic of Ireland*, (Policy Research Centre, National College of Industrial Relations, Dublin, 1994)

Alan Ryan 'Mill in a liberal landscape' in *The Cambridge Companion to Mill*, ed. John Skorupski, (Cambridge, 1998)

G.H. Sabine, *A History of Political Theory*, 3rd edition revised and enlarged (George G. Harrap & Co., London 1963)

J.R. Saidel, G.L. Harlan 'Contracting and Patterns of Nonprofit Governance' *Nonprofit Management and Leadership* Vol. 3, No. 3, 1998

L.M. Salamon 'Partners in Public Service: The Scope and Theory of Government-Nonprofit Relations' in *The Nonprofit Sector: A Research Handbook* ed. W.W. Powell (New Haven and London, 1987)

L.M. Salamon *Partners in Public Service: Government—Nonprofit Relations in the Modern Welfare State* (John Hopkins Press, Baltimore, 1995)

L.M. Salamon 'The Rise of the Nonprofit Sector', *Foreign Affairs*, Vol. 73, No. 4, 1994

L.M. Salamon, H.K. Anheier 'Social Origins of Civil Society: explaining the nonprofit sector cross-nationally' *Voluntas: International Journal of Voluntary and Nonprofit Organisations* Vol. 9, No. 3, 1998

L.M. Salamon and H.K. Anheier *The Emerging NonProfit Sector An Overview*, Johns Hopkins Non Profit Sector Series 1, (Manchester University Press, Manchester, 1996)

L.M. Salamon, H.K. Anheier *The Emerging Sector Revisited A Summary Revised Estimates* The Johns Hopkins Comparative Nonprofit Sector Project, Phase II (Centre For Civil Society Studies, Institute for Policy Studies, The Johns Hopkins University, Baltimore, MD, 1999)

M. Sandel *Democracy's Discontent: America in Search of a Public Philosophy* (Cambridge, Mass., 1996)

J.R. Sardel, S.L. Harlen 'Contracting and patterns of nonprofit governance', *Nonprofit Management and Leadership*, Vol. 8, No. 3, Spring 1998, pp 243–259

W. Richard Scott *Organisations Rational Natural and Open Systems* Third Edition (Englewood Cliffs, N.J. 1992)

D. Selbourne *The Principle of Duty An Essay on the Foundations of the Civic Order*, (Sinclair-Stevenson, London, 1994)

P. Selznick *The Moral Commonwealth: Social Theory and The Promise of Community* (Berkeley, CA, 1992)

A. Shanks *Civil Society, Civil Religion*, (Blackwell, Oxford, 1995)

S.M. Shortell 'New Directions in Hospital Governance' *Hospital and Health Services Administration*, Vol. 34, No. 1, 1989

David Silverman *Interpreting Qualitative Data Mehtods for Analysing Talk, Text and Interaction*, (Sage Publications, London, 1993)

Q. Skinner *The Foundations of Modern Political Thought*, Vol. 1, (Cambridge, 1978)

D. Smail *The Origins of Unhappiness* (London, 1993)

Susan J Smith 'Society, Space and Citizenship: a human geography for the 'new times'?' *Transactions Institute of British Geographers*, New Series, Vol. 14, No. 2, 1989

S.R. Smith, M. Lipsky *Non Profits for Hire: the Welfare State in the Age of Contracting*, (Cambridge Mass., 1993)

Social Policy in Ireland Principles, Practice and Problems eds. S. Healy and B. Reynolds (Dublin, 1998)

Robert E. Stake 'Case Studies' in *Handbook of Qualitative Research* eds. N.K. Denzin and G.S. Lincoln (Sage, London, 1994)

K. Starkey 'Opening Up Corporate Governance' *Human Relations*, Vol. 48, No. 8, 1995

D. Starkweather 'Hospital Board Power' *Health Services Management Research*, Vol. 1, No. 2, July 1988

John Steward and Michael Clarke 'The Public Service Orientation: Issues and Dilemmas' *Public Administration* Vol. 65, No. 2, Summer 1987

Symposium: 'Leadership, Democracy and the New Public Management' *Public Administration Review* Vol. 58, No. 3, May/June 1998

Taken On Board Corporate Governance in the NHS: Developing The Role of Non-Executive Directors Audit Commission Management Paper (HMSO Publications, 1995)

Henry Tam *Communitarianism A New Agenda For Politics and Citizenship* (London, 1998)

B.E. Taylor, R.P. Chait, T.P. Holland 'The New Work of the Nonprofit Board', *Harvard Business Review*, September-October 1996

Marilyn Taylor 'The Changing Role of the Nonprofit Sector in Britain: Moving Toward the Market' in *Government and The Third Sector Emerging Relationships in the Welfare State* eds. B. Gidron, R.M. Kramer, L.M. Salamon (Jossey Bass Publishers, San Francisco, 1992)

L.D. Terry 'Administrative Leadership, Neo-Managerialism and the Public Management Movement' *Public Administration Review* Vol. 58, No. 3, May/June 1998

K. Tester *Civil Society*, (Routledge, London, 1992)

The Autobiography of John Stuart Mill, (1873), ed. A.O.J. Cockshut, (Halifax, 1992)

The Blackwell Encyclopaedia of Political Thought, ed. C. Miller (Blackwell, Oxford, paperback corrected edition, 1991)

The Cambridge Companion to Mill, ed. J. Skorupski, (Cambridge, 1998)

The Contract Culture in Public Services Studies From Britain, Europe and the USA eds. Perri 6, J. Kendall (Aldershot, 1997)

The Evidence for Voluntary Action Being Memoranda by Organisations and Individuals and Other Material Relevant To Voluntary Action eds. Lord Beveridge and A.F. Wells (London, 1949)

The Invention of the Modern Republic ed. B. Fontana (Cambridge, 1994)

The Irish Health System in the 21st Century eds. A.L. Leahy and M. Wiley (Dublin, 1998)

'The Irish Political and Policy-making System and the Current Programme of Change' Papers delivered to the OECD meeting of Senior Officials from Centres of Government, Dublin, September 1997 *Administration* Vol. 45, No. 4, (Winter 1997-8)

The Non-Profit Sector in International Perspective Studies in Comparative Culture and Policy, ed. Estelle James (Oxford, 1989)

The Republican Ideal Current Perspectives ed. N. Porter (Belfast, 1998)

James D. Thompson *Organisations in Action*, (New York, 1967)

R.M. Titmuss *The Gift Relationship From Human Blood to Social Policy*, (London, 1970)

Alexis de Tocqueville *Democracy in America*, ed. J.P. Mayer, (Anchor Books edition, New York, 1969)

Alexis de Tocqueville *The Ancient Régime and the French Revolution*, (Collins, Fontana Library, 1966)

John Trevelyan *Voluntary Service and the State*, (London, 1952)

F. Twine *Citizenship and Social Rights The Interdependence of Self and Society* (Sage Publishers, London, 1994)

Values and Social Change in Ireland, ed. C.T. Whelan (Dublin, 1994)

Curtis Ventriss 'Toward a Public Philosophy of Public Administration: A Civic Perspective of the Public' *Public Administration Review* Vol. 49, No. 2, March/April 1989

Voluntary Action in Ireland North and South: Report of a Research Symposium ed. A. Williamson (Association for Voluntary Action Research in Ireland, Centre for Voluntary Action Studies, University of Ulster, Coleraine, 1998)

Voluntary Sector Management Research Project, School of Business Studies, Trinity College, Dublin, Seminar IV, unpublished Briefing Paper by A. O'Regan, G. Donnelly-Cox on 'Environment'

Voluntary Sector Management Research Project, School of Business Studies, Trinity College, Dublin, Seminar VI, 30 April 1998, unpublished paper, 'Strategy, Implementation and Leadership'

Voluntary Agencies: Challenges of Organisation and Management, (eds) D. Billis & M. Harris (London, 1996)

Voluntary Social Services: Their Place in the Modern State, ed., A.F.C. Bourdillon (Methuen, London, 1945)

Voluntary-Statutory Partnership in Community Care of the Elderly, (National Council for the Elderly, Dublin, 1993)

John Walshe *A New Partnership in Education From Consultation To Legislation in the Nineties* (Institute of Public Administration, Dublin, 1999)

G. Walt *Health Policy An Introduction To Process and Power*, (London, 1994)

M. Walzer *Spheres of Justice*, (Oxford, 1983)

M. Walzer 'The Civil Society Argument' in *Dimensions of Radical Democracy*, ed. C. Mouffe (London, 1992)

B. Weisbrod *The Nonprofit Economy* (Cambridge Mass, 1988)

B. Weisbrod *The Voluntary Nonprofit Sector* (Lexington Mass, 1977)

T. West *Horace Plunkett: Co-operation and Politics An Irish Biography* (Gerrard's Cross, Buckinghamshire, 1986)

A. Wildavsky *Craftways On the Organisation of Scholarly Work* (New Brunswick and London, 1989)

Arthur P. Williamson 'The Voluntary Sector's Central Role in Managing Societal Instability in Northern Ireland' in *Government and The Third Sector Emerging Relationships in the Welfare State* eds. B. Gidron, R.M. Kramer, L.M. Salamon (Jossey-Bass, San Francisco, 1992)

C.R.M. Wilson *New On Board Essentials of Governance for Hospital Trustees* (Canadian Hospital Association Press, Ottawa, 1991)

H.E.S. Woldring 'State and Civil Society in the Political Philosophy of Alexis de Tocqueville' *Voluntas: International Journal of Voluntary and Nonprofit Organizations* Vol. 9, No. 4, 1998

Wolfenden Report *The Future of Voluntary Organisations*, (Croom Helm, London, 1978)

M.M. Wood 'Is Governing Board Behaviour Cyclical?' *Nonprofit Management and Leadership* Vol. 3, No. 2, 1992

Robert K. Yin *Case Study Research Design and Methods* (Revised edition, Sage Publications, London, 1989)

Elizabeth Young-Bruehl *Hannah Arendt For Love of the World* (New Haven and London, 1982)

M. Zald 'The Power and Functions of Boards of Directors: a Theoretical Synthesis' *American Journal of Sociology*, Vol. 75, 1969

Appendix

Accreditation Standards for the Governing Bodies of Hospitals issued by the Canadian Council on Health Facilities Accreditation

GOVERNING BODY STANDARDS

The following standards for the governing board have been reprinted with the express permission of the Canadian Council on Health Facilities Accreditation.

STANDARD I MISSION, PLANNING AND GOALS

The governing body has an overall planning framework for the facility.

1. The governing body provides for and approves a written statement describing the mission of the facility

   The mission statement may include:

   - philosophy of care
   - purpose of the facility
   - services offered
   - limitations of service
   - regional status
   - role in patient care, teaching, research and health promotion
   - role in, and responsibility to the community

   Give date of last approval.

2. The governing body develops the mission statement with input from the management, medical, professional and support staff of the facility and other relevant bodies.

   Mechanisms may include:

   - committees
   - group discussions
   - staff meetings
   - consultation with regional health planning bodies.

3. The governing body ensures that there is a plan for communicating the mission statement to all staff and to the community.

4. The governing body reviews the mission statement at least every three years, revises as necessary and dates accordingly.

4.1 The mission statement is reviewed and revised when there is a major change in:

- funding
- available resources
- regional status
- demographics
- relevant legislation
- programs and services

Give date of last review and/or revision.

5. The governing body provides for and approves a strategic plan to guide the development of current and future services and progams within the facility.

5.1 The strategic plan includes:

- a needs assessment
- goals
- program and service development
- clearly defined interrelationships among acute care, long-term care, rehabilitation services, mental health services, and related community services

Give date of last approval

6. The governing body ensures the input of the management, medical, professional and support staff of the facility to the development of the strategic plan.

7. The governing body reviews the strategic plan at least every three years, revises as necessary and dates accordingly.

7.1 The strategic plan is reviewed and revised when there is a major change in:

- mission
- goals
- needs of the community
- regional planning
- demographics
- available resources

Give date of last review and/or revision.

8. The governing body receives regular reports from management on the evaluation of programs.

8.1 The reports relate to:

- the evaluation of the effectiveness and efficiency of a program in attaining its objectives
- the evaluation of a program's cost in relation to its benefits

9.   The governing body provides for and approves the goals of the facility.

9.1 The goals:

- are what the facility wants to achieve
- support the mission of the facility
- are influenced by available resources

Give date of last approval.

10.   The governing body approves the facility-wide objectives developed by management to achieve the goals of the facility.

Give date of last approval.

11.   The governing body reviews the goals at least every three years, revises as necessary and dates accordingly.

The goals are reviewed and revised when there is a major change in:

- needs of the community
- mission
- strategic plan
- organization of the facility
- demographics
- regional planning
- relevant legislation
- available resources

Give date of last review and/or revision.

STANDARD II ORGANIZATION AND DIRECTION
There is an organized governing body which has overall responsibility for the operation and governance of the health care facility.

1.   The governing body is organized to govern the facility effectively.

1.1 The governing body appoints the necessary committees for the conduct of its affairs.

1.2 The committees of the governing body:

- have terms of reference and reporting lines
- record minutes that reflect the deliberations of the committee

- meet at regular, stated intervals to consider the affairs of the facility and to provide direction
- involve input from medical and other professional staff when dealing with professional issues

1.3 The governing body may delegate any of its authority to an executive committee between regular meetings.

2. There are systematic and effective mechanisms for communication and problem solving among members of the governing body, management and medical staff.

Mechanisms to facilitate communication and problem solving may include:

- a committee with joint representation
- board member attendance at medical staff meetings
- regular reports from management on all operational aspects of the facility.

3. There are mechanisms for the recruitment, appointment, election, tenure, reappointment, re-election and retirement of members of the governing body.

Mechanisms may be determined internally by the governing body or by external bodies who have such responsibility.

4. The governing body appoints and reappoints members of the medical staff.

4.1 The governing body:

- delegates to the medical staff the authority to evaluate the professional competence of its members and all applicants for staff membership
- holds the medical staff responsible for developing a process for, and performance of peer review
- holds the medical staff responsible for making recommendations to the governing body concerning initial staff appointments and reappointments, and the assignment, curtailment and/or withdrawal of privileges
- requires that the medical staff's bylaws include a mechanism whereby applicants may appeal to the governing body any decision made by it in refusing appointment or reappointment, or in limiting privileges
- requires that the medical staff's bylaws include a mechanism for review of decisions, including the physician's right to be heard at each step of the process

5. The governing body evaluates its performance in governing the facility at least every three years.

5.1 The evaluation takes into account:

- assessment of performance in relation to the strategic plan for the facility
- performance of individual board members and the board as a whole in relation to the duties and responsibilities of board members set out in the facility's bylaws

Mechanisms for evaluation may include:

- a structured self-evaluation process
- external review

6. The governing body appoints a chief executive officer to manage the facility.

7. The authority, accountabilities and duties of the chief executive officer are detailed in a written position description adopted by the governing body.

7.1 The accountabilities of the chief executive officer include:

- overall management of the facility
- leadership in the development, implementation and coordination of the strategic plan, program development and evaluation, goals and objectives
- establishing an organized and systematic program of routine communication among governing body, management, medical, professional and support staff, ancillary organizations, patients, the public, media and government
- regular reporting on all operational aspects of the facility to the governing body
- liaison among governing body, professional staff and support services
- developing an organizational plan for the facility
- establishing formal means of accountability for all subordinates
- establishing services and programs as appropriate
- planning and implementing the management activities within the facility
- co-ordinating facility services with identified population needs
- ensuring facility compliance with applicable legislation and regulatory agencies, including review and prompt action on recommendations by such agencies, as directed by the governing body policy
- developing mechanisms to implement the policies established by the governing body
- ensuring facility compliance with governing body policies
- developing and ensuring facility compliance with operational policies and procedures
- implementing a management information system for the facility
- establishing internal controls to ensure the effective use of physical, financial and human resources

311

- ensuring that there is a current organization chart available to the governing body
- implementing a facility-wide quality assurance program
- implementing a facility-wide occupational health and safety program
- implementing facility-wide utilization review activities
- implementing facility-wide risk management activities
- protecting human, physical and financial resources through appropriate methods of managing risk (insurance, etc)

8.   The governing body evaluates the performance of the chief executive officer relative to the agreed upon goals, objectives and expected outcomes.

Mechanism for evaluation may include:

- an ad hoc committee of the governing body
- external review

8.1 While some performance appraisals may occur annually in conjunction with salary reviews, an appraisal on the basis of achieved goals, objectives and outcomes is required at least every three years.

9.   The senior management team participates in an advisory capacity at meetings of the governing body.

9.1 The senior management team includes, but is not limited to:

- the chief executive officer
- the medical director/chief of staff
- the chief executive nurse
- the chief financial officer
- the chief human resources officer

STANDARD III BYLAWS, REGULATIONS, AGREEMENTS AND POLICIES
The governing body has bylaws, regulations and/or agreements in accordance with its legal accountability and its responsibility to the patient population served.

The governing body has policies to provide all staff with clear direction on the scope and limitations of their functions and responsibilities.

The governing body has policies to provide all patients and their families with a clear understanding of their rights and responsibility with the facility.

1.   The governing body adopts bylaws and/or regulations for the facility.

312

1.1 The bylaws and/or regulations include, but are not limited to:

- a definition of the powers and duties of the governing body, officers and committees
- the membership of the governing body which includes a broad representation of the community served (physicians, including those who are members of the medical staff, may be members of the governing body, except where prohibited by provincial law or by the facility's bylaws)
- a description of eligibility for governing body membership
- the method of appointment and/or election, the reappointment and/or re-election and the retirement of members, officers and chairmen of committees of the governing body
- the definition of the tenure of the members of the board
- the duties, responsibilities and authority delegated to the chief executive officer
- a statement of the responsibilities and authority delegated to the medical and professional staff
- the procedure for processing and evaluating applications for medical staff membership and for the granting of clinical privileges
- confirmation that no assignment, referral or delegation of authority by the governing body to the chief executive officer, the medical staff, or anyone else, precludes the governing body from exercising the authority required to meet its responsibility for the conduct of the health care facility
- full disclosure of ownership and control of the health care facility
- bylaws or regulations that delineate the purpose, function and size of any ancillary organization
- a yearly financial audit of the accounts of the facility
- the approval of a process for transfer of functions
- conflict of interest guidelines
- others as determined by provincial or territorial legislation

2. The bylaws and/or regulations of the facility are reviewed at least every three years, revised as necessary and dated accordingly.

   Give date of last review and/or revision.

3. The governing body ensures that there are mechanisms whereby the bylaws and/or regulations of the medical staff are developed and recommended by the medical staff for approval by the governing body.

   Mechanisms may include:

   - Medical Advisory Committee reports to the governing body
   - Medical Staff Bylaws Committee
   - approval by medical staff as a whole
   - Council of Physicians, Dentists and Pharmacists reports to the governing body (Quebec)

3.1 When the governing body does not concur with recommendations from the medical staff concerning clinical privileges, there is provision for a review of the recommendations by a joint committee of the governing body and the medical staff before a final decision is reached by the governing body.

3.2 The governing body specifies the period of time within which applicants are informed of the disposition of their application for staff privileges.

4. The medical staff bylaws and/or regulations are approved by the governing body.

Give date of last approval.

5. The governing body ensures that ancillary organizations, if they exists, delineate their purpose and function in written bylaws and/or regulations.

6. The bylaws and/or regulations for ancillary organizations are approved by the governing body.

Give date of last approval.

7. The governing body is informed of any affiliation agreements with educational institutions.

8. The governing body ensures that there are policies in place which provide guidance to the facility regarding the implementation of its mission.

8.1 The policies include, but are not limited to:
- human rights which endorse that:
  - no individual is excluded from receiving services provided by the facility, or from membership on the governing body or staff of the facility on the basis of race, creed, sex or national origin
- patient's rights and responsibilities which endorse that:
  - the personal dignity of the patient is respected
  - the rights of patients and their families to privacy and confidentiality of health information are respected
  - the rights of patients to access their health record are respected
  - the rights of patients to make decisions concerning their care are respected
  - patients are made aware of their responsibilities
  - optimal care is provided for patients who may require a different method of care delivery and resources not ordinarily utilized by the facility
- ethics which endorse that:
  - there is a process for addressing ethics issues within the facility
  - there are policies for:

- consent (informed and involuntary)
- choice of treatment, refusal of treatment, and accessibility to treatment
- death and dying (withdrawal of resuscitative services, withdrawal of life support, palliative care, etc.)
- abortion
- research, particularly with respect to human experimentation
- dealing with patients' complaints
- organ donation and retrieval

- health and safety which endorses that:

  > the facility will provide a healthy and safe environment for patients, staff and visitors
  > a policy on smoking within the facility

- multiculturalism which endorses that:

  > the facility will respect the cultural differences of the patients and staff of the facility
  > a process for identifying and addressing any cultural differences of patients and staff

- health promotion which endorses that:

  > the facility will encourage health promotion for its patients, staff and community

- non-violence toward patients and staff which endorses that:

  > the facility will take all precautions to protect the physical and mental safety of its patients, staff and visitors
  > the facility has procedures for assisting patients who have been subjected to violence prior to or during admission to the facility
  > the facility has procedures for assisting staff who have been, or are currently subjected to violence within the facility

- conflict of interest which endorses:

  > guidelines for the resolution of any apparent or potential conflict of interest

9. The policies of the governing body are reviewed at least every three years, revised as necessary and dated accordingly.

   Give date of last review and/or revision.

STANDARDS IV HUMAN, PHYSICAL AND FINANCIAL RESOURCES
The governing body is accountable for the provision of the human, physical and financial resources required to fulfill the mission and goals of the facility.

1. The governing body provides for human, physical and financial resources.

1.1 Mechanisms include:

- regional planning
- evaluation of resources availability and adequacy
- review of community need
- program evaluation
- alternative sources of funding

2. The governing body approves a medical human resources plan on the recommendation of the medical staff and consistent with the strategic plan.

2.1 The number of medical staff required to meet clinical needs is determined by:

- regional planning
- the role of the facility
- needs of the facility and the community
- availability of human, physical and financial resources

2.2 In teaching facilities, the plan is developed in conjunction with the affiliated medical school.

3. The governing body appoints and reappoints medical staff in accordance with the medical human resources plan, the facility bylaws, rules and regulations, and, if applicable, provincial rules and regulations.

4. The governing body approves an annual budget for the facility.

4.1 The budget for the facility includes both the operating and capital equipment components.

5. The governing body approves a long-term capital development plan for the facility.

The long-term capital development plan is influenced by:

- The mission
- The strategic plan
- The goals
- Regional planning
- The available resources

6. The governing body provides for an annual audit of the financial controls and production of the financial statements.

7. The governing body reviews and approves the annual audit report.

Give date of last approval.

8. The governing body instructs management to follow up on recommendations made in the annual audit report.

9. The governing body receives feedback from management on follow-up actions resulting from recommendations made in the annual audit report.

STANDARD V ORIENTATION AND CONTINUING EDUCATION
The governing body receives the appropriate orientation and continuing education to enable it to fulfill its mandate.

1. There is an orientation program for all new members of the governing body.

1.1 The orientation program is documented.

1.2 The orientation program may include:

- relevant legislation
- strategic plan
- mission
- goals and objectives
- bylaws, regulations and agreements
- governing body policies
- organization chart of facility
- regional plan
- facility programs and services
- physical layout of facility
- quality assurance program
- utilization review activities
- risk management activities
- occupational health and safety activities
- performance expectations of the governing body

1.3 The orientation program is completed in a timely manner and participation is documented on completion.

2. A program of continuing education is available to all members of the governing body.

2.1 The continuing education program provides opportunities for members to expand their knowledge and understanding of governance and health care issues.

The program may include:

- meetings or seminars relevant to the mission of the facility
- opportunities to assist in identifying developmental needs
- opportunities to assist in planning continuing education programs

317

- opportunities to review literature relevant to the governance of the facility
- participation in professional associations and activities
- self-directed learning
- teleconferences

2.2 Participation in continuing education is documented on completion.

3. Members of the governing body evaluate their orientation and continuing education programs.

Mechanisms for evaluation may include:

- participant feedback
- peer review
- cost/benefit analysis

STANDARD VI QUALITY ASSURANCE
The governing body is accountable for the provision of quality patient care and service.

1. The governing body adopts a policy for a facility-wide quality assurance program to ensure quality patient care and service.

1.1 The policy endorses a facility-wide systematic process of monitoring and evaluating the quality of patient care and service, identifying and resolving problems, and identifying and acting upon opportunities to continually improve patient care and service.

1.2 The governing body provides resources and support systems for the quality assurance program.

2. The governing body establishes mechanisms for receiving the results of the quality assurance program at least on a quarterly basis.

Mechanisms for receiving the results of the quality assurance program may include:

- Quality Assurance Committee
- other committees
- reports from management
- reports from the medical staff
- reports from patient and staff satisfaction surveys
- correspondence from patients

3. The governing body provides feedback on the results of the quality assurance program to the management and medical staff.

Mechanisms for providing feedback may include:

- Quality Assurance Committee
- reports

4. The governing body monitors and evaluates the quality assurance program at least annually.

Mechanisms for monitoring and evaluating the quality assurance program may include:

- Quality Assurance Committee
- other committees
- reports
- questionnaire and surveys

STANDARD VII UTILIZATION REVIEW

The governing body is accountable for the effective and efficient management of resources.

1. The governing body adopts a policy for facility-wide utilization review activities.

1.1 The policy endorses:

- a commitment to utilization review
- the development of valid methods to assess that services within the facility are being used in the most effective manner
- the education of governing body, management and medical staff in utilization review

2. The governing body establishes mechanisms for receiving the results of utilization review activities at least on a quarterly basis.

The mechanisms for receiving the results of utilization review activities may include:

- Utilization Review Committee
- other committees
- reports from management
- reports from medical staff

3. The governing body provides feedback on the results of utilization review activities to the management and to the medical staff.

Mechanisms for providing feedback may include:

- reports

4. The governing body annually monitors and evaluates the facility-wide utilization review activities.

    Mechanisms for monitoring and evaluation may include:

    - establishing reporting mechanisms
    - establishing an evaluative methodology

STANDARD VIII RISK MANAGEMENT

The governing body is accountable for the management of risks to the patients, staff, visitors and property of the facility.

1. The governing body adopts a policy for facility-wide risk management activities to manage risks to the patients, staff, visitors and property of the facility.

1.1 The policy endorses a facility-wide, systematic process of identification, assessment and action to manage risks to the patients, staff, visitors and property of the facility.

1.2 The governing body provides resources and support systems for facility-wide risk management activities.

2. The governing body establishes mechanisms for receiving the results of risk managemnt activities at least on a quarterly basis.

    The mechanisms for receiving the results of risk management activities may include:

    - Risk Management Committee
    - other committees
    - reports from management
    - reports from medical staff
    - reports from patient and staff satisfaction surveys
    - correspondence from patients

3. The governing body provides feedback on the results of risk management activities to the management and to the medical staff

    Mechanisms for providing feedback may include:

    - reports

4. The governing body annually monitors and evaluates the facility-wide risk management activities.

    Mechanisms for monitoring and evaluation may include:

    - Risk Management Committee
    - other committees

- reports
- questionnaires and surveys

STANDARD IX HEALTH AND SAFETY

The governing body is accountable for the provision of a program to ensure the health and safety of patients, staff and visitors of the facility and for disaster and emergency preparedness.

1. The governing body provides for the health and safety of patients, staff and visitors through a facility-wide health and safety program.

1.1 The governing body provides resources and support systems for the health and safety program.

2. The governing body provides for facility preparedness in disaster and emergency situations.

2.1 The governing body provides resources and support systems for disaster and emergency preparedness.

STANDARD X INFECTION CONTROL

The governing body is accountable for the prevention of infections in order to enhance patient care and staff health in the facility.

1. The governing body is accountable for the provision of a facility-wide infection control program.

1.1 The governing body provides resources and support systems for the infection control program.